Passionate Playboys

These millionaires play by their own rules!

**Praise for three best-selling authors –
Lynne Graham, Jacqueline Baird and
Amanda Browning**

About Lynne Graham
'Lynne Graham delivers a
spellbinding love story.'
– *Romantic Times*

About MISTAKEN FOR A MISTRESS
'Jacqueline Baird offers a sensual tale of
hidden pasts…[with] an electric chemistry.'
– *Romantic Times*

About Amanda Browning
'Amanda Browning pens a riveting tale.'
– *Romantic Times*

Passionate Playboys

THE TROPHY HUSBAND
by
Lynne Graham

MISTAKEN FOR A MISTRESS
by
Jacqueline Baird

SEDUCED
by
Amanda Browning

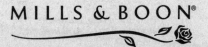

MILLS & BOON®

Harlequin Mills & Boon Limited,
Eton House, 18-24 Paradise Road, Richmond, Surrey, TW9 1SR

PASSIONATE PLAYBOYS
© by Harlequin Enterprises II B.V., 2002

The Trophy Husband, Mistaken for a Mistress and *Seduced*
were first published in Great Britain by Harlequin Mills & Boon Limited
in separate, single volumes.

The Trophy Husband © Lynne Graham 1996
Mistaken for a Mistress © Jacqueline Baird 1997
Seduced © Amanda Browning 1996

ISBN 0 263 83158 2

05-0702

*Printed and bound in Spain
by Litografia Rosés S.A., Barcelona*

Lynne Graham was born in Northern Ireland and has been a keen Mills & Boon® reader since her teens. She is very happily married with an understanding husband, who has learned to cook since she started to write! Her five children keep her on her toes. She has a very large Old English sheepdog, which knocks everything over, and two cats. When time allows, Lynne is a keen gardener.

Lynne loves to hear from readers, you can contact her at: www.lynnegraham.com

Look out for another of Lynne's fabulous books in Modern Romance™

THE HEIRESS BRIDE
by
Lynne Graham
on-sale September 2002

THE TROPHY
HUSBAND
by
Lynne Graham

CHAPTER ONE

SARA paid off the taxi in a breathless rush and raced up the stairs to the flat she shared with Antonia. Had they been burgled? Had someone in the family had an accident? Worse still, had something happened to Brian? Her imagination had gone into overdrive since she had received Antonia's message at work.

'Miss Dalton said you had to come home immediately, that it was very urgent,' the girl on the switchboard had stressed anxiously. 'I hope it isn't bad news, Miss Lacey. She wouldn't even wait for me to put her call through.'

Crossing the landing at speed, Sara unlocked the door of the flat. It was a disorientating experience. Loud music assaulted her ears. Phil Collins' latest album was playing full blast. A single electric-blue court shoe lay abandoned like a question mark on the hall carpet.

'Antonia?' Sara called, a quick frown of bewilderment drawing her fine brows together as she glanced into the empty lounge. The bedroom door was ajar. She pressed it back.

'Antonia?' she said again, and only then did she see the half-naked couple passionately entangled on the rumpled bed.

'*Sara*?' her cousin squealed as she reeled up, her honey-blonde hair wildly mussed up, her pink mouth swollen, pale blue eyes wide with horror.

In the very act of embarrassed retreat, Sara froze. Her attention had lodged on the tousled male head lifting off the white pillows. Recognition hit her like a punch in the stomach. Cruel fingers clutched at her heart and her lungs, tripping her heartbeat, depriving her of the air she needed to breathe.

'Oh, my God...' Brian groaned, grabbing up his shirt and rolling off the bed in one appalled movement.

Antonia was frantically struggling back into her blouse. 'Why the hell aren't you at work?' she screamed.

'You phoned...left a message that I was to come home,' Sara framed unevenly, not even recognising the distant voice that emerged from her bloodless lips as her own.

'*I* phoned? Are you crazy?' Antonia shrieked furiously. 'Whoever phoned, you can be sure it wasn't me!'

'You bitch, Toni!' Brian bit out in stricken condemnation. 'You deliberately set me up—'

'Don't be stupid!' Antonia hissed, but then without warning defiance replaced her angry discomfiture. She rested malicious blue eyes on Sara, who was already backing away on legs that were threatening to fold beneath her. 'But I did warn you that Brian was mine for the asking...didn't I?'

'No...' Brian's voice wavered weakly as his gaze collided with Sara's shattered green eyes—pools of stark pain in the dead white stillness of her triangular face. He made a sudden move towards her, both hands raised and extended as if to draw her back to him. 'This has never happened before, Sara...I *swear* it!'

Sara turned jerkily away and fled. She nearly fell down the last flight of stairs—Brian's frantic calls from the landing above acted on her like a trip-wire. Blocking him out, she steadied herself with one shaking hand on the dingy wall and made herself breathe in slowly and deeply before she walked back out onto the street.

Antonia and Brian. Brian and Antonia. She stared down numbly at the ring on her engagement finger. Her stomach lurched in violent protest. Six weeks off the wedding day...her cousin and her fiancé. It was as if the world had stopped turning suddenly, flinging her off into frightening free fall. She was in shock—so deep in shock that she couldn't even think. But her mcmory was relentlessly throwing up scraps of dialogue from the recent past.

'Brian chose you like he chooses his shirts…you've got to look good at the company dinners and wear a long time!' Antonia had sniped.

'Three years ago I could have lifted one little finger and Brian would have come running… He really had it bad for me.' Antonia had savoured the words.

Sara squared her narrow shoulders, caught a glimpse of herself in a shop window and stared. She saw a small woman with black hair worn in a tidy French plait, dressed in an unexciting navy business suit and white blouse. No competition for a five-foot-ten-inch blonde who had once made it between the covers of *Vogue*. She felt as if she was dying inside. She didn't know what to do, where to go.

A bus was drawing up at the stop several yards away and she started to run. Her dazed eyes skimmed over the man standing in a nearby doorway. He turned his head abruptly, making her wonder if she looked as odd as she felt. She didn't notice that the man swiftly fell into step behind her and climbed on the same bus.

'Do we have to have Antonia as a bridesmaid? My mother can't stand her,' Brian had complained peevishly.

'She's a real tart,' he had muttered with distaste. 'No decent woman would take her clothes off for money…'

Still with the same man tracking patiently in her wake, but quite unaware of his presence, Sara wandered back into the hugely impressive London headquarters of Rossini Industries. When the receptionist on the penultimate floor addressed her, Sara didn't hear her. Blind and deaf, she was moving on automatic pilot. She entered the spacious office which she shared with Pete Hunniford. It was empty. Pete's wife had gone into labour mid-morning, she recalled then. It was like remembering something that had happened a lifetime ago.

Her phone was buzzing like an angry wasp. She sat down and answered it.

'Tasmin Laslo here. I want to speak to Alex,' a taut female voice demanded.

'Mr Rossini is in conference. I am so sorry. Would you like me to—?'

The actress said a very rude word. 'You're lying, aren't you?'

Sara had been lying to Alex Rossini's women for the entire year that she had been employed as his social secretary. Alex Rossini was very rarely available to his lovers during office hours, and when a name was removed from a certain regularly updated list he was never available again. Lying went with the territory, no matter how much Sara despised the necessity.

'He sent me a diamond bracelet while I was filming in Hungary and I knew it was over!' Tasmin suddenly spat tempestuously. 'He's found someone else, hasn't he?'

'You're better off without him, Miss Laslo,' Sara heard herself saying. 'You're a wonderful actress. You're wasted on a slick, womanising swine like Alex Rossini!'

Incredulous silence hummed on the line. 'I beg your pardon?' Tasmin finally gasped.

Sara looked down dazedly at the receiver and thrust it back on the cradle in shock. She was trembling all over. Dear heaven, had she really said that? She rose unsteadily upright again. Her stomach cramped with sudden, unbearable nausea. She lurched into the cloakroom across the corridor and was horribly sick.

Ten minutes later, still shaking like a leaf, she returned to her office. The phone was buzzing again. She ignored it, walked over to Pete's desk and withdrew the bottle of brandy that he kept in the bottom drawer. She poured a liberal amount into a cup and slowly drank it down, grimacing at the unfamiliar taste of alcohol. Maybe it would settle her stomach. Brian and Antonia. Their names linked in a ceaseless refrain inside her pounding head, making her want to smash her head against the wall in protest.

She felt as if she was going mad. Sensible, steady Sara, who always kept her head in a crisis. But Sara had never before faced a crisis in which her whole world had fallen apart. Shivering, she helped herself to another nip of brandy, struggling to get a grip on herself. 'No decent woman…' A choked and humourless laugh escaped her. She tore the ring off her finger, dropped it in a drawer and rammed the drawer shut. She made herself pick up the phone again.

Unfortunately it was her aunt on the line. Something about the wedding rehearsal. Sara froze while Antonia's mother talked. Then she sat down, and drew in a deep, shuddering breath. 'Aunt Janice?' She hesitated and then forced herself on. 'I'm sorry but the wedding's off. Brian and I have broken up.' Even to her own ears she sounded unreal, like someone clumsily cracking a joke in the worst possible taste.

'Don't be silly, Sara,' Janice Dalton murmured sharply. 'What on earth are you talking about?'

'Brian and I have broken up. I'm very sorry…but we've decided we can't get married after all.'

'If you've had some foolish argument with Brian, I suggest you sort it out quickly,' her aunt told her with icy restraint. 'Brian had lunch with us yesterday and there was nothing wrong then!'

The line went dead as her aunt cut the connection. Sara trembled. Antonia's mother…how could she have told her the truth? Janice and Hugh Dalton had given her a home when her own mother had died. How could she possibly tell them the truth? Much better simply to pretend that she and Brian had had a change of heart—much cleaner, much less embarrassing for all concerned. The two families were neighbours and friends. A giant lump thickened her throat. Did Brian *love* Antonia?

'No decent woman…' Antonia had shed her clothes with alacrity when she had been offered the chance to feature in the famous Rossini calendar. Marco, Alex Rossini's kid brother, had smoothly offered Sara the same opportunity, unperturbed by her incredulous embarrassment. 'You've got something your long, tall cousin hasn't got… You're really sexy…and you have a lot of class.'

Marco had made the invitation in front of a highly amused audience at the staff party and it had become a tormenting, running joke in the months which had followed. The instant that Marco had seen Sara redden he had realised that he had found a real live target. Every time he saw Sara, he offered her an increasingly fantastic sum to bare all. No doubt he saw in her what everyone wanted to see, Sara reflected bitterly: a woman the exact, boring opposite of her exciting, beautiful cousin. Prim, quiet, predictable, ludicrously unlikely ever to set the world…or indeed any man…on fire.

Antonia had had Sara christened Prissy Prude at school, and, having created that image for her, had then delighted in shattering it by sharing the news that Sara was illegitimate, the inconvenient result of her youthful mother's holiday fling with a Greek waiter. Some of the girls hadn't laughed at first but they had soon fallen into line and obediently giggled and sneered. After all, Antonia had been the undeniable leader of the pack and peer pressure had been relentless. Sara had duly been persecuted, no other girl daring to stand her ground against Antonia lest she find herself enduring the same ordeal. To escape, Sara had left school at sixteen and taken a secretarial course. And that had not been her dream.

But Brian *had* been her dream…

Suddenly, with a violence that shook her, Sara hated everything about herself—her body, her personality, her inhibitions, her clothing. She *was* boring, laughably out of step with other women in her age group. Old-fashioned, sexually ignorant, eager to give up her job and become a housewife and mother at twenty-three. She should have been born a century ago, not in the nineties.

Out of the corner of her eye, she finally noticed that the door was open. Slowly she lifted her head and panic filled her, her cat-green eyes flying wide to accentuate the exotic slant of her cheekbones. Alex Rossini was standing there as silent as a sleek predator on the prowl...and both phones were ringing off the hook, unanswered. He should have been in Rome this afternoon, not here in London, she thought stupidly.

'Coffee-break?' Alex murmured in a curiously quiet voice instead of letting fly at her as she had expected. The phones stopped abruptly as if the switchboard had cut them off, plunging them into a sudden, thunderous silence.

In a daze, she looked back at him. Six feet three inches of lithe, rawly virile masculinity. Black hair, hard bronze profile with the deep, dark, flashing eyes of his Italian ancestry. A sexually devastating male with an overwhelmingly physical presence that few men could equal. And Sara hated being near him. She hated the way he looked at her. She hated the way he spoke to her.

If the cost of setting up the first marital home hadn't been so extortionate, Sara would have sacrificed her excellent salary and taken a lesser position elsewhere within a week of being exposed to Alex Rossini's sardonic asides and contemptuously amused appraisals. He made her feel so murderously uncomfortable...so self-conscious, so *ridiculous*. He made her feel like a curious specimen trapped behind museum glass.

'Finish your coffee.' A lean, long-fingered brown hand casually closed round the half-full cup of brandy sitting on the edge of her desk and extended it to her.

Didn't he smell the alcohol, realise that it wasn't black coffee? Evidently, obviously not. Jerkily, she reached out and accepted the cup and focused on his beautifully polished shoes, every muscle whip-taut. She tossed back the rest of the brandy in a burning surge. It brought tears to her eyes, which she blinked back furiously.

'Where's Pete?'

'Still at the hospital with his wife.' Sara struggled for some desperate semblance of normality, astonished that he wasn't cutting her to ribbons with the satirical edge of his tongue. She forced herself upright, bracing both hands on the desk. Involuntarily her gaze collided with shimmering dark golden eyes and it was like falling on an electric fence, shock waves making every raw nerve-ending scream. Deliberately she turned her head away, closing him out again. No, she was not susceptible. She had proved that to her satisfaction over and over again.

'Then I'm afraid you'll have to take his place.'

'His place?' Nobody could possibly take Pete Hunniford's place. Pete was Alex's most devoted gofer. Nothing came between Pete and ambition. He had freely admitted to Sara that his first marriage had fallen apart because he was never at home. And right at this minute, if Alex employed his mobile phone, Pete would be out of the labour ward like a rocket.

'Nothing too onerous… *Relax*,' Alex breathed in that distinctively rich dark voice which rolled down her spine like golden honey, burning wherever it touched. 'I only want you to take down a couple of letters.'

Her brow furrowed as she automatically lifted a pad and pencils. He was talking very slowly, not with his usual quick impatience. He hadn't even asked her why she hadn't answered the phones. He stood back for her to precede him from the room, and in her need to keep as much physical space between them as possible she jerked sideways and skidded off balance.

Strong hands whipped out and closed round her upper arms to steady her. Her head swam, her heartbeat kicking wildly against her breastbone. She quivered, fighting off sudden dizziness, and he drew her back. 'OK?' he murmured, still holding her on the threshold.

'F-fine... Sorry.' Her nostrils flared in dismay as the warm, definably male scent of him washed over her. Aromatic, intrinsically familiar...intimate. *Intimate*? What was the matter with her? What the heck was the matter with her? As she stiffened he released her and she walked down the corridor with careful small steps, noticing that the double doors of his office at the end looked peculiarly out of focus. Now near, now far, now skewed. All that brandy. Drunk in charge of a phone. But it felt shamelessly, unbelievably good: a short-term anaesthetic against the enormous pain waiting to jump on her—the pain she could not yet face head-on. As long as she didn't think, she could protect herself.

'Sit down, Sara.' She plotted a course across the thick carpet with immense care and sank down on the nearest seat, suddenly terrified that he would notice the state she was in. Being intoxicated suddenly didn't feel good any more. In Alex Rossini's presence, it felt like sheer insanity. Discovery would be unbelievably demeaning.

Disorientatedly, she glanced up and found him standing over her. She flinched. Her hands trembled and she anchored them tightly round the pad. He didn't sit down. He strolled with silent grace across to the floor-length windows. A stunningly handsome man, he had an innate elegance of movement, his superbly cut mohair and silk-blend charcoal-grey suit the perfect complementary frame to wide shoulders, lean hips and long, powerful thighs.

From beneath luxuriant black lashes he surveyed her. 'Shall I begin?'

He didn't normally request permission. Uncertainly she nodded. He dictated with incredibly long pauses that enabled her more or less to keep up but she still missed bits because her mind wouldn't stay in one place. Shock was giving way to reality, denial giving way to bursts of agonised pain. For how long had Brian been deceiving her with Antonia? Her memory threw up the image of the open bottle of wine in the lounge, the half-filled wineglasses by the bed. No sudden passion there. They had carried the glasses with them into the bedroom. A carefully staged lunchtime encounter when Sara should have been at work.

'Did you get all that?'

The page currently beneath her fingers was blank. Briefly she simply closed her eyes, willing herself to find calm and control.

'It's all right, Sara…the letter isn't important.'

The softness of the assurance astonished her. Dazedly she glanced up, encountered Alex Rossini's brilliant dark eyes and was mesmerised by the sincerity she read there. He was resting against the edge of his polished desk, far too close for comfort. He reached down and removed the pad from her nerveless fingers, setting it carelessly aside.

'Something has upset you…' he drawled.

Her creamy, perfect skin tightened over her fine facial bones as she focused on his silk tie. 'No…'

'You're not wearing your ring.'

Sara went white. The pencil she was fiddling with snapped in two.

'You are clearly distressed,' Alex murmured in the same quiet, disturbingly gentle tone which she had never heard him employ before. 'I believe you were called home unexpectedly this morning. What happened there?'

She was appalled to discover that she wanted to tell him, spill out the poison building up inside her, but instead she bit down hard on her tongue.

'Perhaps you would prefer to go home for the rest of the day?' Alex suggested lethally.

'No…' Sara muttered, horror bringing her back to life. Antonia would be waiting for her and she could not yet face that confrontation.

'Why not?' he prompted her.

'I found my fiancé in bed with my cousin.' As soon as she had said it she could not believe that she had said *that* out loud and to him of all people. A tide of chagrined colour crawled up her slender throat.

But Alex Rossini didn't bat a magnificent eyelash and his response was instantaneous. 'A merciful escape.'

'Escape?' Sara queried blankly.

Alex spread beautifully shaped brown hands expressively. 'Think how much more disturbing it would have been had you discovered such a sordid liaison *after* the wedding.'

'There isn't going to be a wedding now,' Sara said shakily, and whereas telling that same fact to her aunt had seemed like part of a living nightmare it now felt like hard, agonising reality.

'Of course not. No woman would forgive such a betrayal, would she?' Alex drawled softly.

The silence hummed. The tip of her tongue snaked out to moisten her dry lower lip. Forgiveness…understanding. Brian had been asking for both within seconds. He had not stood shoulder to shoulder with Antonia…

'After all,' Alex continued with honeyed persistence. 'How could you ever trust him again? Or her?'

The darkness sank back down over Sara where for an instant she had seen a wild, hopeful chink of light.

'Were you thinking of giving him another chance?' Alex enquired in a tone of polite astonishment.

Sara flinched. 'No,' she muttered sickly, duly forced to see the impossibility of ever trusting again.

Yet she could not believe that she was actually having such a conversation with Alex Rossini, who was not known for his concerned and benevolent interest in his employees' personal problems. Indeed, the Rossini credo was that the best employees left their private life outside the door of Rossini Industries and never, ever allowed that private life to interfere with their work.

'Why are you talking to me like this?' she whispered helplessly.

'Do you have anyone else to confide in?'

Sara tried and failed to swallow. It was almost as if he knew, but how could he possibly *know* how frighteningly isolated she now was? She could not turn to Antonia's parents and she had no other relatives, no close friends who were not also Brian's friends or colleagues. 'No, but—'

'Nothing you have told me will go any further,' Alex asserted, his night-dark eyes, sharp and shrewd as knives, trained on her, but those eyes were no longer cutting, no longer cold, no longer grimly amused.

'You're being so...so kind,' Sara said in a wobbly tone as she fought to conceal her disbelief, for this was a side of his character that she had never thought to see, indeed never dreamt existed.

'You have had a traumatic experience and, naturally, I am concerned.'

'Thank you, but I don't need your pity,' Sara bit out painfully.

'The very last thing you inspire is pity,' Alex assured her, unleashing a wry smile of reproof on her. 'You should be celebrating your freedom. Life is far too short for regrets. You've already wasted two years of it on that little salesman. The future has to offer far more entertaining possibilities—'

'How did you know Brian was a salesman?' Sara breathed, the words slurring slightly.

'Isn't he? He looks like one,' Alex informed her smoothly.

Something not quite right tugged at her instincts and then drifted away again, for nothing in her entire world was right any more.

'You live with your cousin, don't you?' Alex probed.

Again she was disconcerted by his knowledge and perhaps it showed, because he added, 'Marco mentioned it to me.'

'Yes.' Sara flushed, reluctantly recalling all the unwanted, gory details which had been forced on her during Antonia's short-lived affair with Alex's brother. That connection had embarrassed Sara.

'Naturally you do not want to return to your home at this moment,' Alex murmured, and casually tossed a set of keys onto her lap. 'You can use the company apartment until you have made other arrangements.'

Even in the state she was in Sara was staggered by such a proposition. The apartment was a penthouse on the floor above, used only by the Rossini family and, very occasionally, their personal friends. 'I couldn't possibly—'

'Where else have you got to go?'

She clutched the keys, meaning to return them but thinking helplessly of the humiliation of dealing with Antonia as she felt now. Her strained eyes unguarded and vulnerable, Sara stared back at him. 'I'm very grateful.'

'A fresh start,' Alex murmured intently. 'I'm having a dinner party tonight. Why don't you come? You shouldn't be on your own.'

A nervous laugh lodged in her aching throat. *A party?* He thought that she was in the mood for a party? Was he insane or just downright incapable of comprehending the immensity of what had happened to her today?

'I'll be fine,' she returned tremulously, wondering if he needed someone to supervise the caterers. Pete usually attended Alex's dinner parties, checked the seating arrangements, oiled the conversation and ensured that everything went smoothly. Alex Rossini paid for that kind of service. Alex Rossini was so rich that he could afford to burn money for amusement.

'I'll call you later. I'll send a car to pick you up at seven,' Alex told her as if she hadn't spoken.

Dully she fumbled for an excuse. 'I have nothing—'

'I'll buy you a dress to wear. No problem, *cara*. Don't even think about something so trivial.'

'But I—'

Strong brown hands reached down and closed over hers, tugging her gently upright. He angled her towards the door as if she were a walking doll. 'Go up to the apartment and lie down for a while; practise thinking optimistic, happy thoughts. Smile…' he urged softly, and a blunt fingertip skimmed below the trembling curve of her full lower lip and withdrew again, the contact feather-light and strangely soothing.

Unwarily, like someone in a dream, Sara looked up at him, connected with shimmering, mesmeric gold eyes and staggered slightly. He balanced her again with ease. An ache unlike anything she had ever experienced made her shiver. 'Mr Rossini—'

'Alex… *Cristo*!' he exploded, abruptly freeing her.

Sara almost fell over. Numbly she watched him stride over to sweep up the phone that she hadn't even heard ringing. He swung smoothly back to her. 'Go up to the apartment and lie down,' he instructed her again.

Sara backed out slowly and walked back down to her office to collect her bag. Her head was aching. She put a hand up to her hair and undid the tight plait, running her fingers through the loosened tresses. The phone on her desk was ringing. For an instant she hesitated, and then she lifted it.

'Sara?' Pete demanded impatiently. 'Where have you been?'

'I was—'

'Look, I need a favour,' he broke in. 'Alex told me to get Marco's signature on some papers yesterday but I forgot. They're in the top right-hand drawer in my desk. Take a cab over to the studio and get it seen to before Alex asks for them… OK?'

Sara took a deep breath, grimaced and then wearily sighed. 'OK.'

'You're an angel. I bet your replacement won't be half so helpful.'

The reminder that she was actually working out her notice hit Sara hard as she climbed into a taxi. She would be in the dole queue soon, she realised dully. Her successor was already picked, due to take her place in a fortnight's time. Brian hadn't wanted a working wife. And she had no savings. She had poured every penny of her salary into renovating and furnishing the Victorian terrace house that Brian had bought. Weekends and evenings, she had scraped walls, plastered, decorated, cut out and sewn and hung curtains. She had put her heart into transforming that house. The knowledge that now she would never live there sank in on her slowly and then blistered her soul like an acid burn.

Real anger began to rise inside her. Three years ago Sara had stood by, watching Brian pursue Antonia without success. But her cousin would take just for the sake of taking, and throughout the years that Sara had lived in the Dalton home she had been taught that lesson over and over again. Anything she had been foolish enough to value had inevitably been taken from her by her cousin…only this time it had not been a toy or a sentimental keepsake, it had been the man she loved. She clambered dizzily out of the cab with a white, frozen face.

She had never been in Marco Rossini's high-tech photographic studio before. The reception area was incredibly busy. It made her feel claustrophobic. She forced her passage through the throng and trekked down the corridor indicated by the laconic redhead on the desk.

Marco was lying back in a chair inside the perimeter of a blinding circle of lights in an empty studio. He looked half-asleep but his mobile dark brows hit his hairline at speed when he saw Sara hovering, and he sprang upright with a mocking smile. 'To what do I owe the honour? Don't tell me you've finally decided to take me up on my offer? Miss December in red boots and a tasteful sprinkling of holly berries…what do you think?'

Sara gritted her teeth as she felt her cheeks burn. She was in no mood to take one of Marco's baiting sessions. Evading his malicious gaze, she murmured flatly as she extended the file, 'These documents require your signature.'

Marco suddenly laughed.

'What's so funny?' Sara heard herself demand almost aggressively, the words slurring slightly.

'Private joke.'

'If it's about me, it's not private!' Sara told him fiercely, standing her ground.

Marco surveyed her with intense amusement. 'There's a price.'

'A price?'

Marco laughed again. 'You tell me something first…haven't you ever once got the hots in my brother's radius?'

Sara looked back at him blankly. 'Excuse me?'

'Alex is a very good-looking guy, beats the women off with sticks. If he wasn't family, I'd hate the smooth bastard! Come on, you can tell me…if it wasn't for true love, you'd have given him a whirl, right? You know that movie where Robert Redford pays a million bucks for one night with Demi Moore—*Indecent Proposal*? You too could have made your fortune…'

'I don't understand.' It was a lie. Sara just couldn't believe what Marco was insinuating.

Marco dealt her an incredulous glance. 'Are you saying you didn't even notice? Or are you telling me that Alex didn't once chance his arm?'

'If you are trying to imply that your brother is attracted to me, you're wrong—'

'To the tune of a million bucks? He could drop a million

without noticing. No, the sum I heard mentioned was two million,' Marco imparted with undeniable relish. 'I think Alex thought just one was bargain basement.'

Sara's head was swimming again. It was so hot beneath the lights that she couldn't concentrate. 'This is a very distasteful conversation, Marco.'

'So Alex wants to jump your bones...is that some sort of crime? Lust makes the world go round,' he told her impatiently.

Alex Rossini wanted to go to bed with her? Her lashes fluttered in bemusement. She couldn't believe it.

Marco shook his head slowly. 'You really didn't know, did you? Love is truly blind. But hey, don't let your heart soften in his direction. Remind yourself that you don't like him and steer clear. Marry your insurance salesman and live happily ever after,' he advised very drily as he flipped through the file and began scrawling his signature.

Alex Rossini *wanted* her? Rubbish, nonsense, Marco's deliberate mistake—doubtless another example of his nasty sense of humour. 'You don't like him'. Had her dislike of Alex Rossini been so obvious that even his brother was aware of it? She remembered Alex's astonishing kindness and tolerance and a stark arrow of guilt abruptly pierced her.

No, she had never liked Alex Rossini—his arrogance, his impatience, his sardonic tongue, his rich man's self-centred motivation which took no account of anything but his own wishes, his own needs. She had never liked the way he treated women either. As if they were *things* that he could buy and discard when he got bored...and he got bored so fast that your head would spin. Fast cars, fast women, fast-lane life. Nightclubs, movie premières, gambling joints, summer in the South of France, winter in the Alps. When the beautiful face and body of his latest lover palled, she got twenty-four regulation red roses and a diamond bracelet. Imaginative in that line he wasn't.

Why should he be? Women were easy around Alex Rossini. *He* didn't need to lie and cheat and deceive. *He* had no need to make promises that he had no intention of keeping...

Oh, Brian, how could you do this to me?

For the first time Sara met her own anguish head-on, and she swayed slightly, her temples pounding. The heat was suffocating her. Her blouse was sticking to her skin. In a clumsy movement she tugged off her jacket and breathed in deeply. Two million pounds... She wanted to laugh like a hysteric. It was so ridiculous...

'You know getting married costs a lot,' Marco murmured reflectively, watching Sara with fascinated eyes as the jacket slid from her limp fingers to the floor. 'Why don't you reconsider my offer? Nobody need ever know. I wouldn't be planning on publishing the shots. It could be your secret...and mine.'

As Sara attempted to focus on him, there was a sudden commotion out beyond the lights. A raw burst of Italian scorched her eardrums. A fist hit Marco on the shoulder, hard enough to knock him back, and suddenly Alex was there, ranting at his brother and with every blistering sentence punching him on the shoulder again, forcing him into retreat, like a boxer playing with a weak opponent.

White-faced, Marco leapt behind Sara. '*Dio*...switch him off before he kills somebody!'

CHAPTER TWO

SARA'S emerald-green eyes were wide with shock and incomprehension.

'I'm ashamed of you!' Alex roared at Marco, his strong features a mask of dark fury. 'For a bet, for a lousy fifty K. She's smashed out of her mind! She doesn't even know what day it is!'

'She's still a hell of a lot safer with me than she is with you!' Marco condemned furiously. 'And why shouldn't I have asked her?'

'Get out of my sight, you little jerk! Think yourself lucky it didn't go one step further—'

'All I did was make her an offer!' Marco shouted back.

'Then why's she got her jacket off?' Alex demanded with clenched fists.

'She took it off herself! Big deal! She wears more bloody clothes than Scott did in the Antarctic! Can nobody take a joke around here? I'm sorry, Sara,' Marco breathed harshly, turning back to her. 'I didn't know about your engagement, but now the deck is clear I would go for that two million and not a penny less!'

Shoulders unbowed, Marco walked away out beyond the lights.

'What the hell did you think you were doing coming over here in the state you're in?' Alex demanded with ferocious bite.

It was *her* turn, Sara registered numbly.

'Didn't I tell you to go and lie down? You could have fallen under a bus or something! When I realised you'd gone out again, I couldn't believe it!' Alex gritted, perfect white teeth flashing against sun-bronzed skin.

23

'I n-needed his signature on some papers.'

'So why did you take your jacket off?' Alex persisted.

'I was hot,' she muttered heavily.

Alex swept down a lean, impatient hand and lifted the article. '*Dio*…I should've worked that out for myself. A woman who wears her skirts below the knee and covers up every inch even in the heat of midsummer is highly unlikely to strip off for the camera. You're too much of a prude.'

Sara went suddenly rigid. Anger roared up through her without warning. 'I am *not* a prude!'

Alex had fallen very still. 'So you do have a temper,' he murmured in a tone of discovery.

'Just don't put me down,' she warned him unevenly, shaken now by the anger that had mushroomed up inside her and demanded an exit.

Alex drew fluidly back several paces and spread graceful brown hands. 'I was worried about you. You see, my creepy little brother laid a bet with me six months ago—'

'A bet?' Sara echoed with a frown.

'He bet me fifty thousand pounds that he could get you to pose in the nude.'

Sara shuddered, sick mortification flooding her.

'It never occurred to me that there was the slightest possibility you would fulfil that bet. You're not the type. It was a joke, Sara. Marco loves a good joke; sometimes, like today, he's tempted to take it too far.'

Sara studied the floor with burning eyes. She could feel the tears but they were mercifully dammed up. 'A good joke'. Her stomach twisted. A lousy male bet had lain behind Marco's constant baiting. A choked laugh fell from her tremulous mouth. She couldn't meet Alex's gaze. Marco had never had the smallest hope of winning his puerile bet but Alex had still chased after her. Why? Alex was already painfully well aware that she had gone off the rails once today. All along, she registered in anguished embarrassment, he had known that she was drunk.

'I've made an ass of myself,' she whispered with stinging bitterness.

'You *haven't* made an ass of yourself,' Alex breathed with raw emphasis. 'You've had a rough day. That's all.'

She quivered, a turmoil of emotion sweeping over her. She wanted Brian's arms round her so badly that she thought she would break apart. But Brian would never put his arms round her again. That was finished, dead, destroyed. More pain than she would have believed possible was suddenly coming at her from all sides. Her hands knotted together.

'You really love that bastard,' Alex murmured flatly.

She covered her cold face with spread fingers, as if she could somehow hold in what she was feeling. She fought to get a grip on herself again.

A pair of determined hands drew her forward and balanced her. With enormous effort, she managed to slide her arms obediently into the jacket which Alex extended.

'What was the crack about the two million?'

Sara's slender length tensed as she shakily tugged her hair out from beneath the collar of her jacket and shook it back out of her way.

'You have the most beautiful hair. I always wanted to see it loose.' Alex's dark eyes rested on the silky black torrent tumbling down to her waist. 'Don't ever get it cut.'

She slowly lifted her head, bewildered green eyes colliding with smouldering gold. It was electrifying. Stunned, she kept on looking at him. 'Marco said…Marco said you'd pay two million pounds for one night with me…'

Alex tautened, dark colour accentuating his hard cheekbones. 'You are even more drunk than I thought you were.'

Her glazed eyes fell from his. 'I've put my foot in my mouth—'

'I intend to put my fist in Marco's.'

'I was only joking.'

Alex pressed her towards the door. 'He wasn't…'

'H-honestly?' she stammered in disbelief.

'You think I'd be here if it wasn't true?'

He guided her out through the buzzing reception area. Her blitzed brain was endeavouring to absorb what he had confirmed. Alex Rossini *wanted* her. He found her desirable. What would have threatened and appalled her a mere twelve hours earlier now, for some reason, fascinated her. 'You were so kind this afternoon—'

'And I wouldn't be kind without a hidden agenda?'

'No,' she said without even thinking about it.

A chauffeur was standing by the door of a silver limousine. Sara climbed in, slid along the richly upholstered leather seat. Her luxurious surroundings made no impression on her at all. Don't think about Brian, don't think about Brian, she urged herself feverishly. 'Why didn't you…? I mean, you never showed—'

'Sara, I'm not a lovesick teenager. I find you physically very attractive. That is chemistry.'

'Sex.'

'Sex,' Alex agreed drily.

Was that the way Brian wanted Antonia? Did it matter whether it was love or infatuation or simply lust which had motivated him? Would love hurt any more than the way she was already feeling? Had it only been guilt which had made him chase out of the flat in her wake? *Stop it…stop it* a little voice shrieked inside her. It's over, Sara. Accept it. Alex was right. You could never trust Brian again.

'You think I'm very naïve,' Sara muttered, closing out the seething turmoil threatening her again.

'No. I don't think this is the time for this conversation.'

'I don't believe in love any more.' For hadn't Brian done all the right things? Romantic cards, constant phone calls. Last night he had been with *her*, holding hands, smiling...the consummate actor, and she had been the blind fool, for she had noticed nothing different.

'How would you like to sink into an alcoholic stupor and have a nice long sleep?' Alex enquired with unconcealed hope.

'Very, very much,' she whispered painfully.

The silence pulsed with undertones that she didn't understand.

'I really didn't know your feelings went this deep.' A grim laugh splintered from him.

She didn't show her feelings. She had learnt that young. But today she had been brutally wrenched out of her protective shell. 'How could you know?'

'I thought you were more in love with the bridal trappings...not to mention the wallpaper books, fabric swatches and paint-cards,' Alex enumerated with sardonic bite.

'I wanted a home that was really mine. Easy to mock what you've always had, Alex.' Sara shot him a look of angry intensity that challenged him and then tore her gaze away again, but he stayed etched in her mind's eye. The gleaming black hair, the slashing brows, the hard, arrogant slant of his mouth and nose. *Hard*—that was the definitive word. He might be possessed of a quite intoxicating masculine beauty but the raw stamp of power and fierce force of will overlaid those spectacular dark good looks like bonded steel.

Her head was pounding sickly. 'I'm not even asking you where we're going...'

'You're safe with me. Tonight you don't have to think for yourself.'

She closed her aching eyes. The one male in the world whom she would never, ever have trusted and yet all of a sudden she instinctively did trust him. Alex Rossini, protector. She ought to have laughed at the idea but instead she fell asleep.

*   *   *

Sara surfaced from a nightmare, shivering and perspiring. She sat up with a dizzy start and found herself in a completely unfamiliar room. The bedside lamps were lit on either side of the wide divan bed. The sheet tangled round her was silk. She lifted an uncertain hand to the thin, strappy nightdress clinging to the damp thrust of her breasts and fell still only when she saw the tall, dark male rising from a chair in the shadows.

'Alex…' she whispered shakily as it all came back in jagged bits and pieces and she breathed in sharply in relief, helplessly reassured by his presence.

'Feel like something to eat?' He sounded so normal, so casual.

'Where am I…? Oh, Lord, to have to *ask* that,' she muttered between clenched teeth.

'This is my house. I didn't think leaving you alone in the company apartment would be very wise—'

'Your dinner party.'

'Cancelled. Not one of my better ideas.'

From below the screen of her lashes she surveyed him with inescapable fascination. Nothing seemed real—not the day's events, certainly not the extraordinary alteration that had taken place in their relationship within the space of hours. She had not looked before she'd leapt today. He had looked for her, watched over her, kept her safe. *Why*? Did he want her so much that he was prepared to put up with her as she was now?

'I'll order some food.'

The door flipped quietly shut in his wake but still she looked to where he had been. She had got blindly, foolishly drunk and Alex Rossini had picked up the pieces. But he hadn't expected her to react that way… What had he expected? Why should he have *expected* anything when he couldn't have known what would happen to her today? The dinner party—'Not one of my better ideas'. He had talked almost as though the dinner party had been stage-managed in advance for her entertainment, which was crazy. She must have misunderstood him.

She slid out of bed. Her head was still swimming a little. She grimaced at the foul taste in her mouth and was exceedingly grateful to find a bathroom through the other door that she had espied. Her own tousled reflection in the mirror shook her. Peeling off the nightdress, she switched on the shower and stepped into the cubicle, grateful for the warm water and the rich lather of the soap that would wash her clean.

Who had undressed her and put her to bed? Alex? How strange that she shouldn't be plunged into stricken mortification over the idea. Yesterday she would have died a thousand deaths. Today—tonight—she knew that she had already betrayed so much to Alex Rossini that the once slavishly cherished sanctity of her own body no longer seemed worthy of such earth-shattering importance.

And why didn't she face it? She had very probably *driven* Brian into Antonia's arms! She had refused to sleep with him before they got married. Deaf to his every protest, she had been determined to wait for their wedding night, had smugly believed that the sexual restraint would lend an extra-special meaning to the vows they would take. Only now there wasn't going to be a wedding day…and it was cold comfort to acknowledge that she had saved her virginity but lost the man she loved. Maybe she had got exactly what she deserved. She had put her wretched principles first and where had it got her? She slid back into bed, forcing her cold face into the pillow, raw with the bitter pain of rejection and humiliation. Nothing was ever going to give her her pride back.

She didn't hear the door open; she went rigid when she was gathered up into strong male arms, and then her nostrils flared on the scent of Alex and she trembled, her arms uncoiling and curving round him very, very slowly. No, I mustn't do this…she thought. But it felt so good, so

damned good to be held close. The breath shortened in her
dry throat. Her fingers splayed centimetre by centimetre
across one powerful shoulder and stayed there. She was
almost paralysed by her own daring.

The silence thundered in her ears.

He released his breath in a faint hiss and she could feel
the savage tension in his taut, muscular frame and the
pounding of his accelerated heartbeat against hers. And
Sara smiled for the first time in hours with a sense of grat-
ified wonder and curved even closer, her other hand sliding
against his silk shirt-front, feeling the heat of his flesh burning through the fine fabric. His response was intoxicating.

'Is this a solo party…or a masquerade?' Alex demanded
softly. 'I am not *him*. You will not close your eyes in my
arms and pretend that I am.'

Shocked, she tipped her head back, eyes wide, and met
a vibrant gold challenge. 'I know who you are,' she whispered dazedly, yet in his arms, even with her eyes open,
she felt as if she was living some fantastic dream.

Lean hands closed gently round her wrists and pushed
her back against the pillows. He curved one long-fingered
hand to her cheekbone and held her still, raking her bewildered face with grim intensity. 'You want me to want you
now,' he said tautly.

It was the truth, although she hadn't seen it for herself.
Hectic colour lashed her cheeks beneath that appraisal.
'Yes…'

'Not like this,' Alex swore, his eloquent mouth hardening. 'And not tonight.'

She had been stumbling round like a clown half the day
under his gaze. No doubt whatever imagined attraction he
had endowed her with had evaporated fast when he had
been faced with such pathetic reality. Alex Rossini was
accustomed to sophisticated women and none of those experienced ladies would ever have made such a fool of herself in his presence as she had. As he released her a semi-

hysterical laugh was torn from her. It came out of nowhere and shook her.

'Don't…' Alex reproved her thickly. 'I want to make love to you very badly. I've wanted you for a long time but I won't take advantage of you when you don't know what you're doing.'

But she *did* know, for she knew herself far better than he did and she wasn't the type to have an affair with her boss, or the sort of woman who longed to see herself made notorious in newsprint as Alex Rossini's latest bed-partner for a few adventurous weeks. There would be no tomorrow for them; there was only tonight. He couldn't take his eyes off her, she registered in fascination.

'Sara…?' he prompted rawly, his blunt cheekbones overlaid with dark colour and prominent with ferocious tension.

Green eyes gazed back at him in defiant challenge. 'One night…and it won't cost you two million. It won't cost you anything. I don't put a price on myself,' she told him with a bitter edge to her voice because she knew now that once she had put a price on her body and that price had been a wedding ring.

'*Cristo*…' Alex seethed down at her in sudden incredulous frustration. 'What's come over you that you're talking like this?'

Her jewel-like eyes were relentlessly nailed to his as an unfamiliar feeling of power took her over. 'I want…I want to be wanted tonight…'

'OK…' Alex sprang upright in one driven motion and stared fulminatingly down at her. 'But you remember that this is not how *I* wanted it to be between us.'

And how had he imagined it would be? The two million for one wild night? Had that been his sexual fantasy? Or a few candlelit dinners, a lot of Italian charm and compliments and so to bed? Alex usually conducted his affairs with style. With flowers, gifts, country weekends, cruises on his fabulous yacht, *Sea Spring*. This was more honest—

much more honest—than either proposition and she did know exactly what she was doing, didn't she…? *Didn't* she? For an instant Sara had a frightening glimpse of her own emotional turmoil and knew that she was actually on the brink of an abyss, knew that she simply couldn't bear the thought of the long, lonely hours of the night which stretched ahead, knew that Alex's desire was balm to her savaged ego.

But had any woman but her ever wanted Alex Rossini for company rather than physical gratification? She wasn't expecting the latter, wasn't expecting any rolling waves to hit any metaphoric seashores, could be honest enough now to admit to herself that she had never been particularly interested in that aspect of human relations, even with Brian. It had been no sacrifice for *her* to practise celibacy. All that clumsy, awkward, heavy-breathing stuff had, frankly, left her cold, but she was intelligent enough to accept that other women didn't feel that way. She had often heard her own sex talk unashamedly about their sexual urges and once she had worried that there was something lacking in her because she did not feel the same needs as they apparently did. Then she had come to terms with her own essential coolness in that field.

She heard the shower switch off, the door open again, the sound of his footfalls on the thick carpet and thought, Dear heaven, what am I doing? Am I crazy, am I on the edge of a breakdown to be inviting an intimacy that I don't even want? And then Alex reached for her, pulling her up against him with a long, powerful arm. A stifled gasp of shock escaped her as he drew her into remorseless contact with every lean, hard line of his masculine physique. He rolled lithely over on the bed, taking her with him, and gazed down at her with burning golden eyes.

'You can change your mind,' he told her not quite evenly.

Eyes to drown in, eyes to tempt a saint, so wickedly

beautiful in that hard male face that they took her breath away. Sara looked up at him, bereft of words, suddenly hopelessly entrapped by that all-enveloping gaze. She wondered, in a state of complete abstraction, what it would be like to be kissed by him, which was about as far as her craven imagination was inclined to take her.

'I want the lights on...I don't want you to forget...*bella mia*,' he murmured with a sudden fractured roughness that tingled down her spinal cord and made her shiver. Forget what? she almost asked, but she couldn't make her voice work and it didn't seem important.

He wound his forefinger into a silky strand of her hair and slowly lowered his dark head, almost as if he expected her to shout, No! at the last possible moment, but Sara was wholly entranced. *Bella*...beautiful, she was savouring dreamily.

And then she found out what his mouth felt like on hers and she froze when his tongue probed between her parted lips. She had never liked *that*...but his sensual mouth became more insistent, more demanding and she trembled, pulses suddenly racing, heart accelerating madly, and she discovered that she had no resistance, no urge to pull back from that intoxicating pleasure.

Her head swam, a kind of stunned disbelief threatening to demand utterance, but he kissed her breathless and it would have taken restraint to initiate dialogue and she had none at all. She was carried blindly from one seductive kiss to the next, as badly hooked as an addict on heady delight.

Sure fingers moved against the full thrust of her breasts and a surge of such tormenting excitement took her in its grasp that her mind was a complete blank. She couldn't think, indeed she could barely breathe as she felt her own flesh swell, her nipples pinching into tight, prominent buds. He ran his mouth down the extended line of her throat, strung a line of inflaming kisses along her collar-bone, dallied on pulse-points and places she didn't know she had until that moment, and left her weak but with every skin cell alive with quivering, devastating anticipation.

'Look at me…' Alex demanded.

Her lashes flew up on command. She looked, lingered, drowned in smouldering gold. 'Alex,' she mumbled shakily, the fingers of one seeking hand pushing through his thick dark hair, shaping his head in an involuntary caress that also held him fast.

A brilliant smile flashed across his sensual mouth. He ran the tip of his tongue teasingly down the valley between her breasts and she shivered violently. 'Alex,' she said again without the smallest shade of doubt.

He peeled the nightdress out of his determined path, slowly shaped the quivering thrust of her achingly sensitive flesh with expert hands and then imprisoned a throbbing pink nipple in his mouth, suckling hungrily at the tender bud. Her whole body jerked in the surge of scorching heat that he evoked, the sudden, shattering, first-time pull of nerve-endings awakening to sexual passion taking her over. What remained of her control vanished simultaneously.

She heard a voice moaning, didn't recognise it as her own, her fingers tightly gripping the hot, sleek smoothness of his shoulders as her back arched. Pleasure she had never dreamt of was shooting through her in agonising waves and there was hardly a pause between one peak and the next. She twisted beneath him, couldn't stay still, wanting, needing, her thighs trembling, tightening on the ache building inside her.

He said something caressing in Italian, and the last thought that she would afterwards recall was that Italian was definitely the language of love in that incredibly rich, deep voice of his, and then he skimmed a hand through the damp curls at the base of her taut stomach and the world became a delirious, multicoloured shower of lights behind her lowered eyelids as he discovered the moist heat at the very heart of her. She cried out, gasped, shuddered. The hungry ache fired higher and higher, the strength of her own need biting so deep that it hurt, driving her to the edge of torment and making her plant desperate little kisses over any part of him that she could reach, her tongue tasting him, her teeth grazing him as her slender hips rose pleadingly against his most intimate caresses.

'Wait...' Alex groaned raggedly.

A split second after he drew back from her Sara tugged him back again with insistent hands and covered his mouth wildly, feverishly with her own, automatically utilising everything that he had taught her to keep him in the circle of her arms. He stiffened and then with an earthy groan surrendered with raw enthusiasm, his long, muscular length shuddering as his hands settled on her thighs and he moved against her, freeing her swollen lips, gazing down at her with ferocious hunger. 'If this is a dream, I don't ever want to wake up,' he confessed with passionate conviction.

'Alex...' she gasped tautly, her entire quivering body reaching up to his in helpless need, reacting with liquid-honey-enticement to the tantalising, hot, hard probe of his flesh against hers.

The surge of pain caught her on the crest of tortured anticipation. She gasped in shock, eyes flying wide to meet similar shock in his startled gaze. '*Cristo cara...*' he said in hoarse disbelief, but the momentary frown etched between his ebony brows was swiftly wiped away and the dark eyes glittered more golden than ever.

And then he moved again lithely, powerfully deepening his penetration, and a truly stunning wave of breathtaking sensation swept her back into that wild oblivion where only the demands of her own hungry body held sway. With every driving thrust he took her with him, made the fire burning inside her flame ever higher, ever more unbearably, until her teeth clenched and her heartbeat thundered and her nails raked fiercely down his damp back because the wild, hot pleasure that went on and on only made her more desperate. The explosive burst of her own climax was electrifying. It blew her apart, left her trembling in devastated aftershock from a sheer overload of pleasure.

'I feel better in my bed.' Alex was sweeping her up, letting his mouth caress hers again tenderly, then there was movement. That was all her punch-drunk senses could recognise. She felt the faint chill of colder air and then a cool sheet against her back before the heat and muscularity of Alex connected with her again.

'Don't go to sleep,' he instructed her, his dark drawl impossibly vibrant and wide awake as he wrapped his arms around her possessively and vented a deeply satisfied sigh of slumberous relaxation.

Not waves on shores so much as a golden sun of glory around which she had revolved, she conceded sleepily. So much effort to think…so much easier simply to feel, and she felt wonderfully at peace.

'We spend the weekend on the yacht. I'm in Paris on Monday…you'll *love* Paris, *cara*. What do you think?' he probed.

What did she think? Sara struggled valiantly to think. She thought that he sounded as if he had closed a tremendously difficult and lucrative business deal which had lost some poor fool a fortune and made him another mountain of money that he didn't need: immensely, shamelessly self-satisfied. At that point her brain switched off and she shifted with positive contentment into the warm, comforting solidarity of him.

Her nose twitched on the heady scent of flowers. She lifted heavy eyelids slowly, focused on a giant, beribboned basket of flowers and then another basket…and then another. Her mouth went dry. She woke up in a hurry, jerking upright in an unfamiliar bed in an unfamiliar bedroom and gaped at all the flowers surrounding her. Her attention lodged on a man's silk tie lying in a tiny splash of crimson on top of a dense, creamy carpet and her heart plunged as if she had gone down at supersonic speed in a lift.

She nearly fell out of the bed in her haste to vacate it. Memory took her back and then forward. She turned as white as a sheet and suddenly knew without any prompting what being sober *really* felt like. A case she recognised as her own was sitting by the window. With a pained groan of disbelief, she stared at it. He had somehow got her clothes out of the flat? Oh, dear Lord, what had she done? What *had* she done?

With frantic hands she tore into the case. Taped to the inner lid was a big piece of paper, slashed with Antonia's untidy scrawl. 'What the hell is going on?' it said.

Sara grabbed up a handful of clothes and dived into the *en suite* bathroom. She studied herself in the mirror—red, swollen mouth, shadowed eyes, wildly tousled black hair. Trollop, tart, she castigated herself with tears of rage and shame burning her eyes. How could she have behaved like that with Alex Rossini? She wanted to sink into a great black hole—no, she wanted to put him into a great black hole and pour tons of concrete over him so that he could never escape and she would never have to meet his eyes again!

Thankfully he had already left for the office... Oh, dear heaven, *the office*! It was already after nine. She would say that she had missed the bus. Nobody would think anything of that; nobody need ever know...but if she had had any choice she wouldn't have walked into Rossini Industries ever again. However, there would certainly be talk if she suddenly disappeared and failed to work out the last ten days of her notice—much better to grit her teeth and finish her time there. In any case, she conceded bitterly, she badly needed her month's salary because her bank account was almost empty.

Fumbling, with little of her usual dexterity, she contrived

to confine her hair into a murderously tight bun at the nape of her neck.

She crept out of the bedroom, her arm nearly falling off from the weight of the case she was hauling with her. Tight-mouthed, she dragged it along to the landing at the top of the stairs. With every movement, she was more and more aware of the complaint of newly discovered muscles in unmentionable places and the undeniable ache in the least mentionable place of all, and her rage thundered higher with very step.

'Buon giorno, cara…'

Her throat thickened. Slowly she straightened, stricken eyes flying to the tall, devastatingly attractive male standing at the head of the staircase.

'I was coming up to see if you wanted to join me for breakfast…but we can do without the luggage,' Alex assured her very softly, measuring dark eyes speeding over her furiously flushed face and lingering with incipient shrewdness. 'Don't do it—don't say what's brimming on your lips… Don't disappoint me, *cara.'*

She wanted to kick him down the stairs. A temper that she had never had any trouble controlling until now was suddenly threatening to explode. She sucked in air, freezing her facial muscles. 'I happen to be late for work, Mr Rossini.' Ice dripped from every syllable.

She hit her lowest ebb as she watched his sensual mouth twist and then compress. She didn't need to be told how ridiculous she had sounded. Then his strong dark face tautened. Brilliant dark eyes rested on her. 'Sara…I want you to count to ten and think about last night without prejudice. Is that possible for you?'

'No,' she said woodenly, honestly, dragging her mortified gaze from his—an act which took so much willpower that she felt drained.

'We shared something very special which I don't want…or intend…to lose. It doesn't matter that you were on the rebound…the only thing that matters is how we both feel now,' Alex drawled very quietly. 'Clean page, open book.'

'Close it,' Sara said between gritted teeth.

'I don't mind you cutting off your nose to spite your face…*per Dio*, I mind very much if you attempt to make a similar sacrifice of me!' Alex covered the space between them in one long, fluid stride.

'I made a mistake, damn you!' Sara spat, tears scorching her eyes.

'No, *cara*. That's where you're wrong. What happened between us was no mistake—not for me and not for you either.'

'Am I entitled to voice an opinion of my own?'

'Not right now…no.' Alex lifted the case from her, set it arrogantly aside. 'The prudish streak is threatening to go on the rampage.'

Sara flinched as though he had struck her.

'*Bella mia…*' Alex sighed reprovingly, smoothing long brown fingers caressingly over one pale, taut cheekbone, his accented drawl low and very soft. Even though she didn't want to stand there and allow him to touch her again, something frightening, something stronger than she was kept her still, unresisting, her slender length leaning involuntarily closer as if she wanted to curve into that hand and stretch like a sensual cat. 'Don't leave. I promise not to try and force anything more. You need time and space to think. I'll give it to you. I'll be patient…I'll stay in the background.'

'Alex…' Her voice fractured as she fought to free herself from the spell he cast even while she mentally reeled at the impossible image of Alex Rossini endeavouring to sink into the woodwork.

'There's nothing to be ashamed of, nothing to regret—'

'But I don't *want* this!' Sara gasped, suddenly finding that freedom to speak her own thoughts. She jerked her head away from him. 'I don't want to have an affair with you. Last night was madness—'

'Sweet insanity that worked like a dream... Don't deny what you're feeling right now.'

'I feel nothing...*nothing*!' she swore violently, and, snatching up her case again with an energy born of desperation, she started down the stairs.

'Sara, you cannot possibly go back into the office after this.'

He caught up with her in the hall. A firm hand closed round hers and tugged her back and round to face him again.

'You think I'm going to be your mistress, you think wrong!' Sara threw at him rawly.

'What did I tell you to be sure to remember today? That this was not how I wanted it to be between us,' Alex reminded her with controlled anger. 'But you wouldn't settle for anything less and now you blame me for it. That's very female but bloody unfair.'

Her shocked eyes fell from his. 'I'm not blaming you. I just want to forget this happened, that's all.'

'But I will not play that game...and take your hair out of that excruciatingly ugly old-maid style!' Alex suddenly gritted, and hauled her even closer, banding one strong arm round her narrow back as his free hand roved free to the thick coil of hair and released it from its confinement. 'You're a beautiful young woman; rejoice in that beauty...don't stifle it!'

'Let go of me!' Sara told him shrilly.

'All I want to do is take you back to bed,' Alex confided in an undertone of angrily suppressed passion as he brought her up against him, a lean hand splaying to the feminine swell of her hips with a lover's intimacy.

Appalled cat-green eyes collided with his gaze and the atmosphere sizzled. She blinked bemusedly, feeling the piercingly sweet heat reawaken low in the pit of her stomach, the sudden ache of her nipples as her breasts stirred beneath her bra. Her soft mouth trembled. Alex smiled lazily down at her, shifted with fluid emphasis against her and she felt the force of his arousal with shock. Her lower limbs turned to cotton wool. Her ability to breathe and think for herself diminished with terrifying rapidity. 'Stop it…' she whispered breathlessly.

'One kiss, *bella mia*, and I'll let you go into work,' he bargained mockingly.

'No!' she spat as her heartbeat pounded like a trapped bird in a cage.

'Stubborn…' Alex breathed thickly, amused. 'You want that kiss as much as I do.'

'I'm sorry…I didn't realise…I used the rear entrance,' another voice intervened.

Alex's hand dropped instantly. Sara sprang back from him, eyes wide with horror when she saw Pete Hunniford standing several feet away, his mobile features momentarily transfixed with incredulity and then swiftly rearranged into total impassivity.

CHAPTER THREE

SARA stood there like a graven image as Pete handed a file
to Alex.

'Sara needs a lift back to the office.' Alex quirked a
sardonic black brow as he glanced reflectively at her. 'Unless you've changed your mind, *cara*?'

'No.' She wrenched open the heavy front door for herself, and frankly couldn't get out of the huge house quickly
enough.

Alex dropped an arm round her and walked her out onto
the top step, seemingly indifferent to a degree of icy, re-
pulsing rigidity which would have frozen off the continuing
advances of any normal male. 'Lunch at one…Sara?'

Sara was staring in consternation at the man who had
darted out from his position by the railings and focused a
camera on them both. *Click*! Grinning, he then ran across
the street and jumped into a car. 'How unfortunate,' Alex
said, and he didn't even attempt to sound convincing.

The thick atmosphere between Sara and Pete on the drive
back to the office would have defied the sharpest knife.

'Right,' Pete began grimly. 'Now the first thing you do
is lie like a trooper to dear Brian. You worked late, had to
stay over…you say I was there too. You do not confess;
do you understand that, Sara? Believe me, Brian does not
want the whole truth and nothing but the truth in this in-
stance. That story covers you on all fronts. The paparazzi
are always watching Alex. So there'll be a photo of you
emerging from his house at ten in the morning in tomorrow's papers… What does that prove? Nothing.'

Paper-pale, Sara parted her lips, unsurprised by his cynical advice but deeply embarrassed by his frankness. 'Pete, I—'

'I can't believe it… *You*!' he muttered, shaking his smoothly styled head. 'I thought you were bombproof around Alex. I feel responsible. I only gave you the job because you were engaged. Only the day before yesterday you were handing Alex a cup of coffee as though he was the carrier of some dread social disease, and this morning…?'

'Please, let's not talk about it,' Sara mumbled. She thought of yesterday's sunny awakening, her blinkered innocence of what the day would bring. And then this morning's devastating dawn.

'Obviously Alex finally made a move on you. Well, heaven knows, I've been waiting for it to happen. I've worked around Alex a long time. Believe it or not, I *like* Alex…but if he looked at my sister the way he's always looked at you I'd lock her up and throw away the key…because Alex is very bad news with women. He's emotionally cold and detached. I've seen him in action too many times not to know that—'

'Pete…' Had everyone *but* her been aware of Alex's interest in her?

'Your two predecessors fell head over heels for him and made a blasted nuisance of themselves! I thought you had more sense.'

Sense? When and where had sense figured in yesterday's turmoil? She felt cheap and stupid and desperately ashamed of herself. Was that prudish? But she couldn't discard the values of a lifetime overnight. She had invited…no, far worse, virtually *pleaded* for Alex's sexual attentions. She had thrown herself at his head. Her stomach cramped with nausea.

How could she have done that? Why had she done it? Had she sunk so low in self-esteem that she had been grateful to Alex Rossini for finding her desirable? Had she needed the proof that she could still attract a man after seeing Brian in Antonia's arms? Or on some level had she sought revenge for that agonising betrayal? If that had been her motivation, she was now discovering that revenge was a two-edged sword that could turn back on you and inflict piercing pain and regret.

When she and Pete arrived at the office Gina, the svelte receptionist, gave her a curious, veiled look as she murmured a greeting. Two executive secretaries were out in the corridor having a close conversation, but fell silent as she walked past. Their greetings were very muted indeed. Sara didn't have to wait long to find out why.

'Miss Lacey?' A uniformed waiter whipped the covers from a selection of food on a heated trolley. 'Breakfast, compliments of Mr Rossini.'

'Bloody hell,' Pete said only half under his breath as he drew to a halt beside her. Clearing his throat, he said rather loudly, 'I hope there's enough for two. Working so late, I slept in—didn't have time for much this morning.'

Sara was so taken aback that she couldn't even throw Pete a look of gratitude for his efforts to cover up for her. In any case, who was likely to believe that Alex had demanded Pete to leave his wife's side and work overtime last night?

She sank down behind her desk, watched numbly as the food was served. She hadn't eaten since breakfast yesterday, but she might have eaten last night had she not been far more intent on seducing Alex Rossini into spending the night with her. Hectic colour fired her creamy skin. Alex hadn't wanted her to return to the office. He would be well aware that such an extravagant gesture would create gossip—the kind of gossip that Sara shrank from. Could he be cruel enough to use that as a weapon against her?

'What did Molly have…a boy or a girl?' she asked, striving valiantly for normality.

'Didn't Alex tell you? He was on the phone a good ten

minutes with me yesterday...' Pete flushed. 'Sorry—little girl. We're going to call her Flora.'

'Congratulations.' Sara lifted her knife and fork, her fingers all thumbs.

'Sara...you look like death warmed over,' Pete said, tight-mouthed.

'I'm fine.'

She wondered if she would ever feel fine again. As she forced herself to eat, she drowned in a torrent of brutally unwelcome erotic images. She sat there growing ever more appalled, ever more bewildered by the wanton creature that she had become in Alex Rossini's arms. If only it had been unpleasant, sordid, disappointing even... She hated him all the more for the fact that it hadn't been! She did not think that she could ever forgive herself for finding Alex Rossini more physically exciting than the man she loved. What did that say about her?

Maybe her aunt had been right about her all along. Janice Dalton had regularly lectured Sara on the dangers of promiscuity. As a quiet, far from precocious teenager, Sara had found those sessions deeply humiliating and she had bitterly resented the knowledge that the older woman feared the hereditary factor. 'I don't want you turning out like your mother did,' her aunt had told her. Had the mother she barely remembered slept around? The concept had been distastefully implied more than once. There had always been a grim irony in Janice Dalton's blind refusal to see how her own daughter lived her life.

'Sara?' Pete was in the doorway.

Sara glanced up from the accounts that she was checking. Her job covered a lot of ground. She had overall responsibility for the day-to-day running of Alex's various homes round the world. She dealt with minor household crises, changes of staff, repair and maintenance bills, indeed all the boring minutiae that Alex didn't have time to deal with but which had to be dealt with if the smooth running of his domestic arrangements was to continue with the faultless efficiency that he took for granted.

'I understand that Alex gave an order that you were to receive no personal calls yesterday afternoon.'

'Did he?'

Pete grimaced. 'Brian is on his way up in the lift.'

Every scrap of colour ebbed from her cheeks.

'See him in here. I'll take myself off.'

'But Alex—'

'So Alex doesn't allow personal visitors…but then Alex isn't in yet.'

Sara stood up slowly. Brian appeared on the threshold. He looked as if he'd been up all night—pasty pale, tense, his eyes bloodshot. Pete closed the door on his way out, giving her a ludicrous thumbs-up sign behind Brian's back.

'Sara…' Brian swallowed. 'What do I say to you?'

It was as if a glass wall stood between them, as though a thousand years had passed since yesterday. 'There's nothing to say.' She felt nothing, absolutely nothing at all, only a terrible emptiness.

'She'd been chasing after me for weeks,' he muttered unevenly. 'I'm not making excuses…but—'

'It gave you a kick because she wasn't interested three years ago.'

He flushed and then nodded with compressed lips.

'And you just couldn't help yourself.'

His strained brown eyes met hers. 'That's where you're wrong. I don't even like Toni. I know what she's like. It was just…you know…a physical thing. Damn it, Sara, how do I say to you that I just wanted to go to bed with her and then forget she existed? But that's how it was!' he told her with sudden fierceness, and she could feel him willing her to believe him. 'There was no emotion involved. I know you have to think that's disgusting but it's *you* that I love, *you* that I want to marry.'

His pleading gaze met hers. A knife twisted inside her then. 'You have to know that that is impossible now,' she managed shakily.

'Look, let me tell you it all from the beginning—'

'No, I don't want to know! It's upsetting for both of us to drag this out. I couldn't ever *forget*…you see,' she said chokily, and then she remembered Alex and what she herself had done and spun away, too upset to say anything more.

The door clicked open. Alex lounged there, his densely lashed dark eyes, no shade of gold in their depths, shooting to her with a burning anger that didn't show on his strong dark face but which Sara discovered that she could *feel* with every fibre of her shrinking body. The atmosphere vibrated and she registered in stricken bewilderment that that one scorching look from Alex had filled *her* with guilt. Alex was outraged to find her even talking to Brian.

'I believe you've overstayed your welcome, Shorter,' Alex drawled chillingly. 'Don't come here again.'

Complete bewilderment flashed across Brian's face.

'Alex…' Sara whispered in shock, for in that threatening gaze she recognised the kind of savage, territorial instincts which more properly belonged in the jungle, not in civilised society. She had the frightening suspicion that if Brian said one word out of line Alex would use it as an excuse to throw him down the lift shaft.

'What's going on here?' Brian asked, shaking his blond head. 'I don't understand…'

Alex strolled forward like a prowling panther and slid a fluid arm round Sara's rigid back. 'Sara and I are going for lunch. You're wasting your time,' he delivered very drily.

Brian's jaw dropped. 'Sara?'

Sara didn't know where to put herself. Alex took care of that problem too. He simply swept her out of the office, down the corridor and into the lift. Before the doors slid shut she had a perfect view of Gina's incredulous expression.

'Did you return the ring?' Alex enquired flatly.

Sara finally unglued her tongue from the roof of her shocked mouth. 'How dare you do that to me? How *dare* you speak to Brian like that?'

'How long was he in there with you?' Alex demanded. 'Evidently long enough to tell you a sob story!'

'It's none of your business how long I was with him.'

'You slept in my arms all last night. If that doesn't make it my business, what does?' he responded with devastating frankness. '*Dio*...I'm sure you didn't tell him that.'

A tide of painful heat engulfed every inch of Sara's exposed body. Alex Rossini had been put on earth purely to torment her, she thought in anguished disbelief. He steamrollered over every sensibility she possessed.

'I presume you *did* tell him that he was yesterday's news?'

His expectant silence sizzled.

'What does it matter to you whether I did or not?' she flung at him wildly.

'I don't share my women. It's an old Italian custom,' Alex returned with sardonic bite.

Sara stumbled out into the cool of the underground car park. 'I am not one of your women!'

He swung round. 'Then what are you?'

Her eyes clashing with that coolly enquiring dark gaze, Sara went rigid, her breath catching in her throat. 'I'm in love with another man—'

'Who's already history.' Alex studied her with cool intent. 'A man you never even shared a bed with. What kind of love was that?'

'The kind of love I'm sure you couldn't understand!'

'Pure, perfect love,' Alex mocked. 'It had to be perfect for you, Sara...that was the most important part, wasn't it?'

'I don't know what you're talking about.'

He pressed her into the waiting limousine. 'The white wedding, the virgin sacrifice. It's medieval. What were you going to do if you finally got into the marriage bed and found you didn't like what he did there?'

'Don't be disgusting!' Sara gasped.

'You'd have been a martyr. You'd have gritted your teeth and mentally flipped through a wallpaper book while the poor devil got on with it.'

Outrage leapt through her. 'I refuse to listen to this.'

'You were shocked by your own response last night…'

'No!' she gasped, jerking her dark head away, trembling with the force of her own jagged reactions. Emotions were all churning about on the surface—emotions she wasn't used to handling.

'And you weren't the only one shocked,' Alex breathed, his dark drawl fracturing. 'It never occurred to me that you could still be a virgin, and I would never have got into that bed with you had I known that. I'm not in the habit of taking advantage of untutored innocence.'

'I don't want to talk about it.' Her strained voice quivered. 'I don't even know what I'm doing here with you.'

'You wanted an escape from Brian,' Alex told her grimly. 'That's why you're here.'

Dazedly she closed her eyes. He might as well have reached inside her and read a label. Was she so transparent? Until he'd said it she hadn't even appreciated why she had allowed Alex's arrogant intervention. It had been easier, less painful than prolonging an encounter which could only have gone round in ever more distressing circles. Had Antonia been Brian's dream woman? A dream he had finally set aside? Had he knowingly settled for second best when he'd chosen Sara—someone who shared his interests, his outlook, his goals, but still a woman as different from Antonia as any woman could be? There had been nothing left to talk about with Brian.

'You don't even blame him, do you?' Alex murmured.

Sara searched herself, learnt that once again Alex could hit the target with disturbing accuracy. Her anger had settled into sad acceptance. 'She's very beautiful, very tempting,' she said gruffly.

'She's a blue-eyed blonde with good teeth and long legs. There's a lot of them out there,' Alex returned dismissively.

Momentarily she was transfixed by such a description of her glamorous cousin. Then she reminded herself that on Alex's international scale of beautiful women Antonia might well strike him as being not that special…only that did not explain—indeed it made all the more impossible to understand—*why* Alex should think a five-foot-one-inch brunette secretary worthy of such attention as she was receiving!

And then she understood why and was astonished that she had not solved the riddle sooner. Alex got bored so easily with women. Listening to Pete, wryly concealing her awareness of his helpless masculine envy, she had heard time and time again about just how eager women were to attract Alex Rossini's attention. Sara's greatest attraction could only have been her lack of interest.

Her apparent indifference had singled her out from the rest of the female staff. She couldn't think of a single one who didn't go a little fluttery in Alex's presence. Even happily married, older women were *aware* of Alex's undeniable sexual charge…but Sara had blocked her awareness out, scornfully denying her own instinctively physical response to those spectacular dark good looks of his. Stubborn self-discipline had made it possible for her to close him out…until yesterday, when alcohol and shock had decimated her natural defences.

Alex assisted her out of the car, the warmth of his hand on her arm making her shiver and stiffen. She wanted nothing more to do with him. She had to tell him that. Very possibly he felt grimly responsible for her after what had happened between them. After all, she had turned out to be far less sexually experienced than he had cynically assumed.

The stylish restaurant was disconcertingly empty. Sara blinked as she sank into the chair pulled out for her. A pianist was playing quietly in the corner. Waiters *en masse* engulfed them in the most expensive variety of silent service.

'Where is everyone?' she asked weakly.

'I wanted privacy for us to talk…and I didn't think you would wish to return to my house.'

He had paid for the privilege of an empty room for her benefit? She swallowed hard. A light first course was swiftly served. Alex lounged back with a glass of wine in one shapely hand and surveyed her with immense calm. 'Eat,' he encouraged her softly.

'Let's get the talking over with,' she suggested brittlely.

A rueful smile curved his wide, sensual mouth. 'Sometimes you are very young, *cara*.'

'Just not used to this kind of treatment.'

'Very, very young,' Alex said wryly. 'And if you looked in the mirror without superimposing your cousin's standard of attractiveness you would see what I see. Perfect bone structure, eyes with the colour and depth of emeralds, translucent skin, a wonderfully sultry mouth and a figure that would tempt a saint from celibacy…and I am no saint, *bella mia*.'

Her mouth went dry, soft pink highlighting her cheekbones.

'When I look at you, I see a very lovely woman who walks, talks and behaves as if she's very plain and ordinary. That was what first drew my attention—that complete lack of self-awareness. You made me curious. I thought at first that it was an act, designed to actually attract attention…' As she stiffened he shifted a lithe hand, silencing her. 'Then I watched you look back at me and freeze and I knew that whatever you were you weren't indifferent.'

'If you're trying to say that I actually asked for—'

'If your wedding plans hadn't fallen through I would never have approached you,' Alex asserted softly. 'But no man who desires a woman ignores an opportunity when it comes his way. I didn't plan to take you to bed last night…it was too soon and, in the light of your inexperience, most ill judged, but I had no idea that I would be the first. Don't try to turn what we shared into a tawdry one-night stand. It wasn't, and what is more you know it wasn't.'

Sara dropped her head, forced against her volition to recall his lovemaking, a helpless curl of heat igniting in the pit of her stomach, making her pale and tauten in angry rejection of her body's weakness. 'But that doesn't change how I feel and think. We have different standards. What happened,' she framed tightly, 'shouldn't have happened.'

'But it did and there's no going back.'

'Maybe there wouldn't be if I fancied myself in love with you or something like that.' Her skin warmed, her generous mouth tightening. 'But I don't!'

'Love!' Alex repeated with audible exasperation.

'Obviously not something that comes into your affairs and probably never has done!' She had forced herself to be as honest as she could be. A sexual relationship without any deeper feelings was not for her. She might have leapt out of the frying-pan into the fire last night but she had enough strength of will to admit her own error and still stand her ground.

Alex vented a curiously chilling laugh, his dark eyes as hard as gemstones as he gazed back at her. 'Oh, I've been in love, Sara…a lot more deeply in love than I suspect you have ever been. I was nineteen. She was ten years older. It lasted two fantastic years and then one morning I woke up and she wasn't there any more. I spent six months trying to find her and at the end of that six months I would still

have given every penny I possessed to have her back...
Now that *is* love.'

Sara was shaken by the confession. For a split second
she found herself envisaging Alex as the adoring, very vulnerable satellite of an older woman, but her imagination
could not hold that image for long. At thirty-four there was
nothing of the boy left in Alex. He was an overwhelmingly
self-assured adult male. 'Why did she leave?' she heard
herself ask, unable to stifle a flare of natural curiosity.

'She convinced herself that she was wrong for me.' Alex
shrugged a broad shoulder, his mobile mouth twisting. 'But
she also helped me to free myself from any illusions about
love. Take a degree of mutual respect and liking and add
in sexual attraction and you have a far more secure basis
than you'll ever find with love.'

'I don't believe that.'

'Yet you had your illusions smashed only yesterday,'
Alex reminded her with velvet-smooth cruelty. 'You took
him for granted. You instinctively trusted him not to betray
you. You built a whole rack of unreal expectations on the
basis of the belief that love conquers all. Now, if you hadn't
been *in* love, you wouldn't have made such sweeping assumptions and you wouldn't have felt so safe that you were
blind to the signs that his attention was straying.'

'There may be a certain amount of truth in that but I
would still say that for most people the benefits of loving
and being loved more than outweigh the risks.'

'The feel-good factor,' Alex slotted in with satire. 'But
whether you like it or not we both felt very good last
night...and love had nothing whatsoever to do with it.'

Sara reddened furiously, loathing and helplessly resenting the way he kept on backing her into corners and arguing
with her. Brian and she had almost never argued. She had
seen that as a symbol of the strength of their relationship,
a sign that they were wonderfully well matched. No doubt

another one of the illusions of love which Alex had so coolly delineated.

'Emotionally cold and detached,' Pete had said. For the first time she really saw that aspect of Alex, and it sent a cold tingle down her spine as she contrasted that cool intellect with the apparent warmth and undeniable physical passion that he had shown her yesterday. No, she wouldn't like to be the fool who fell in love with Alex Rossini. The warmth could only have been an illusion, aimed to impress and reassure.

'Last night was last night—time out of time if you want to call it that,' Sara breathed. 'But I won't have an affair with you and I won't be your mistress either.'

'Why not?' Alex said lazily.

Her control snapped. 'Because we have nothing in common. Because we live in different worlds with different values—'

'But *not* because you're not interested.'

Silently fuming, Sara settled back into the limousine. 'Will you allow me to work out my notice without harassment of any kind?'

'Breakfast…was harassment?'

She bit her lower lip and tasted blood. 'You know what I mean…'

'Is what people might think so important to you that you would allow it to rule your life?'

'That's not fair!'

Alex reached for her clenched fingers where they rested on the seat. Momentarily she attempted to draw back from the contact and then, for a reason she could not begin to comprehend, her fingers stayed where they were, curled within his larger hand. She trembled; she didn't know what was happening to her. She had a sudden, terrifying urge to throw herself on Alex and sob her heart out. In all her life she had never felt more confused. He drew her relentlessly closer.

'Alex…no…' she whispered pleadingly.

But Alex didn't listen. He twined lean fingers into her fall of hair, tugging her round to face him. Her eyes burned as she met his shimmering gold enquiry and every tiny muscle tensed. Her pulsebeat thumped at the foot of her throat, a terrible excitement rising inside her no matter how hard she fought to suppress it. 'No…' she said again, as much for her own benefit as for his.

But an aching, compulsive wanting held her still. In dazed silence she recognised the shocking strength of promptings entirely new to her experience. Alex lowered his dark head and took her mouth with hungry urgency. Fire in the hold, she thought wildly, madly, feeling the instantaneous charge of her own helpless response. She wanted to grip him, hold him, mesh with every hard, muscular angle of his lean, virile length. The scent of him, the touch of him inflamed her senses with a drowning passion that was utterly self-absorbed. Tiny little sounds escaped her throat. Hot, electrifying pleasure engulfed her with every thrust of his tongue.

Her fingers slid with shameless hunger beneath his silk shirt, skimming luxuriantly over skin as smooth as velvet, feeling the taut contraction of his sleek muscles as he jerked and groaned beneath her exploration. He swept her up and pulled her down on top of him, expert hands gliding up the quivering stretch of her thighs, hitching up her confining skirt and then bringing her down again, sealing her into raw contact with the hard, throbbing length straining against his zip.

Shuddering, Alex released her swollen mouth, eyes of smouldering gold blazing over her rapt face. 'Come home with me…lie in bed with me…forget everything else,' he breathed raggedly.

In that split second the passenger door beside him sprung

open with a thick clunk. Sara focused dazedly on his chauffeur's mirror-shiny shoes standing on the pavement and then she leapt off Alex with an agility and speed that a mountain goat would have envied, almost falling out of the limousine in her desperate haste to vacate it. Alex grated out something, called her name, but Sara kept on walking, right on past the clutch of Rossini employees who were still staring open-mouthed and incredulous at what they had witnessed.

'Pete…' she said ten minutes later when she had tracked him down, 'I'm afraid I'm about to leave you in the lurch. I think it's time I went home.'

CHAPTER FOUR

'HEAVEN knows, Brian's entitled to an explanation. You've behaved disgracefully!' Janice Dalton railed in angry condemnation. 'The whole village is talking…and how do you think the Shorters feel about all this? They treated you like a daughter!'

'I'm sorry,' Sara whispered shakily.

'You *lied* to me. You told me that you and Brian had decided that you couldn't get married; you didn't have the decency to tell me or him that there was another man involved!'

Say nothing, don't argue and the sooner it will blow over. But after three solid days of recriminations following the publication of that wretched photo of her with Alex that belief was beginning to wear more than a little thin. It had not occurred to Sara when she'd decided to leave London and come home that she might find herself cast as the guilty partner. Brian was playing the martyr, the innocent…letting her take all the flak.

'Give it a rest, Ma.' Antonia appeared in the kitchen doorway, wearing her sunniest and most generous smile. 'At least the wedding invitations weren't in the post.'

'I'll bring the washing in.' Sara headed for the back door with alacrity. When she hit the fresh air, she drank in deeply.

'Blood will out, it seems…' Her aunt's strained voice carried out through the window. 'But nobody could have been more careful than I was raising Sara…'

Sara moved out of earshot and began to take the washing off the line. It was a beautiful May day and she couldn't even appreciate it. She felt like a rat in a trap. The nightmare just seemed to go on and on. Antonia had driven down from London only an hour ago, perfectly groomed, blonde mane fresh from the hairdresser's, not a frazzled nerve in sight. Her cousin simply took it for granted that Sara would not dare to reveal the fact that she had found her in bed with Brian.

But then two wrongs did not make a right. Brian and Antonia's betrayal did not justify her own behaviour with Alex Rossini. But she wasn't trying to excuse herself any more. One misjudged night would not bring her world to an end. What tormented her was the bitter knowledge that Alex's intrusion on the scene had turned what would have been a simple broken engagement into a positive disaster. Her aunt and uncle were outraged by the belief that she had deceived Brian and then dumped him in apparent pursuit of a rich tycoon. That the aforementioned rich tycoon had then seemingly abandoned her was her aunt's sole consolation. Janice Dalton liked to see bad behaviour rewarded by just desserts.

Alex… She tensed, a ground swell of uneasy confusion engulfing her. Sometimes running away was the only way to protect yourself. She did not regret walking out of Rossini Industries that same day. It had been the only possible solution. She had made an absolute ass of herself and that had hit her pride hard, but nobody had ever died from reaping a salutary lesson in common sense.

She couldn't handle Alex Rossini. She couldn't handle a passion that smashed every safe boundary that she had ever observed. Alex had viewed her as an entertaining challenge. Alex had made her a target, amused by the unfamiliar cut and thrust of actually having to try and talk a woman into continuing to share his bed. But ultimately Alex had simply played the one winning card he did have…her undeniable desire for him.

It still appalled Sara that one rogue male could wreak that much havoc. Everything she'd thought she knew about herself had been ripped apart and put together again in a new arrangement that felt entirely alien…and all within the space of twenty-four hours. Little wonder that she had been guilty of such serious misjudgement; little wonder that she had been in turmoil, at the mercy of a seething sexual attraction which had betrayed her when she'd been desperate enough to seek any form of comfort.

'I knew you wouldn't tell tales…'

Sara spun from the low wall that separated the rambling garden from the fields. Antonia was standing a few feet away.

'Only because I didn't see that it would achieve anything but more distress all round.' Sara tilted her chin.

Antonia uttered a sharp little laugh. 'Brian won't even speak to me. He still thinks I made that phone call.'

'Of course you did,' Sara said drily, not having wasted one ounce of mental energy on that minor point.

'I didn't!' her cousin launched back at her furiously. 'I *didn't* make that call! Someone who knew about Brian and me obviously decided it would be fun to drop us in it! Maybe someone he works with, someone who saw us out together… I don't know…but it *wasn't* me!'

Sara didn't care who had made that call to the office. But she was grimly amused by her cousin's vociferous self-defence. Guilty of sleeping with Brian and guilty of complete absence of remorse, but not guilty of making that phone call.

'So tell me the true story about Alex Rossini,' Antonia demanded.

'Why?'

'I could do with a laugh to lighten my day,' Antonia derided. 'Ma has to be out of her mind to imagine that Alex would look at you twice, never mind take you home for the night! Alex Rossini wouldn't even give *me* the time of day the one time I met him. Why do you think I settled for Marco? I bet the most intimate thing you ever did for Alex Rossini was take dictation over breakfast!'

Sara turned back to the wall and braced her hands on the worn stone. She thought of all the years that she had wasted trying to make a friend of Antonia, wondered now why she had bothered when she had been beaten from the outset. Antonia had never forgiven her for depriving her of her cherished only-child status in her family home. Even though her cousin had effortlessly continued to bask in the limelight constantly shone on her by her besotted parents, Sara had remained a bitterly resented intruder.

When Sara had begun dating Brian, the pairing had been popular with both families. Brian's mother loathed Antonia, had been seriously worried when her son had shown an interest in her, and had been seriously relieved when, after a decent interval, he'd switched his interest to Sara instead. As for her uncle and aunt…they liked Brian but would have been very disappointed had their beautiful daughter settled for him. They expected Antonia to marry into wealth and status.

That Sara should get married first had rather astonished the Daltons. But her aunt had thoroughly enjoyed all the fuss of the wedding arrangements and over the past year Sara had grown closer to her than ever before. It hurt now to see that stronger bond broken and at such a cost to everyone concerned. Only Antonia, self-centred as ever, stood clear of the fallout. But then Antonia never took responsibility for anything she did.

'Why did you do it?' Sara asked now, not really expecting a response.

'Brian doesn't love you, he loves me…he just hasn't got the guts to admit it!' Antonia snapped, suddenly on the defensive.

Sara slowly turned, a frown of surprise etched between her brows.

'His mother hates me. She thinks I'm a tart. Brian does

too… Why do you think he went for you? He wants me but he doesn't want me, so he played safe!'

Recognising the bitter resentment in Antonia's eyes, Sara was shaken. Ironically it had not occurred to her that her cousin might actually *care* about Brian. She had assumed that the entire episode had been yet another demonstration of Antonia's helpless need to smash anything which she herself valued. An act of spite and superiority.

'But there's only one thing I want to talk about,' Antonia continued angrily. 'Brian's acting like an idiot, chasing after you, refusing to have anything to do with me…but that's only because he's feeling guilty. Let him off the hook. Tell him you understand and that you accept that your engagement is over. I don't want him to feel trapped with me.'

'Trapped?' Sara echoed, not following.

Antonia looked unconvincingly coy and then shrugged a slim shoulder with quite unhidden self-satisfaction. 'I think I may be pregnant…'

'I think I may be pregnant…' It was like a body-blow to Sara. She went white. In an instant she learnt that her pain was not yet at an end. She had faced up squarely to their betrayal…but still the concept of Antonia pregnant with Brian's child could only make her feel sick. *She* had expected to have Brian's child.

'And I'm not telling him until he's stopped this stupid guilt trip about you!'

'I might as well have told tales…' Sara mumbled.

'No!' Antonia told her sharply. 'There's no reason for anyone to know *when* I got caught. You take yourself off back to London. I will be seen consoling Brian and then we'll go abroad and get hitched on a beach somewhere without any fuss. Everyone will think we were madly impulsive but I doubt if they'll suspect it was a shotgun do!'

'You have it all worked out.' No humiliation for Antonia.

'Brian was mine,' her cousin said with flat emphasis.

'And I can't say sorry when I don't feel sorry. Just you make sure you tell him I didn't make that phone call.'

A hysterical laugh clogged Sara's throat. Antonia didn't only expect her to take the heat for her, she also expected her to intercede on her behalf with Brian. So her cousin wasn't as sure of Brian as she wanted to be. But then why else would she be pregnant? That, given Antonia's experience, was unlikely to be an accident. Dear Lord, for how long had they been meeting behind her back?

In the kitchen Janice Dalton was fussing frantically over a tea-tray. 'Brian and his parents have come over!' she said, tight-mouthed. 'What are your uncle and I supposed to say to them?'

Sara almost laughed but she was afraid that if she did she wouldn't be able to stop. Brian here? And with his parents in tow? She had already heard all about how shocked and furious the Shorters were. Everyone was jumping on the same bandwagon. In the Dark Ages she'd have been dragged out to the village common and burnt as a witch for the sin of having offended so many people.

Be careful of what you wish for in case you get it… Last week she had passionately hated her dull, 'nice girl' image; this week she would have given ten years of her life to have her reputation back, to be able to walk down the village street again without nudges, turned backs and coldly disapproving stares. Notoriety wasn't fun, not in a small, close-knit community where so many people reserved the right to stand in moral judgement.

The doorbell shrilled. Halfway down the polished hall she was intercepted by Brian as he emerged from the lounge. 'Sara…I had to see you. We have to sort this out.'

'Tell them the truth!' she gasped, incredulous at his persistence and attempting to drag her arm free of his hold.

'Why did you tell your aunt we were finished? Why the blazes did you have to get caught in that stupid photo with Alex Rossini?' Brian demanded resentfully. 'Don't you realise what an idiot that's made me look? I know there's nothing going on between you and Rossini…there *couldn't* be…but it's made things even more complicated.'

The doorbell went again as if someone had a finger welded to the button. The piercing noise ground along her already jagged nerve-endings like a knife being sharpened.

'Let go of me,' Sara pleaded in despair, her voice shaking.

'I love you and I still want to marry you… If we don't talk, how are we going to work this out?'

Sara couldn't bear to listen to him. It was as if Brian was living in some fantasy world of his own. She tore herself free of his grasp with such force that she almost crashed against the front door. She hauled it open, her strained face a mask of desperation.

It was Alex. The shock of it rocked her back on her heels. But she experienced a flood of relief so powerful that it left her dizzy. She swayed, her head swimming. Strong arms reached out and caught her before her knees could buckle beneath her.

'What the hell has been going on here?' Alex demanded chillingly.

'Alex…' Sara whispered as she leant up against him, entirely supported by his superior strength and so grateful for his presence that she felt weak. 'Get me out of here…*please*!'

'Take your hands off her!' Brian raked at him after an astounded pause.

Alex ignored him. Swinging on his heel, he walked Sara out to a black Bugatti sports car, calmly slotted her into the passenger seat and murmured softly, 'I'll be back in a minute, *cara*.'

Sara snatched in an unsteady breath. Who do you think Alex is—some white knight riding gallantly to your rescue? a little voice asked drily. She shut the voice off. All she knew was that she had never been so glad to see anyone. At that moment it was more than enough.

She watched Alex emerge from the house again, couldn't even summon up the curiosity to wonder why he had gone back in. His black hair was ruffled by the breeze but so perfectly cut that it fell straight back into place. Dark eyes mirrored the sunlight—flashing gold against the hard symmetry of his masculine features. He looked quite extravagantly gorgeous in a pearl-grey suit that was very Italian in style. The overall effect was one of quite breathtaking elegance and sophistication. *Who* was she? she found herself wondering helplessly. Who was the woman who had walked away when Alex had laid his heart at her feet?

He swung in beside her. 'You have some preference about where you would like to go?'

'Anywhere…'

He laughed spontaneously. '*Dio*, I timed my arrival well. I also have plans of my own…'

That was scarcely a revelation. Alex would always know exactly where he was going and what he was doing. Unlike Brian…Brian, who she had once fondly believed to be strong, decisive and forthright, she reflected painfully. Right now Brian seemed lost in a turmoil of his own making, and he had been loyal to neither her nor Antonia. Had Brian come to her that day in her office and told her that he *loved* her cousin, she would have respected him more and understood him better.

'You've lost weight,' Alex remarked casually.

'Scarlet women do.'

'You get much thinner and you'll slide through a grating. There wasn't a lot of you to begin with.'

Was she getting too thin? She glanced down anxiously at the slender curves filling out her pink cotton T-shirt and jeans, and for some reason also recalled that she had no makeup on. Her cheeks flushed. For goodness' sake! It wasn't as if she was out on a hot date!

'Why did you come down?' she asked.

'I missed you?'

'Try again.'

'I was a little worried about the effect of all the publicity?'

'The little-office-girl-makes-good bit...or the Alex-Rossini-goes-down-market bit?'

'If being with you is slumming, there's not an office girl in the City safe.' Alex casually tossed a newspaper onto her lap. 'Have you seen the latest?'

Sara stiffened. 'I thought I'd had my fifteen minutes of fame.'

With a sinking heart, she read the gossip column. Tasmin Laslo was reportedly furious to learn that she had been replaced by a woman she described as 'an impertinent little typist', and the actress had gone on to share the news that the same typist had called her employer 'a slick, womanising swine'.

'I said it,' Sara whispered sickly. 'I said it that day when she phoned...that she was well rid of you.'

'Honesty got the better of you?'

'You have every right to be angry with me,' Sara conceded tautly.

'It was a fair assessment of my character to date. I don't give a damn, but if I know Tasmin she'll find a way to make this story run and run.'

Yet even in receipt of that daunting assurance Sara could feel a sense of calm stealing over her for the first time in days. It was the most incredible relief to escape the hothouse pressure and angry tensions of the Dalton household.

'Antonia's pregnant.' It leapt straight out of her subconscious onto her tongue.

Alex burst out laughing. Sara dealt him a stunned look.

'Sorry, *cara*. That was not very kind of me...but it does cross one's mind that, whatever else she is, she's a remarkably determined young woman.'

'Brian doesn't know yet. Of course, when he does…he'll leave me alone.'

'Is that what you want?'

'Yes…absolutely,' Sara returned, fiercely defensive on that point.

'I suspect the heat is already off you,' Alex delivered smoothly. 'When I went back into the house, I told them.'

Her seat belt pulled tight as Sara's back jerked blade-straight. 'Told them what?'

'I only wanted to make myself known to your family. Under fire, you surely did not expect me to pose alongside you as a martyred miscreant?'

Sara's jaw dropped as she gazed back at him wide-eyed. 'What did you tell them?'

'I merely pointed out that our relationship only began after you discovered that your fiancé and your cousin had been seeing each other behind your back. I was far kinder to them than they were to you,' Alex imparted, quite untouched by her consternation. 'I did not refer to the fact that you found them between the sheets. I find it quite impossible to comprehend why you should have felt the need to protect them in the face of the kind of treatment you have obviously been receiving.'

'It'll devastate my aunt and uncle—'

'Let them be devastated. She is their daughter and you are not her keeper.'

'You had no right to tell them!' Sara gasped.

'In the light of what I overheard before I entered the room, I enjoyed telling them. Your cousin staged a most unconvincing faint. Your ex put on a fetching impression of a trout on a hook. And then, as I was withdrawing to leave them all to it, the rather large blonde woman in the pearls made a decidedly offensive remark about your cousin's morals…something which rankled so severely that your cousin literally couldn't take it lying down.' Alex's accented drawl trembled with betraying amusement. 'She came up out of her faint like a vampire rising from the tomb and began screeching at the top of her voice!'

'Quite priceless entertainment, I gather?' But Sara's own voice had developed an involuntary wobble. She was genuinely shocked by Alex's sublime indifference to the feelings of everyone concerned but the picture that he had drawn was so vivid, so innately rich with black comedy that she couldn't help the ripple of amusement which briefly gripped her.

'You see, *bella mia*...you can laugh and smile again,' Alex murmured with satisfaction.

'Even when I hate myself for it? Even when I have no right to feel superior to Brian and Antonia?' she muttered feverishly. 'The same day...I slept with you.'

'But you would never have done that had you still considered yourself morally bound to him. You're too loyal. Nor can I believe that you would have practised such deceit as they did.'

'You could talk me right out of my conscience,' Sara whispered.

'It might be an improvement if you stopped behaving like a schoolgirl fresh out of a convent. Nobody's perfect,' Alex reminded her, taking some of the sting out of that initial statement.

'I owe Antonia's parents a great deal. If they hadn't given me a home when I was five, I would have gone into care. They took me in and brought me up just as if I was their own child.'

'Liar. I saw a dozen photos of her decorating the room, none whatsoever of you. They are comfortably off yet you left school at sixteen and made your own way in life.'

'My choice. You couldn't have expected them to do more. My aunt didn't even particularly want to take me on. I'm illegitimate,' Sara pointed out stiffly.

'Not so uncommon these days.'

'My father was a Greek waiter.'

'Rich, warm Mediterranean blood…do I apologise for mine?' Alex elevated an ebony brow with decided hauteur.

Sara was betrayed into a rueful laugh. 'I wasn't apologising—'

'You were. How did your parents meet?'

'My mother was on holiday. She was only out there a week. She was twenty-one,' Sara told him. 'Nobody wanted her to keep me but she did. So they told her she could manage on her own… It's fair enough that they weren't exactly over the moon when I landed back on their doorstep. My grandparents were too old to take me on. Antonia was only a year older. My aunt and uncle stepped in. They didn't *have* to.'

Alex made no comment. Sara rested her head back, the tension draining out of her, her limbs slowly sinking into relaxation. 'As usual I'm not asking where we're going.'

'You don't really care.'

Her skin reddened. 'No…I'm just grateful for a break.'

'I don't want gratitude, *cara*.'

An odd chill ran down her spine. As she watched the countryside flying by she never forgot for one moment that she was sitting beside Alex Rossini. Her awareness of him was so intense that she couldn't hide from it. The frozen front that she had once contrived to put up in his presence was now quite impossible to maintain.

'We're almost there.' Alex swung off the road and drove down a long, tree-lined lane past a Gothic gatehouse.

'Where is ''there''?' She tested a smile, found it was not so difficult as she had imagined it would be.

'Ladymead Hall. It's on the market and I have an appointment to view it.'

'You want a house in the country?'

'A base within easy reach of London.' Alex brought the powerful car to an abrupt halt before it hit a string of potholes. There was already a Mercedes parked ahead of them. Sara gazed out at the mellowed brick frontage of the

Elizabethan manor house. Interest flickered and then slowly flamed. She climbed out. Sunlight glinted off the mullioned windows, several of which were boarded up. The ancient building had the same sad air of neglect as the overgrown grounds.

'Do you want me to wait in the car?' Sara asked abruptly across the bonnet.

'Of course not.' Alex strolled forward to greet the suavely suited estate agent, but Sara changed course and walked over to the entrance, not wishing to intrude.

'We'll explore alone.' Rejoining her, Alex planted a glossy brochure carelessly in her hand. 'You can give me the feminine viewpoint.'

The interior was better preserved than the exterior had suggested. The great hall had a massive stone fireplace and a wonderful flagstone floor. From room to room Sara wandered silently by Alex's side, her rapt face taking in the intact linenfold panelling, the elaborate if filthy plasterwork on the ceilings. The kitchen still rejoiced in massive built-in dressers. She pictured an Aga…a green one…in the fireplace. No, not there—that old black range ought to be cleaned up and preserved, she decided. The Aga would have to go at the other end.

A mouse ran over her foot; she didn't notice it. She roamed industriously through the maze of little dirty rooms which ran off the kitchen, mentally labelling them—logs, laundry, cloakroom, boiler room, junk—and frowned in intense concentration when she ran out of labels. She climbed the lavishly carved oak staircase, her fingers lingering here and there on the elaborate exuberance of the Jacobean ornamentation. Not a single word passed her lips.

Finally, at the head of the long gallery, sunlight beaming in from the windows in diamond patterns, dust motes dancing in the air, Sara uttered a dreamy sigh of enchantment and then endeavoured to be rationally judgemental for Alex's benefit. 'It's a very large house.'

'Do you think so? I thought it was rather modest,' Alex admitted softly.

Sara gazed out of a tall window and another smile curved her generous mouth. 'There's a topiary garden down there. I wonder if it could be saved? I suppose there once would have been a herb garden too.'

'An enormous amount of renovation would be required.'

Sara's head spun round, dismayed green eyes flying to him. 'You surely wouldn't let that put you off?'

'I have to confess that I would prefer to buy after someone else had done the dirty work.'

She thought of his immaculate Georgian house in London, the cool, contemporary decor of the few rooms that she had glimpsed, and nodded in rueful understanding.

'But I can see this as a family house...as a home,' Alex said, his accent feathering almost seductively over the syllables.

'Yes,' she sighed, thinking, Definitely not down Alex's street.

'Marry me and make it that...'

Her lashes flew up on stunned emerald eyes, her breath tripping in her throat. She stared back at him in a daze of disbelief.

'I want a wife, and...eventually...children.' Alex selected the last word with the same utterly complete calm. 'I also want you. We both appear to want the same things at this stage in our lives. Why should we not seek them together?'

The tip of her tongue stole out to moisten her full lower lip. Her mind was a total blank, and then she met Alex's dark golden gaze and the electrifying effect scorched along every nerve-ending, igniting a sudden surge of colour in her cheeks. She trembled, shattered by the immediacy of a response over which she had absolutely no control.

He took a prowling step closer. 'We already have the passion without which no marriage of convenience could hope to prosper. You want me, *bella mia*…do not be ashamed to admit that.'

'I can't believe that you want to get married—'

'I'm thirty-four, Sara…and I openly confess to having enjoyed my freedom for many years. However, women are not the only ones who get the urge to settle down with one partner.'

'I know but—'

'A practical marriage and a civilised relationship—that is what I am offering you. Where there is no strong emotion there will be no pain either,' Alex pointed out, his night-dark eyes skimming over her troubled face. 'In short, I will not hurt you, Sara.'

Alex didn't want a wife who was madly in love with him. He didn't want to become the focus of emotions that he had no intention of returning. That made a cold kind of sense to her. Women in love could be very demanding creatures. A woman in love with a man who did not love her might easily become jealous, possessive and insecure if the inequality within the relationship began to threaten her self-respect.

'Why me…for heavens' sake?' Sara murmured not quite steadily. 'You hardly know me.'

'I beg to differ. You have worked for me for a year. I know you to be cool under pressure, efficient, something of a perfectionist and an excellent organiser. You are more likely to be early for an appointment than late. You are respected and liked by your subordinates but regarded as rather reserved because you never participate in the office gossip.'

Sara was blushing fierily. 'I do hope you'll put all that in a reference for when I go job-hunting again. I sound like a model employee.'

'You were, but you were never ambitious in the career stakes.'

Sara turned away, her lower limbs feeling as if they were stuffed with cotton wool. 'No,' she conceded wryly.

'Which also suits my purposes. I travel a great deal. A wife with a demanding career of her own would have little time to spare for home and family in my absence.'

'Home and family'? Damn him, damn him, damn him for the calculating, coolly assured character assessor that he was! Alex knew what she had so lately lost, could only be aware of the strength of the lure that he was casting out to her when she was facing a wretchedly uncertain future, bereft of everything that she had expected to be hers.

'And, if you will forgive me for making the point, I believe I have also seen you at your worst.'

Her narrow back went rigid. 'Falling-down drunk and desperate?'

'You were still strong, still worthy of my respect…you threw no tantrums, wallowed in no self-pity and indulged in no vindictive outbursts. You behaved with remarkable self-restraint. I admired that.'

He had to be a lethal poker player. Sara had an insane image of herself going down on her knees and kissing his feet in gratitude for such assurances. But Alex *had* treated her with respect, consideration and understanding, without any overtones of superiority or pity. All those things Alex had given her and she had taken, not even truly valuing what she was receiving at the time.

Yet Brian, whom she had loved and trusted and believed in, had almost destroyed her. Brian…still talking about reconciliation with the arrogant and distasteful conviction that no matter what he had done she would ultimately forgive him. Brian, coolly disparaging her worth with his incredulity that a male of Alex's wealth and importance could find her deserving of interest. She had never seen that conceit and egotism in Brian until now.

There was a savage irony in making a comparison between two such radically different men, one whom she had adoringly placed on a pedestal and endowed with every conceivable virtue, the other whom she had disliked and misjudged and distrusted. She was ashamed of that now—ashamed that her gauche unease in Alex's disturbingly physical presence had led her into such unjustifiable prejudice.

'Alex…I can't deny that you're tempting me…but I don't think that I'm in a state of mind right now to be dealing with such a major decision,' Sara returned unsteadily, her jewel-like eyes unguarded and anxious.

'No doubt you feel that you don't know me well enough.'

'I know you well enough, Alex,' Sara said a little shyly, reflecting that while she had been at her worst Alex had been at his best. 'And the one thing this mess with Brian has taught me is that even though I've known him almost all my life I didn't *really* know him at all when the chips were down. I didn't suspect that he was still attracted to Antonia and I didn't once notice anything odd in his behaviour, but then, as you said, love makes you take people for granted, gives you a false, rosy picture and too many high-flown ideas. Was it like that for you— I mean with…?'

'Elissa? Naturally. At that age I was a great romantic. But the pain fades…I can assure you of that,' he replied very drily.

Elissa—lovely name, she thought abstractedly as she gazed at Alex's chiselled golden profile. He was so very, very good-looking that even at a time like this, when it was so important that she should not be distracted, she was.

'You're a very rich man,' Sara pointed out in some embarrassment. 'There must be loads of women…you know…who would be much more suitable than me…'

Alex dealt her a cynically amused smile. 'But you are very special, *cara*. My embarrassment of riches did not tempt you an inch away from your moral standards last week. I liked that too. I would not like to be married solely on the basis of what I can deliver materially.'

It crossed her mind that Alex believed he had her so well taped that she would provide him with no unwelcome surprises. Perhaps all that she had despised in herself a mere week ago was ironically Alex's standard of what his wife should be. An old-fashioned home-maker with traditional values, highly unlikely to take off with the chauffeur one day, or announce that pregnancy might ruin her figure, or make spoilt-rich-girl demands on a male who was very much accustomed to having everything go *his* way.

'I don't know what to say...'

'You say yes.' Alex stretched out his hands and she reached for them, helplessly revelling in the warmth of physical contact.

'It would be crazy.'

'If you think that, my talents as a negotiator must be failing.'

Alex was a brilliant negotiator, pulling off the kind of stunning deals which made his competitors howl in anguish. But to negotiate a marriage proposal seemed so...so *cold*. Hurriedly she squashed the suspicion. There was nothing cold about the male arms relentlessly tugging her closer, nothing cold about utilising intelligence and cool, calm forethought in so important a field as choosing a life partner, she told herself.

'I can't think straight...'

He laughed softly, dark eyes flashing gold with innate male satisfaction. He knew why she was in such a condition, knew that he could draw her, unresisting and quivering, into contact with every hard, muscular line of his length and extract a response that she had not yet learned to control.

With a shapely hand he stroked a silky strand of black hair back from her brow. Her heartbeat was racing like crazy, her breasts lifting within a light cotton bra which suddenly felt unbearably restrictive. 'I also like the fact that I excite you…' Alex purred.

A flush of horribly self-conscious heat marked out her slanted cheekbones as he glanced down at the thrusting evidence of her stiffened nipples poking through the cotton jersey. 'Don't be shy,' he reproved her, leaning her back against the wall, sliding his hands below the T-shirt to skim caressingly up over the smooth skin of her taut ribcage.

Sara stopped breathing, held still by the smoulder of his golden eyes. With breathtaking cool, he flipped the bra out of his path. Her breasts sprang full and heavy into his shaping hands. Sensation fired a bitter-sweet ache between her thighs. She trembled. His thumbs grazed the achingly sensitive buds and she moaned and jerked, looking down at her wantonly bare flesh in mingled disbelief and excitement.

His dark head lowered. He ran the tip of his tongue along her full lower lip and then, with innately erotic precision, intruded sexily into the moist interior already invitingly opened to him. A stifled moan was torn from her, her hands rising of their own volition and clutching at his shoulders to prevent her sliding down the wall in an inelegant heap of shuddering responsiveness.

'If you don't become my wife, I'll make you my mistress,' Alex warned softly. 'I am not going to go away, not about to politely withdraw in gentlemanly defeat.'

He straightened, expertly replaced her disarranged clothing. Sara was shaking but not so controlled by the dissatisfied ache of her shamefully willing body that she was deaf to the message he wanted her to receive. Angry humiliation leapt up in place of passion. She stepped back and flung him a look of warning. 'If you ever do that to me again, Alex, I'll slap your face—hard! I am not some brainless little toy you can play with and I'm not a wind-up doll either. I will not be controlled or manipulated by you!'

'But you will marry me.'

The conviction with which he made that assurance threw Sara even further off balance.

'I...I need to think about it,' she muttered unevenly.

'Back in that madhouse? How could you think there? I want an answer now,' Alex declared. 'Yes or no will suffice...for this round.'

She wrenched her eyes from him, struggled to rise above the quite startling temptation to tell him to take his proposal and jump off a cliff. Her brain told her that she was too emotionally charged up right now to make a level-headed decision but every other natural prompting urged blind, immediate acceptance.

Alex was offering her everything that she had ever wanted on terms that she could fulfil, and on one level there was a part of her, which she tried and failed to overcome, that was helplessly, deeply influenced by the knowledge that Alex wanted her and valued her. That awareness was balm to her salvaged ego and Alex was offering her an unbelievably welcome escape from a situation that was threatening to become quite intolerable.

'Yes.' The instant she said it she almost retracted it again, but then she thought of how it would feel to stand on the sidelines while Antonia married Brian. She would be an object of pity, the spectre at the feast, the onlooker who embarrassed everyone. In one small family there was no room for the rejected bride *and* her replacement. Why put herself through such humiliation? Nobody could possibly feel sorry for Alex Rossini's chosen wife...could they?

CHAPTER FIVE

'IT'S a magnificent gown. Of course we couldn't have afforded anything this elaborate,' Janice Dalton remarked stiffly. 'I expect with the number of important people coming Alex wanted you to look really special. But your uncle and I will feel total frauds sitting at the top table. We haven't done a thing to help... But then it's all been done in such a frantic rush...'

Sara sent the older woman a veiled glance, troubled by her constrained manner. Alex's revelation about Antonia and Brian had shattered her aunt. Both the Daltons had been very upset by their daughter's behaviour. Brian and Antonia's deceit had been a bitter pill to swallow, unsweetened by Antonia's refusal to express the slightest regret.

'Sara...it's still not too late to change your mind,' her aunt muttered tightly.

The wedding was a mere two hours away. Sara almost laughed at the idea. 'I don't want to change my mind.'

'Alex is very rich and very handsome,' the older woman added with a rather peevish edge to her delivery. 'But he's also a rather overwhelming personality. Naturally, I want you to be happy...but are you really sure you're making the right decision?'

'I want to marry Alex.' That belief had buoyed Sara up over every day of the past month. It was like a rock that she clung to when the winds of change threatened to howl around her. As long as she had focused on Alex, her future home and her approaching wedding, she had been able to sit safe inside a neat little emotional cocoon. Brian and Antonia had gone back to London. She had seen neither of them since that day when Alex had swept her off in the

Bugatti to Ladymead. Both her cousin and her ex-fiancé had found retreat from family recriminations the most comfortable option.

Ladymead… An abstracted smile curved Sara's lips. Alex had bought her dream house. He had sent her back to the car with the satirical assurance that he didn't want the estate agent to catch one glimpse of her enchanted face. 'Do you know if there's anybody else interested?' she had pressed anxiously.

'There is precious little that I desire that I cannot buy.' For an instant, assailed by the dryness of that tone and the sudden coolness of those brilliant dark eyes, Sara had experienced the most peculiar inner chill.

She shook off the memory, choosing to recall instead her aunt and uncle's shaken response to Alex's announcement that same evening that they were getting married as soon as it could be arranged. 'A rather overwhelming personality'… Yes, the Daltons had been so overpowered by Alex that they hadn't uttered a word of protest, had indeed struggled valiantly to conceal their astonishment, but there had also been perceptible relief in their reaction. If Sara had found another bridegroom, nobody needed to feel quite so bad.

Alex had assured them that he would handle all the arrangements. And he had…or his staff had. Sara hadn't had an input either and hadn't wanted one. She had spent the past year up to her throat and revelling in all the endless tiny details of bridal fervour. This time she was grateful not to be involved, not to be reminded of that *other* wedding which would now never take place. Alex had been supremely tactful, she thought gratefully.

The doorbell went. Her aunt went downstairs. Sara frowned when she heard her uncle Hugh's voice. He sounded upset. She walked out onto the landing.

'Tell me it isn't true,' her uncle was protesting dazedly. 'You can't make an announcement like that on Sara's wedding day!' her aunt was saying vehemently to someone standing out of view in the hall below. 'What would people think of you?'

'What's going on?' Sara asked tautly.

Antonia strolled forward and looked up. 'Brian and I got married in a register office yesterday.'

Sara went very still. 'Congratulations,' she murmured. 'I am very pleased for you both.'

Ignoring the burst of angry speech from her uncle, Sara walked back into her bedroom. Well, she had known it was coming, hadn't she? And she was marrying Alex in a couple of hours. The bridesmaids, whom she had not even met, would be arriving soon—Alex's three half-sisters, all flown in from abroad for the occasion and putting up at the Savoy. Her eyes burned. She quivered, drew in a deep breath and slowly let it escape again. She even contrived a wry smile. Antonia had, as usual, beaten her to the starting line. And she did wish them happy. It was just…just that she would rather not have known today…that was all.

'You and Alex Rossini…'

Sara jerked around. She hadn't heard the door open. Antonia stood on the threshold, her eyes glittering feverishly beneath the stylish brimmed hat she wore.

'Please don't cause a scene,' Janice Dalton pleaded tautly, preceding her daughter into the room.

'Sara makes me sick,' Antonia hissed rawly, ignoring her mother. 'Always says the right thing, always does the right thing. And—whoopee—she grabs a billionaire the same day she loses Brian! I bet Alex Rossini is madly in love with her too…he certainly can't wait to get her to the altar! I bet her mother-in-law adores her just like that old witch Shorter does! I bet she's going to spend the rest of her life in the lap of luxury, cosseted and appreciated and adored. It would make *anyone* want to throw up!'

And with that bitterly resentful conclusion Antonia

stalked out again. The only sound that broke the thrumming silence was the thunderous slam of the front door.

Tight-mouthed, Sara's aunt sank into a chair. 'She's so horribly jealous of you. She always was…'

Jealous? Antonia jealous of *her*? Sara was stunned by the concept.

'We spoilt her more when we saw how she felt. We thought that would make her feel more secure. But it didn't change her feelings and it really isn't her fault, you know,' the older woman continued defensively. 'After all, she wasn't asked for her opinion when we took you into the family.'

'I can't believe Antonia could be jealous of me.'

Her aunt gave her a humourless smile. 'Of course she's jealous, Sara. People always seem to like you more than they like her. Other women are envious of her looks and can't bear the competition. All too many people are willing to judge Antonia for becoming involved with Brian…when really it's something that could have happened to anyone. But that's why I've invited them both to your wedding.'

Sara slowly turned from the mirror. 'You invited *them*…you invited Brian?' she whispered sickly, belatedly understanding the significance of Antonia's very dressy outfit.

Her aunt lifted her greying head high. 'I thought it would look better if they both came. It will show our friends that there's no acrimony, just a rather last-minute change of partners.' Her voice hardened. 'I don't want people thinking badly of my daughter, Sara.'

'No.' Sara understood that, but, while she could have borne Antonia out of respect to her uncle and aunt, she *still* didn't want Brian at her wedding.

The arrival of Alex's sisters in their finery was a very welcome diversion. Sara had not yet fathomed the complex Rossini family tree that was the result of Alex's father currently being on his fifth wife. Alex's mother had been

Sandro Rossini's first wife and the only one to pass on into history through death rather than divorce. Donatella and the identical twins, Cara and Lucilla, all crowded into Sara's far from large bedroom, bubbling with curiosity, excitement and mercifully excellent English.

'So like Alex to do the unexpected,' Donatella laughed, and spontaneously grasped Sara's hands. An attractive brunette, she was only a couple of years younger than Alex, still single and a water-colour artist of growing reputation in Italy. 'I would kiss you but I might smudge your makeup.'

'You're so beautiful!' Cara carolled with a fourteen-year-old's exuberance. 'I'm not surprised it took Alex a whole year to catch you! Papà is so relieved he's getting married at last. He thought Alex was never going to get over Elissa!'

'Let me help you with your gown.' Donatella stepped into the breach of sudden silence with easy tact while Lucilla nudged her twin in the ribs. Cara's cheeks were already burning fierily.

Elissa, blasted Elissa being mentioned *again*! Sara was astonished by the amount of annoyance running through her. For heaven's sake, Alex hadn't laid eyes on the wretched woman for thirteen years! Surely even the most passionate youthful love affair was little more than a sentimental memory after that length of time?

An hour later Sara walked up the aisle of the local church on her uncle's arm. Alex turned and dealt her a slow smile. Her nervous tension evaporated but her sense of unreality somehow increased. So many strange faces, so few familiar in the crowds that surrounded them while the photos were being taken after the ceremony. She watched security guards keeping the Press at bay. One of them looked eerily familiar, a premature and very noticeable streak of grey evident in his otherwise black hair... Where had she seen him before? The question nagged annoyingly at the back of her mind.

Alex's father, Sandro, embraced her with flattering enthusiasm. His six-foot-tall blonde wife, Francine, gave her an easy smile and shook hands. 'Welcome to the family, Sara,' she murmured in her distinctive American drawl.

As the limousine drew away from the church, Alex angled a wry glance at her. 'So we are finally together. Believe me, it wasn't my intention that we should scarcely see each other before the wedding. But the trips to New York and Milan were scheduled weeks ago.'

'I kept myself busy.' Sara hurried to assure him, keen to make him believe that she had not felt neglected and that she wasn't the type to moan and nag when business took him abroad. But in truth, she acknowledged, she had been thoroughly fed up. Two evenings out in three weeks, one of which had had to include her aunt and uncle, had done little to remove the lowering suspicion that once Alex had gained her agreement to marry him he had switched his entire attention back to more important things...like making more money, when he already had so much that he couldn't spend it in a lifetime!

'Yes. I understand you've been over at Ladymead on a very regular basis—'

'I wanted to be present when the surveys were being done, and that architect you recommended was marvellously helpful,' Sara responded with enthusiasm. 'And you remember that specialist I mentioned...?'

'Which one?' Alex enquired with a lack of interest so profound that even Sara could not have missed it.

Sara reddened. 'Sorry, am I being a bore?'

'You've kept me fully up to date with developments on the phone,' Alex reminded her with a rather grim smile.

'You do *like* Ladymead?' It shook Sara at that instant to recognise the fact that she had never asked Alex that question before.

'What a foolish question, *cara*. Of course I do.' He reached out and linked her taut fingers with his. 'You make a ravishing bride.'

'It's a gorgeous dress—'

'Don't do that...don't put yourself down. I would not have married a less than ravishingly beautiful woman,' Alex informed her with lazy mockery.

Much of the tension that he had awakened evaporated. Had she imagined that shadow darkening his lean features? She reminded herself that Alex was volatile and that, whether she liked it or not, she had to learn not to be over-sensitive to his fairly rapid changes in mood. And since she had always been the calm type, surely that wouldn't be too difficult?

'Antonia and Brian got married yesterday,' she told him tautly, wondering if her cousin and her ex would show up at the reception. She hadn't seen them at the church but then it was perfectly possible that she could have missed them in the crush.

'I hope it was as hole-and-corner as the courtship,' Alex said very drily.

'My aunt invited them both to the wedding.'

Alex withdrew his hand with a jerk and turned shimmering dark eyes on her. 'She did *what*?'

'Antonia *is* their daughter, Alex,' Sara pointed out rue-fully. 'And my aunt felt that it would cause more comment if they weren't invited as a couple. Brian's mother has already been saying some very nasty things about Antonia to anyone prepared to listen—'

'When are *you* going to say them? *Dio*...love thy enemy,' Alex grated with impatience. 'I didn't want either of them present today.'

'I can understand why *I* could feel that way...but not why you should.' In the back of her mind loomed the horrid realisation that within an hour of the wedding they were having their first fight. 'After all, Brian is going to be like my brother-in-law now.' And her voice fractured slightly on that daunting realisation.

Alex treated her to a sizzling glance. 'Finding it difficult to adjust?'

Sara studied the hands now knotted on her lap. 'No…but I only heard an hour before I left the house this morning. I'm getting used to the idea already—'

'But not quick enough, *cara*,' Alex breathed with chilling bite. 'Not quick enough.'

That chill went right down inside her and hurt, making her feel rejected and shut out. She had been inexcusably tactless, she told herself angrily. Naturally Alex did not want to hear about Brian on their wedding day. Why hadn't she kept her stupid mouth shut? she asked herself as she slid out of the limo outside the fabulous country hotel where the reception was being staged.

'Much better than two million…you're a girl after my own heart,' Marco teased her as he kissed her on the cheek. 'No hard feelings?'

'No more cracks about boots and berries, little brother,' Alex interposed, making Marco flush.

'I'm not about to take my life in my hands.'

Pete drew her to one side, his anxious eyes meeting hers. 'You didn't tell Alex all that nonsense I spouted that morning, did you?' he prompted worriedly.

'Of course not.'

'I mean, *obviously*,' Pete stressed with an amused shake of his head as he perceptibly relaxed, 'Alex is nuts about you! I was way out of line.'

No, Pete hadn't been as far out of line as he fondly imagined, Sara found herself thinking irritably. She was a bit fed up with people saying how madly in love Alex was with her when it was so patently obvious that he was not. Oh, yes, he might be behaving as any bridegroom was expected to behave, but Sara knew that he was only putting on a good show. Why advertise the fact that this was a marriage of convenience? That was private, not for public consumption.

Five minutes before the meal began, Sara saw Antonia and Brian slipping into the only two seats left vacant. Her cousin was wearing a fixed smile. By her side Brian looked grim and uncomfortable. Nothing could have concealed the marks of strain that had thinned his face and lent a harsher line to his mouth.

'The happy twosome,' Alex commented flatly. 'They deserve each other, don't you think?'

Sara focused on her wineglass. 'I wish them well. I really do.'

'If you tell yourself that often enough, I might actually start to believe it too,' Alex breathed with an undertone of rawness that sent her tension screaming up another notch.

After the meal Alex whirled her round the dance-floor with breathtaking expertise. It was Sara who mumbled apologies when she collided with his feet and who couldn't wait to sit down again because she felt that her lack of dexterity, her sheer clumsiness must be embarrassing him when every eye in the room was upon them.

A little while later she was chatting to family friends when she felt a hand touch her shoulder. She turned her head with an enquiring smile. She had to force the smile to stay in place when she saw Brian.

'Care to dance?' he asked loudly.

Sara hesitated, alarmingly conscious of their audience. 'If you like,' she said grudgingly.

'Antonia was determined to come, so don't blame me,' Brian muttered in an embittered undertone as he pulled her onto the floor. 'Dear God, Sara...what happened to us?'

'You know exactly what happened, Brian.'

'But I feel like some bloody pawn people push around for fun!' he vented down at her, his face furiously flushed. 'I was set up, Sara. Last week I found out that some private investigator had been snooping around after me, pestering my colleagues at work, blasted well paying for information about my movements!'

Sara wondered uneasily if he was drunk. 'A private investigator?' she queried, incredulous at the suggestion as they proceeded round the floor at the snail's pace of the vaguely dancing shuffle which had always been their style.

'You tell me how anyone knew Antonia and I were going to be in the flat that day at that time. It was a last-minute arrangement. And who made that phone call which brought you there to find us *in flagrante delicto*?' he completed bitterly.

Her mouth compressed. 'I really don't see that it matters now—'

'The only person I know who could afford a private investigator is your new husband!' Brian cut in with clenched teeth. 'He's rich, he's devious and he hates me like poison, and if you ask me I'm lucky I'm still alive! Back in his homeland that smooth, calculating bastard would probably just have hired a hit man to get me out of the way!'

'Have you any idea how ridiculous you sound?' Sara enquired in disbelief, tugging back from him because anger was making him grip her far too tightly and closely for comfort. 'Why should Alex have hired a private investigator?'

'Well, you ask yourself who got what he most wanted out of this nightmare. And Rossini must have wanted you very badly to marry you this quickly! Very neat, wasn't it—how he was in the right place at the right time to step into my shoes…not off abroad the way he usually is, not involved with another woman… No, he was right there waiting to catch you on the rebound, wasn't he?'

'Forgive me for interrupting this touching reunion…'

Alex's smoothly controlled drawl sent a shiver down Sara's taut spinal cord as her head whipped round in shock. She had never heard that much menace, wasn't surprised when Brian paled and abruptly dropped his arms from her.

'Hates me like poison', Brian had said, and it occurred to her that that bit was certainly true.

Bypassing Brian, Alex drew her close, his strong face tight with suppressed anger.

Sara stumbled and said, 'Why do you dislike him so much?'

'He's still breathing, walking around, causing trouble.'

An uneasy laugh was torn from her. 'Alex...he wasn't trying to make a pass at me.'

'Were you hoping he would? Or was it enough of a power play merely to let his wife watch the two of you clinging to each other and so totally absorbed that neither of you noticed that the music had stopped?' Alex demanded with roughened quietness, dark eyes icy with condemnation.

Sara paled under the unexpected attack. 'It wasn't like that—'

'He's still in love with you...or at least he *thinks* he is, but he's married to another woman now. Your behaviour was inappropriate,' Alex spelt out grimly. 'As was his. But it is you whom I choose to censure, for you are my wife and I expect certain standards to be maintained, particularly in public. If you cannot maintain those standards around your former fiancé, how can you possibly remain in contact with your family? There will be no ongoing problems in that department, *cara*. I assure you of that.'

Sara was shaken and angered by his rebuke. In all her life she could not recall any male ever telling her that her behaviour had been unacceptable. Her pride smarted furiously. Possibly she should have been more distant with Brian in so public a setting when all too many people were aware of how recently their relationship had been severed, but she did not feel that she deserved to be dragged mortifyingly over the coals of Alex's grim disapproval as if she were a child who had let herself down in front of the grown-ups!

'If you had heard what Brian was saying, you might have understood why I was still standing there after the music had finished!' Sara returned defensively.

'You couldn't tear yourself away from him?'

She bridled. 'No, only not for the reasons you imagine. I couldn't believe what he was saying! Brian was accusing you of having put a private investigator on him, of having set him up to be caught in the act with Antonia…for h-heaven's sake…' As she noticed the sudden narrowing of Alex's dark gaze, his immediate, poised stillness, her voice tripped and then slowly drained away.

She had expected him to laugh with that wonderful spontaneity of his, or at worst react with angry exasperation at such an absurd allegation. But Alex did neither. His chiselled golden features clenched, his expressive mouth flattening, and then, in that pulsing silence, one of his twin sisters bounced in between them and grabbed his hand. Throwing Sara a mischievous glance, she tugged her big brother back onto the dance-floor.

As Sara hovered with an uncertain frown pleating her brows, she saw the man with the grey streak in his hair bending down to speak to Sandro Rossini. And it came to her then where she had seen that man before. Outside the flat that day when she had been fleeing from the sight of Brian and Antonia in each other's arms. Yet he was one of Alex's security guards. Maybe he lived in the same street. Coincidence, nothing more… How could it be anything more?

Alex couldn't *possibly* have had any connection with that episode. The very idea was ridiculous! Was Brian's paranoia contagious? But when had she ever known Brian to be paranoiac? Or Alex silent?

An image swam back up in her memory. She remembered Alex coming into her office that afternoon, not a single word of criticism passing his lips about the unanswered phones, his uncharacteristic quietness, his astonishing inability to distinguish between brandy and black coffee in spite of the fact that the bottle had been sitting in open view on Pete's desk... And even if he hadn't noticed all that he must surely have known that she was sloshed out of her stupid mind when she couldn't even walk in a straight line down the corridor!

The more likely scenario would have run very differently. Alex would have demanded to know why she wasn't answering the phones, seen the brandy bottle at one glance and incredulously insisted on an explanation. And only then did she recall the minor fact which she had forgotten in all the excitement. Alex *should* have been flying to Rome that afternoon...but he hadn't gone anywhere. Another coincidence?

With his sisters fussing around her, Sara went to change out of her wedding gown. How had Alex known that Brian was a salesman? That she lived with her cousin? Alex had known *too* much. And what about the dinner party he had mentioned, the keys of the company apartment right there in his pocket so that he could offer them without delay? Her heartbeat was pounding so loudly that it felt as though it was sitting at the foot of her throat. Smooth, slick womaniser...

'No woman would forgive such a betrayal...'

'How could you ever trust him again...?'

What she was imagining was sheer madness, she told herself weakly, but she could not forget Alex's silence. He had neither laughed nor defended himself. His impassivity had challenged her disbelief, indeed openly invited her suspicions...

Sheathed in an elegant suit in cream and black and showered in confetti, she slid breathlessly into the limousine that was to take them to the airport.

'Alex...' Sara licked uneasily at her dry lower lip. 'I'm about to ask you what is probably a very stupid question.'

'The investigator?'

Sara tried and failed to swallow, her intensely green eyes snapping to his diamond-sharp dark gaze.

'Guilty as charged. Yes…I put an investigator on him.'

'Y-yes?' Sara felt as if her voice was fighting through layers of concrete to be heard. To have had her wild suspicion flatly, unemotionally confirmed without the smallest preamble sent shock rolling over her in thunderous waves.

'I wanted you a great deal, Sara.'

'You set an investigator on Brian?' she whispered shakily, her flesh clammy.

'And his liaison with your cousin was duly discovered. I will be very frank; my initial intent was simply to tell you that he was having an affair.'

'Was it?' she asked stupidly.

'But the kill-the-messenger principle, allied with the fear that you might well disbelieve me, convinced me that such a direct approach would be unwise. Nor was our working relationship conducive to the delivery of such a very personal revelation,' Alex spelt out levelly. 'Sadly, it was necessary that you should discover them with your own eyes.'

'S-sadly?' Sara quavered, her entire attention nailed to him with a kind of sick fascination.

'I did not know that you would surprise them in bed,' Alex continued reflectively. 'I could hardly have arranged that.'

'But it was remarkably likely, wasn't it?' Sara's voice wobbled again. 'The phone call?'

'I arranged—'

'The security guard who works for you? I saw him in the street outside the flat.'

'A precaution for your safety…' Alex was beginning to sound very slightly defensive, as if her attitude was not quite what he had envisaged. 'I knew you might be upset—'

'*Might be*?' Sara stressed in agonised disbelief.

'I wanted to know where you were, what you were doing

and that you were safe from any harm. I felt responsible for you.'

Her whole image of Alex shattered there and then. Brick by brick it fell apart, and then even the bricks crumbled to dust. She trembled in the face of the enormity of what he'd confessed with such incredible cool. He had set her up for the worst ordeal of her life and then calmly strolled in to play the good Samaritan and *plunder* what was left with the innate deviousness of a born manipulator. Sara was absolutely devastated.

'Sara…you had a right to know about their affair.'

'That's what reporters say when they rip someone's life apart for the public's entertainment—a right to know,' she repeated unevenly.

'As events swiftly proved, you would have found out anyway,' Alex reminded her grimly. 'Your cousin is pregnant. She was not about to stand idly by and watch you marry the father of her child.'

'That doesn't matter.' Numbly she moved her head to stress that negative response. She could feel the agony of betrayal threatening to smash a composure that consisted purely of shock. It was her second betrayal, her second acquaintance with the weakness of her own judgement in the space of a month. She had *trusted* Alex, and without that trust what was there?

'You played God with my life…' Sara shuddered at the awareness, suddenly understanding why Brian had said that he felt like a pawn. To have been manipulated to such a degree was intolerable. It made her feel super-small and powerless and unbelievably dumb. But what savaged her most of all was the reality that she had so blindly put Alex on a pedestal too, trusting him, listening to him, feeling grateful that he was so tolerant and sympathetic that ghastly day. Now she saw everything she had felt, everything she had thought since about Alex as suspect and unreal.

'I did intend to tell you the truth eventually.'

'Maybe never.'

'Sara…he didn't deserve you.'

'And you did? Heaven knows, you must have got some kick out of playing the concerned employer for the first time in your wretched, self-centred life!' Sara condemned. 'And it was all a sham, Alex. None of it was real!'

'My sympathy and my concern were.'

'Like hell they were!' Sara snapped, feeling the acrid scorch of tears hitting the back of her eyes. 'You must have been delighted at how wonderfully it all went to plan! I even came back to the office to make it easier for you…I got drunk, I fell into your hands like an overripe plum, didn't I?' Her trembling voice broke right down the middle and she turned her head away sharply, forcing her vocal cords to do her bidding again. 'I hate you now… I'll never forgive you for this!'

At the airport she climbed out of the limousine on wobbling legs, fighting the tears off like mad. She, who never, ever cried, wanted to throw herself down in a humiliating heap and sob like a hysteric! When Alex dared to reach for her hand, she jerked away and discovered that in addition to crying she wanted to physically attack him. Never before in her life had she experienced such violent rage. So nobody was perfect…? Well, Alex hadn't touched the tip of the iceberg when he'd said that!

The instant the Rossini private jet was airborne Sara removed her seat belt and headed for the rear cabin. Alex followed her, his strong features taut. 'We have to talk—'

'Brian said that too and I should have bloody listened, shouldn't I?' Sara flung at him in her distress. 'Maybe he had his suspicions then, maybe we could have worked out that there was an *agent provocateur* involved.'

'It's a little late now…we're married.'

'And that certainly wasn't part of the original game plan, was it?' Sara accused him painfully, her head pounding fit to burst. 'You intended to catch me on the rebound and talk me into bed...but I even did that for you, didn't I? I dragged *you* into bed the same day!'

'Sara, don't... It wasn't like that.'

'I know what it was like...I was there!' Sara threw back rawly. 'You were prepared to wreck my future with the man I loved just for the sake of some sordid little fling! And if I had been stupid enough to agree to that I would now be clutching twenty-four red roses and a diamond bracelet! Another Alex Rossini cast-off to be sniggered at by the gutter press!'

'I asked you to marry me,' Alex gritted, a dark flush highlighting his slashing cheekbones.

'Wow, I'm such a lucky girl! I've landed myself a real hero. You're treacherous and dishonest and the only reason you proposed marriage was because it finally sunk in on that boundless ego of yours that that was the only way you were going to get me!'

'If we are to stoop to that level,' Alex drawled with a flash of white teeth and blazing golden eyes, 'I would remind you that when I proposed I had already had that particular pleasure.'

Sara went white and spun clumsily away from him. The reminder outraged her. She needed to hit back so badly that she was burning up inside. 'Well, you didn't get such a great bargain...a wife who's still hopelessly in love with another man! Maybe that makes us about equal,' she taunted bitterly out of savaged pride.

But the soft click of the door shutting on his exit was her only reply. A sob of stifled distress abruptly broke from Sara's compressed lips, and then another. She flung herself on the built-in bed and pushed her convulsing face into the softness of a pillow. Torn in two by the violence of her emotions, she let the tears flow because for the first time in many years of unyielding self-discipline she couldn't hold them back. In any case, there was no Antonia here now to sneer and laugh at such pathetic weakness.

How could Alex have done that to her? How could he have coolly admitted to such vile and inexcusable interference? Didn't he realise that this totally smashed the fragile foundations of their relationship? That there was nothing left—nothing but hatred and resentment and bitter regret inside her now.

CHAPTER SIX

UNFAMILIAR sounds woke Sara by degrees: quick, firm footsteps, the chiming clink of glass and china, then the swish of heavy curtains slowly being drawn back. Sunlight warmed her drowsy face and she opened her eyes.

'Buon giorno, signora.' A middle-aged woman was extending a satin and lace wrap to her with a smile.

Sara, sitting up with a start, found herself deftly enveloped in the garment. The pillows were plumped and a tray set before her. Venice… She was in Venice in the magnificent *palazzo* which had been in the Rossini family for centuries. They had arrived very late last night to be greeted by the housekeeper, Marcella. Declining the offer of supper, Sara had been shown up to this exquisitely furnished room, so exhausted that it had been an effort to spare her fabulously ornate surroundings more than a dull-eyed glance. As she glanced at her watch now she realised in astonishment that she had slept the morning away.

Only when the bustling Marcella skimmed curious dark eyes across the pristine white pillow beside hers did Sara recall that last night had been her wedding night. Her creamy skin reddened with sudden embarrassment. It was perfectly obvious that she had spent the night alone and undisturbed. Why on earth should she be blushing over the fact? she asked herself furiously.

Yet she *had* somehow still expected to wake up with Alex beside her. The discovery of that inexplicable conviction infuriated her even more. Why on earth should she have expected that? She could only be grateful that Alex had accepted the reality that nothing would persuade her to share a bed with him now! After all, she had maintained a frigid silence from the instant the jet had landed, speaking only when forced to do so, making her hostility pointedly obvious. So why did the memory of that mute response in the face of his teeth-clenchingly perfect manners now make her squirm?

Some ten minutes later, still savouring the last bite of the delicious light meal she had eaten, Sara thrust away the tray and sprang out of bed. The skyline beyond the windows was a visual feast of domes, pinnacles, oddly shaped chimneys and campaniles. The Grand Canal below was as busy as any city highway at rush hour but the traffic was far more interesting. A speedboat foamed past, followed at a more sedate pace by a chugging *vaporetti* crammed to capacity and then a little barge heaped with vegetable produce, tailed by an old-fashioned fishing boat. Sara couldn't help being charmed by the sheer colourful vivacity of the scene.

In the adjoining bathroom she sank into a sumptuous sunken bath so large that it reminded her of a miniature swimming pool. But even such sybaritic splendour couldn't make her relax. She had rushed into marriage at breakneck speed. Who was to say that she hadn't asked for what she got? Who was to say that she didn't thoroughly deserve the mess she was now in? No such thing as a perfect hero, Sara, she told herself. But a male with a scruple or two— had that been too much to hope for?

Alex had no regrets either. Why should he care how it felt to be forced to see oneself as a purely sexual object…a female *thing*, desired for her body and for nothing else? For when you stripped all the pretences away that was the true sum of her worth to Alex. He had used all the right buzzwords like 'home' and 'family', blinding her with specious flattery and clever argument, but ultimately his sole objective had been her voluntary placing of her physical self into the bed of his choosing.

With her in love with another man and mere weeks from

her wedding, the average male would have seen her as out of reach. But Alex lived in the rarefied society of the very rich, where anything could be acquired for the right price…or the right tactics. And Alex was famous for being so tortuously serpentine in his business negotiations and so innately secretive that even his top executives could be surprised, red-faced and drop-jawed when he pulled off some deal entirely on his own.

'You never really know what Alex is up to. It fairly keeps you on your toes,' Pete had grumbled once.

The decision to expose Brian's infidelity had cost Alex not one sleepless night. Shrewdly flicking through his options, Alex had known that nothing could better a first-hand encounter with her fiancé's feet of clay. And in one chillingly precise move he had ensured that her engagement would be broken so that he could smoothly step into the breach to persuade her that *he* was the 'far more entertaining possibility' that her future could offer.

Whatever else Alex was he was ruthless, aggressively resourceful and he thrived on challenge. Only what you saw was not necessarily what you got with Alex Rossini, she conceded painfully. Like some science-fiction shape-shifter, Alex could fit himself to any required backdrop, so that within a head-spinning handful of days Sara had been treated to Alex the reformed womaniser, hearing the pure clarion call of domesticity, talking about *settling down*, Alex the family man… Tears stung Sara's embittered eyes. Well, they said that there was a fool born every minute. She had swallowed every lying word whole!

'Did you sleep well?'

Dredged from her all-absorbing thoughts with a vengeance, Sara flinched in horror before she abruptly catapulted upright in a wave of noisily displaced water and snatched at a towel to shield her dripping length from the brazen male poised scant feet from her. Wide-eyed with disbelief, she clutched frantically at the towel and gaped at him. 'How dare you?' she shrilled.

An ebony brow was elevated. 'How dare I what?'

'Invade my privacy!' Sara gasped, hotly flushed as she struggled to anchor the fleecy towel round her, but the foot of it had already trailed in the water and the sodden weight of fabric was anything but easy to handle. 'Get out of here!'

'I see you have miraculously rediscovered your tongue.' Supremely at ease, Alex sank down on a corner of the bath, an unhidden smile of amusement curving his expressive mouth. Densely lashed golden eyes engaged on a boldly unapologetic survey of every gleaming wet inch of pale flesh on view. 'What a promising start to the new day…'

'I want you to listen to me.'

'I am a captive audience,' Alex assured her cheerfully.

Sara quivered with rage. If there was one thing she couldn't bear, it was *not* to be taken seriously. 'You're trying to behave as if yesterday never happened!'

A lean brown hand snaked out and caught her left hand, one long forefinger suggestively brushing the circle of bridal gold she wore. 'Didn't it?'

Deprived of one hand's anchorage, the towel dipped down dangerously low over her breasts and with a strangled hiss of mingled temper and mortification Sara dropped down into the water again. 'Go away!' she roared at him furiously.

'You're changing… You're changing into the woman you've always kept hidden and stifled,' Alex murmured with quiet satisfaction. 'The woman you were born to be. Fiery and passionate, not quiet and submissive. I saw it in Marco's studio first—all that you would conceal and all that I would set free.'

Sara opened her sultry mouth and closed it again, trembling with thwarted fury. 'Don't try to change the subject,' she finally shot back at him.

'Why would I do that? You needed to know the truth. I

made no attempt to conceal it,' Alex reminded her. 'The brandy bottle was the one unknown, *cara*. I suspect that without that handicap you would have suspected the truth the same day. I did not foresee how rapidly events would move...or how swiftly our relationship would develop. I was prepared to *wait* for you to turn to me.'

'You don't even seem to appreciate the evil of what you've done!' Sara launched at him.

'The evil was Shorter's, *cara*. Don't make the mistake of laying the original sin at my door,' Alex warned her softly. 'Had he been faithful, I would have been powerless to interfere.'

'You had no *right* to interfere!'

'I saw my advantage and I used it. What else would you have expected me to do? If I hadn't intervened, you would have suffered a far more public betrayal. I don't believe that your fiancé had any intention of replacing you with your cousin...but the lady had other ideas,' Alex imparted with grim dark eyes. 'How much closer to the wedding would you have liked to come?'

Her teeth gritted. 'That's not relevant!'

'You think not? Without my "evil" intervention, *bella mia*, the invitations would have been out, the wedding presents arriving. Your cousin has a sense of the dramatic. I think she would have left it to the eleventh hour. You would have been greeted out of the blue by the announcement that they were in love. Would you have preferred that scenario?'

'Shut up, Alex!' Sara blitzed back at him rawly, wanting to cover her ears from his devious reasoning. '*Shut up!*'

Alex dealt her a uniquely cynical appraisal, his handsome mouth twisting. 'No, you would not have fallen over yourself for the opportunity to play the jilted bride, a sad object of pity to all concerned. You are far too proud to willingly subject yourself to such humiliation.'

'Damn you, Alex…I hate you!' Resentment was blazing out of control like a forest fire inside her.

'You married me to save face, *cara*… If I have to live with that reality, why shouldn't you?' Alex drawled murderously quietly.

'You sneaky, manipulative swine!' Lunging forward without hesitation, Sara closed two angry hands over the hem of his immaculate grey jacket and tipped him backwards into the bath.

There was a burst of startled Italian, a resounding splash, a sudden dismaying weight on her extended lower limbs and then an instant of stark silence. And then Alex laughed. He threw back his handsome dark head and laughed with uninhibited appreciation.

'You asked for that,' Sara bit out mutinously, refusing to share in his amusement. 'Now perhaps you'll remove yourself.'

Alex bent forward and flipped off his shoes and socks. 'I don't think so,' he murmured, straightening his back lithely and shrugging his shoulders out of his jacket, pitching it carelessly aside.

'And what's that supposed to mean?'

He jerked his tie loose, then embarked on unbuttoning his shirt. 'I am where I want to be—'

'Let me up,' she instructed feverishly, pinned in place by the weight of his hard length.

Alex angled up his lean flanks to unzip his trousers and Sara took advantage of the movement to snake her legs back, but he was far too quick and agile for her. He flipped over and caught her arms before she could complete her escape and brought his mouth down hard on hers.

In a rage of incredulity, she meant to bite him, scratch him, pummel him with both furiously clenched fists. But at the same second that he fiercely probed her lips apart and delved between them with the stab of his tongue, she ran out of breath and reason and physical coordination. He devoured her with hot, hungry urgency and her hands briefly loosened and then clutched with helpless desperation as he yanked her up against him, crushing her bare breasts to the hard, muscular wall of his chest. She wanted more, so much more that every intoxicating second was only a frustrating preparation for the next. And then he released her.

In a daze she blinked as he sprang out of the bath, peeling off his shirt and dispensing with his sodden trousers and the clinging black briefs in a few impatient movements. He reached down into the water and swept her up as if she were an inanimate and dainty doll. Breathless confusion overwhelmed her. 'Put me down...put me down, Alex!'

'Getting me wet was a bad move, *cara*.' Brilliant golden eyes danced over her bemused face. '*Dio*...it made the odds of you escaping unscathed from this bedroom about ninety-nine to one.'

'If you don't let go of...*me*!' Her wrathful response ended in a strangled yell as he dropped her down on the welcoming luxuriousness of the bed and she bounced.

Alex descended lithely onto the mattress, only to imprison her again, closing both hands over her wildly clawing ones and pressing them flat while at the same time lowering his lean, hard length to keep the rest of her in one place. 'Now...calm down—think,' he urged smoothly.

It struck her that about the very last thing she felt capable of just then was thinking. With every lethally sexy centimetre of Alex pinned to her damp, quivering flesh, rational thought was suspended by a sensation closer to pure panic than anything else. Already she could feel a sort of insidious heat and restive tension threatening her already shattered composure.

'Please—'

'I wanted you so much, *bella mia*...how could that ever be a crime?' Alex enquired, subjecting her to the full onslaught of eyes screened to a smouldering sliver of gold beneath inky black lashes. 'For a whole year I desired you and you held me at bay with cold, dismissive glances and scornful little smiles. You treated me like my father's wives once treated me—like an unavoidable but greatly to be regretted accident of birth. No man with red blood in his veins would have resisted the challenge.'

'Stop it,' Sara gasped, blocking him out by closing her eyes. She was trying so hard not to listen while at the same time endeavouring to stamp out the burgeoning and quite appalling sexual awareness leaping to life within her every skin cell, making her breath shorten, her heartbeat race and her pulses accelerate.

'You are my wife,' Alex reminded her very softly.

'I don't want to be!' Sara bit out shakily, tiny little quivers assailing her as she angrily fought to stamp out her own hatefully physical reaction to his proximity.

'This is very sudden,' Alex husked.

Temper took her again, strengthening her defiance. 'You think that if you chip away at me for long enough you can change the way I think…but you can't! Marco said I'd be safer with him that day and he was right. He told me to go for the two million and he was right about that too! You're just using me!' Sara condemned in sudden, bitter pain. 'And I'd rather be used for money than find myself trapped in a marriage that's a sleazy mockery of everything I believe in. At least the money would have been an *honest* exchange!'

Without warning, Alex freed her hands and sprang back from her. His strong dark features were harshly set. 'Is that what you really believe, *cara*?'

With a shaking hand, Sara fumbled for the sheet, wanting to cover herself all of a sudden from that look of icy derision in Alex's eyes. 'Yes,' she muttered chokily, knowing that she had told the truth of her feelings.

Of course he would never have offered and she would never have taken money, but the scenario she had forced herself to draw was far more apt in her opinion than the dubious respectability of the wedding ring she wore. A cruel, cheating charade was what Alex had really given her but she had entered their marriage with very different expectations, stupidly, naïvely trusting and believing in every assurance he had made. She recalled the manner in which he had smoothly tacked on the word 'eventually' to his supposed desire for children and she understood why now.

Alex had never planned on permanence. Alex had merely dangled a wedding ring as bait so that he could satisfy his lust and his ferocious need to win, whatever the cost. If she hadn't been so overly emotional, so eagerly willing to be swayed by his arguments, she would have suspected that reality far sooner. A male like Alex Rossini, with a father who changed wives the way other men changed their shirts, was highly unlikely to see the institution of marriage as an unbreakable bond. Alex had simply told her what she'd wanted and needed to hear.

Tears pricked her eyes again and filled her with a furious impatience at her own continuing and dismayingly unfamiliar emotionalism. She rolled herself under the sheet as if she were settling into her shroud.

Alex was already standing in the adjoining dressing room, rifling through drawers and cupboards, withdrawing fresh clothing. The significance of what he was doing slowly sank in on her as she abstractedly watched his every lithe, graceful movement. His sudden withdrawal had left her treacherous body aching, and her teeth clenched in shamed acknowledgement of the fact.

'This is your room?' she asked across the yawning gulf of silence, which she found quite unbearable.

'You were sleeping so soundly last night, I did not wish to disturb you.' His startlingly handsome features were shuttered, a cold contempt in his eyes which he made no attempt to conceal.

And for the first time Sara registered that Alex could affect her on a level that she had previously denied. A growing sense of fear and rejection was taking her over. Fear and rejection, she acknowledged dazedly. 'I will not hurt you', he had said, and yet he *was* hurting her. In fact all of a sudden her mind was toying with the cowardly notion that she had said too much, gone too far, offended too deeply... In dismay, she bit down so hard on her tongue to trap it between her teeth that she tasted blood. 'Submissive', he had called her. No, she was not going to be submissive or apologetic for honestly stating her own feelings. She had a right to say what she felt.

A right...a *right*—all too often suppressed and surrendered throughout her childhood. She had let herself be forced into a quiet, introverted little slot at an early age because if she'd dared to flex a finger out of that slot Antonia had been waiting, ready to break it. And she had been so grateful that her aunt and uncle had given her a home that she hadn't fought, hadn't defended herself, hadn't expressed herself in any way which might have caused offence or brought her into more open conflict with the daughter they adored. A little martyr of a peacemaker— that was what she had been and much good it had done her!

And where would she end up if one ferociously dirty look from Alex made her want to rush in and tactfully smooth things over as she had done with everyone all her life to date? She couldn't possibly be becoming emotionally attached to Alex. You hate him now, she reminded herself...but you *still* don't want him to leave this room. The discovery shattered her.

Alex emerged from the dressing room, immaculate again in a supremely sophisticated cream suit that was a spectacular foil for his golden skin and exotically dark eyes. And when did you start gaping at him all the time as if he were first prize in a lottery, eyeing him up like some sort of sex-obsessed teenager with uncontrollable hormones? she asked herself derisively.

In the midst of her increasingly frantic self-examination, Alex vented a soft, chilling laugh. Sara permitted her anxious gaze to wander guiltily back to him.

'You want to know why I married you?' he drawled. 'I thought you were different but I should have recalled that old adage that there's nothing new under the sun.'

'I thought you were different too.' But she wasn't going to share the fact that she had actually believed that he had miraculously been transformed from an arrogant, ruthless womaniser into a family man.

'You didn't care.' Alex shot her a glance from glittering dark eyes, his scorn palpable. 'Your cosy future was smashed and you wanted it back, whatever the cost or the risk. I had the means to give it to you—'

'I don't know what you're getting at.'

'Before my very eyes, I watched you fall in love with what I could buy you…and I shouldn't complain. I picked Ladymead out of two dozen properties as the one most likely to appeal. I played a winning bet. *Dio mio*…it did not occur to me that sometimes winning can feel more like losing.'

Sara had stilled, shaken by the information that he had taken her quite deliberately to Ladymead. That he could actually blame her for the results of his own relentlessly manipulative approach disconcerted her even more. 'You're not being fair—'

'I don't feel like being fair.' His wide mouth narrowed, clenched. 'For the first time I feel a certain sympathy for Shorter. I'm not surprised that he was tempted by a normal flesh-and-blood woman, who only wanted him and not some picture-book fantasy with a fairy castle and a perfect hero.'

'I didn't expect you to be perfect.' Her voice wobbled, betraying the strength of the blow he had dealt her. To hear herself compared unfavourably with Antonia pierced her on her weakest flank. 'But I did expect…honesty.'

'Only you don't like it when you get it. If I'd lied yesterday, you could have kept your rigid little principles intact and you would have generously shared your body with me last night,' he derided. 'But that wasn't the option I chose. I told you the truth without hesitation.'

'It's a matter of trust…can't you understand that?' Sara was horrified to realise that she was on the brink of tears again. 'I *trusted* you!'

'I don't think trust played that big a role in your decision to marry me,' Alex countered very drily, his expressive mouth twisting.

'Of course it did!'

'No, Sara. Your objective was to marry well and save face. I do believe I'm the male equivalent of a trophy wife in so far as you actually take notice of my existence. So don't accuse me of using you, *cara*. As I see it, I'm the one who's allowed himself to be used.'

'No—' she began painfully, her cheeks blazing so hotly that she felt as if she was burning up.

'You took not the smallest interest in the preparations for our wedding. As it was the opening chapter on our future together, I was less than impressed by the level of your commitment. Indeed, had I not intervened, you might well have gone up the aisle in the same dress you had chosen for another man's benefit!'

'No…' Sara mumbled sickly, belatedly grasping how very much she had taken for granted.

'I called you every day and all you could talk about was medieval glass, oak panelling and the complexities of renovating listed buildings! But the ultimate insult has to have been the presence of your ex at our wedding,' Alex informed her with icy precision. 'You had the time and the opportunity to prevent that development, but you didn't. There is no pretence of love between us but I found the spectacle of you clinging like a limpet to another man in front of *my* family and friends deeply offensive.'

Her stomach was churning with nausea now. Seen through Alex's eyes, her behaviour both before and during the wedding reached heights of crass insensitivity that she had never dreamt she could be capable of. She lowered her head, swallowing hard. 'No pretence of love between us', she thought wretchedly. No safe, secure raft of liking and bonding to fall back on when there was a crisis.

'And if you ever tell me again that you love him I will throw you out,' Alex completed with absolute conviction. 'I have not the faintest desire for your love but I will not tolerate the use of that kind of smug self-indulgence as a weapon...most especially not when it relates to a weak, lying, cheating little jerk who couldn't keep his pants on even within the family circle!'

The door shut with a thud. That was some exit, Alex, she conceded dazedly. Nothing like going out with a big bang. Nothing like pulling the ground from beneath my feet and changing the whole tenor of my outlook within the space of five agonisingly mortifying minutes.

Everything he had thrown at her had hit home hard. Guilty of bowing out on the wedding arrangements, guilty of yapping on ceaselessly about Ladymead, guilty of not having the guts to tell her relatives that she refused to have Brian at their wedding. After all, Alex, not her family, had paid for it all. And Brian's presence had ruined the day, making Sara feel self-conscious, strained and guiltily on the defensive.

Yes, she had fallen in love with Ladymead, but that was surely not a crime? The real problem had been that when Alex had phoned her their relationship had felt unreal to her. The house had seemed a safe subject to concentrate on. In a sense, too, she had been showing off. See, I can take care of all these things very efficiently without bothering you. See, I can turn that house into a home so fast you'll be really impressed, was what she had been trying to tell him. Only Alex had been anything but impressed.

And why should he have been? Alex had married her for sexual gratification, not for her home-making abilities…hadn't he? Yet that demeaning assumption no longer seemed to fall so neatly into place. Had she been overreacting to what she had learnt yesterday, letting her imagination, her insecurity run away with her? After all, she might still be shattered by the lengths to which Alex had gone in his determination to get her, but those same extremes surely indicated a great deal more than a mere fleeting sexual interest…didn't they?

Hesitantly Sara breathed in, a sense of greater calm enfolding her. For goodness' sake, she had been reacting like a neurotic! Alex had cunningly contrived the very existence of their relationship but that did not mean that absolutely everything he had told her was a lie! Alex might desire her but she could not believe that he would have sacrificed his freedom on that basis alone. Had her sole attraction been physical, Alex would have concentrated his brilliant powers of negotiation on persuading her into having an affair instead.

And on one other count Alex had also been right: it was wrong of her to keep on throwing up Brian. Brian was married to Antonia now…and it was extraordinary, she conceded, how little emotion she could currently stir in response to that reality. No, she was no longer hopelessly in love with her former fiancé. How could you continue to love a man who had turned out to be a figment of your imagination?

Brian had lied, cheated and deceived her, then abandoned her to the heat of everyone's anger while protecting himself. But she understood now what it seemed that her cousin had understood all along. Brian had really wanted both of them—Sara to be the good little wife, home-maker and supportive partner, Antonia for excitement, glamour and passion. And she herself had not given him that passion, so how could she really blame him for seeking it elsewhere? A rueful smile tinged Sara's mouth as she began to get dressed.

It was Alex she had to worry about now. So she had made mistakes...but then Alex had to. He had been too impatient. He had pushed the wedding through far too fast, denying her the time she had needed to adjust to their relationship. Well, whether Alex liked it or not, her necessary breathing space had come before the wedding and he had not aided his own cause by seeing her only twice during that period. Somehow, at the end of a phone line Alex had felt more like her boss again. She laughed at the idea, helplessly recalling Alex tipping backwards into the bath.

She was walking towards the grand staircase when a smiling young maid caught up with her. The girl extended a silver tray bearing an envelope with only one word slashed where the address should have been. Sara smiled too, seeing her own name inscribed in Alex's handwriting.

Alone again, she flipped open the envelope, her eyes sparkling with curiosity.

It was a cheque made out in her name for the sum of two million pounds.

CHAPTER SEVEN

HER cheeks as pink as wild roses, her heartbeat thundering at the foot of her throat, Sara crossed the floor of the echoing salon. The sheer grandeur of the vast reception room overpowered her.

'I thought we would dine out this evening,' Alex drawled. 'Would you like a drink before we leave?'

Sara shook her head in a quick, nervous motion, glossy streamers of ebony hair falling forward as she stole a glance down at the little black dress which had seemed the last word in sophistication when she'd bought it a week earlier. Now, set against the splendour of her surroundings, with Alex in a superb white dinner jacket, she had the suspicion that if she added an apron she would be easily mistaken for a waitress. She hovered, waiting for him to say something about the cheque, which she had immediately returned by the same method he had employed to deliver it.

Alex drained his crystal glass and set it down. 'Shall we go, then?'

Her teeth gritted. Was it for this response that she had spent an entire afternoon agonising upstairs? She had been so angry that she hadn't trusted herself to go near him, had deemed it wiser to take stock and cool down. 'That cheque...' she began stiltedly.

'I've opened an account for you instead. An honest exchange, you said.' Alex sent her a cool dark glance. 'Now that we understand each other I see no need for the commercial element to be discussed again.'

Sara drew in a deep breath, her heart lurching behind her breastbone. 'Alex...do you want a divorce?'

In the act of moving towards the door, Alex stopped dead and swung abruptly back to her.

'Because if that is what all this is about, why don't you just say so?' Sara continued, green eyes flashing like jewels against her pallor. 'I mean, let's not beat around the bush here, Alex. I have already received the message that I am a big disappointment and that nothing I have done over the last month has met with your approval—'

'I don't want a divorce.' His strong face was clenched hard, his dark gaze diamond-bright.

'Well, right now I just want to swim back to the airport,' Sara confided with an uneven little laugh, her stomach churning with nausea. 'I see ''MISTAKE'' looming in letters ten feet tall over that ceremony yesterday. I'm so very sorry for falling for the house you dangled like bait for my benefit...but I did not agree to marry you because you were rich! And until you wrote that cheque it didn't seriously occur to me that you could even think I could be that greedy. But if this is what you call marrying well I'm afraid you can blasted well keep it, Alex!'

As her voice fractured, betraying her distress, she spun away and began walking fast towards the door. But Alex moved faster, tugging her back to him with lean, determined hands. Closing his arms round her from behind, he expelled his breath in a pent-up hiss. 'I owe you an apology,' he grated roughly.

Sara was rigid. She squeezed her stinging eyes shut and trembled. So much pain—more pain than she had ever experienced, and that in itself was frightening. How did she say to him that she *did* have feelings for him but that she didn't know where they had begun or indeed even what they were but that the concept of losing him filled her with panic? And she couldn't even say that she liked him because, right now, she didn't like Alex at all. The cruelty of that cheque when he must surely have known that she was talking nonsense in her distress earlier—well, that kind of cruelty was utterly foreign to Sara's nature. It scared her to feel in any way dependent on a male who could behave like that.

'It was my pride,' Alex confessed in a savage undertone as he bent his head down over hers. 'No woman has ever treated me with such indifference.'

'It wasn't indifference. You weren't there. It was all like a dream…coming up to the wedding,' she explained jerkily. 'We didn't feel real but the house *did*. And you were so distant on the phone…I felt awkward. I didn't know what you expected from me—'

'Too much.'

Her soft mouth wobbled and then compressed. 'I wanted you to be there. Too bad if you don't want to hear that—'

'*Dio*…it's exactly what I want to hear.'

'Is it?' she gulped.

'Even workaholics like to be missed now and again.' An uncertain shiver of amusement rippled through Sara as Alex spun her round to face him again.

He gazed down at her, and a long forefinger followed the silvery path of a tear stain on her cheek before taking a detour to the tremulous softness of her lower lip. There he lingered to trace that sensitive fullness. Her breath got snarled up in her throat, her slender body tautening in involuntary response to the sizzling sexual energy emanating from him. 'If I'd known, I'd have flown you out,' he remarked reflectively. 'You wouldn't have seen much of me by day but at least we would have had the nights.'

Maybe all men had a one-track mind, Sara found herself thinking, with a regret that was not for sharing. It would have been more of a compliment if Alex had contrived to think of something other than the sexual benefits of her company. But then perhaps she was also guilty of expecting too much too soon. A marriage of convenience had to start somewhere, she reminded herself squarely.

'I wasn't *using* you,' Sara whispered feverishly, struggling to put her thoughts in order but finding it impossible. All she could really feel was enormous relief that the cold gulf that he had imposed between them had been bridged. 'You were there and I...needed you.'

His dark face tautened. 'And I need you now, *cara*.' Alex delivered the words with another meaning entirely as he dropped one hand down to the swell of her hips and arranged her into more intimate contact with his powerful thighs. A clenching sensation low in the pit of her stomach made her jerk as she felt the hard thrust of his manhood. Her knees suddenly had all the consistency of jelly and her hands flew up to grip his shoulders. 'A month is a very long time for me.'

And dinner was now a long way off, she sensed, her cheeks burning fierily. With a husky laugh of satisfaction, Alex raked shimmering golden eyes of desire over her and suddenly swept her off her feet and up into his arms. 'You still blush like a virgin,' he teased, starting towards the door.

She felt hot all over when he put her down again in the bedroom and slid down the zip on her dress. This is all right, she told herself urgently; this is normal, natural, healthy behaviour. We're married. It's OK to want him so much that you're ashamed of yourself. It is not OK to start imagining you're just a sex object again. Narrow-minded prudes are boring.

The dress pooled round her feet. She resisted an instinctive urge to cover herself. Alex's gaze locked with hers. His sensual mouth slashed into a knowing smile.

She broke breathlessly into speech. 'Alex, I—'

But, reaching for her, he bent his dark, well-shaped head and silenced her with the heat of his hungry mouth. And the ground shifted below her feet. He kissed her and there was nothing but him and the hot, swirling darkness behind her lowered eyelids. She stood on tiptoe and kissed him back with all the helpless urgency of her own need, her heartbeat a wild thunder in her ears, the blood in her veins pulsing at supersonic speed. She was dizzy when he lifted his head again, her passion-glazed eyes clinging to his.

He undid the catch on her lacy white bra and she stopped breathing altogether as he curved a hand round the pointed swell of one bared breast and brushed his thumb across its pouting pink nipple. A whimper of sound escaped low in her throat as an electric jolt of pleasure shot through her, the distended peaks of her breasts achingly sensitive to his awakening touch. He backed her down onto the bed, stood over her while he undressed. Smouldering golden eyes raked over her and he smiled with satisfaction.

'You *always* wanted me,' he said.

Her mind locked back into gear. 'No...'

But the accusation lingered and sent her memory flying back through countless uneasy encounters when she had dipped her eyes, turned her head and closed her mind even to an admission of what she was doing. She had blocked Alex out over and over again—so often that it had become a habit never, ever to relax around him, always to feel strained, threatened...

'You had iron self-discipline...and you were stubborn. You knew the attraction was there between us but you wouldn't admit it. It drove me crazy,' Alex told her, peeling off his shirt without once removing his intent gaze from her bemused face. 'I was afraid to make a move in case you walked out. You kept a wall between us, you never came close...you never touched me, not even accidentally.'

Involuntarily she recalled innumerable instances of her own pronounced caution in his radius. Remembering scared her. It was scary to accept that all along her body had been conscious of this powerful attraction but that her mind had resisted even acknowledging it until that day when he had walked into her office and she had told herself that she was *not* susceptible. That had been her first conscious admission of what Alex could make her feel. 'I didn't know,' she muttered

'You do now.' Alex folded himself lithely down on the bed beside her and tugged her into his arms, and the thinking stopped there as if he had pushed a button. Her nostrils flared with the scent of him and she trembled as his long, lean muscularity connected with her. She met his eyes and burned in the defenceless heat of anticipation, her breasts rising and falling with the quickening of her breathing, excitement stirring so fast again that it took her by storm.

He lowered his head and let the tip of his tongue graze a rose-pink bud, skimming a hand up over the tautness of her quivering ribcage, discovering the thunder of her racing heartbeat as her whole body leapt in response to that tiny caress.

'Alex…' she gasped.

'Feeling like this is special, *bella mia*,' he muttered raggedly. '*Dio*…you are so beautiful.'

With unsteady fingers she caressed his cheekbone, wanting, wanting him so much that it was like a pain inside her as her thighs tightened on the ache in her loins. His eyes narrowed with smoky desire and then he curved his hands round her pale breasts, touching, inciting her pouting nipples before he dropped his mouth there and tugged at the tormented peaks with an erotic precision that engulfed her in a scorching surge of sensation. Her fingernails dug into the hard muscles of his back and then pushed through his hair as her body rose up to his of its own volition, tiny little gasps of sensual pleasure tearing free from deep in her throat.

His fingers stroked the smooth skin of her inner thigh, mounting higher by torturous degrees that made her clutch at him in involuntary protest, drag him up again, find his mouth again for herself and exult in the hungry thrust of his tongue. He skimmed a finger over the satin mound of her bikini pants so that she twisted and moaned under his mouth in a sweet agony of desperate need. And then the frustrating barrier was gone and he was expertly exploring the honeyed dampness beneath, sending her swerving violently out of control, every muscle screaming with tension as her heartbeat hammered.

'*Now*…' Alex groaned when she was on the brink of an intolerable excitement.

Her gaze collided blindly with his and then he pulled her up to receive him and drove into her hard and fast and her head fell back and she cried out with the hot, torturous pleasure of that penetration, her body yielding to the forceful possession of his. He moved again with sinuous eroticism and the pleasure increased to such unbearable limits that she lost herself entirely. With every tormenting stroke he took her higher and her nails raked down his smooth back as her spine arched and the sunburst heat in her loins suddenly expanded, every muscle clenching in response as she went flying over the edge into a release that convulsed her in violent waves.

In the aftermath she clung to him, recalling the wondrously intimate feel of him shuddering with that same satisfaction in the circle of her arms. A glorious sense of wellbeing enclosed her. She was at peace, perfectly at peace, until she became aware of the intense happiness which was fostering that quiet contentment. It was that unquestionable feeling of joy which shook Sara the most.

Alex rolled over, carrying her with him, and her arms instinctively tightened round his hot, damp, sleekly muscled length because…because she didn't want to let him go. Concealed by the wild tumble of her hair as she rested her cheek against his shoulder, her eyes flew wide at that alarming awareness. She also recognised within herself a surge of raw feminine possessiveness and that made her shiver in shock.

'Cold?' Alex tugged the sheet up carefully over her and shifted again beneath her, like a cat stretching in sunlight.

She knew that he was smiling. 'Much better without the brandy,' he murmured huskily.

Sara tensed. 'I wasn't drunk.'

'But you weren't *quite* sober either,' Alex interposed with rueful emphasis. 'I promised you that you could trust me that night. I wasn't lying when I said that, *bella mia*. But I overestimated the limits of my self-control. I didn't really care why you wanted me. It was enough that you did.'

One crazy night, Sara thought, and it had changed her life. 'Why all the flowers?' she whispered curiously.

'Guilt,' he said succinctly.

'Guilt?' She pushed her hair out of her eyes and looked up at him with a frown.

His expressive mouth twisted. 'I wasn't expecting it to be your first time, *cara*. For a woman that is a significant event and you weren't a teenager any more, you were twenty-three, which suggested that abstention had been a deliberate policy. I didn't think you were likely to feel as reckless in the morning as you had the night before.'

'You were right.' Her creamy skin turned pink and if she hadn't still been too shy to discuss their intimacy of that night she might have told him that he had made it a very significant event. Even in her angry turmoil of regret, she had known that Alex had made their lovemaking feel special. But then why not? she reflected ruefully. Alex was a very experienced lover. At a tender nineteen, an age when *she* had still been at the stage of fumbling kisses on doorsteps, Alex had been living in no doubt very exciting sin with an older woman. Who had seduced whom? she wondered, and then suppressed the thought, scolding herself for such tasteless, inappropriate curiosity.

Alex absorbed the distant look in her green eyes. His dark scrutiny glittering, he lifted her away from him and tumbled her carelessly down onto a cool patch in the spacious bed as he slid out of it. 'I'm hungry, *cara*. There's still plenty of time to make dinner.'

His abrupt withdrawal sharply disconcerted Sara. She watched him stroll into the bathroom, stared in consternation at the scratches marring the smooth, bronzed perfection of his back and dropped her head again, the warmth of that curious joy inside her ebbing fast. She began to wonder fearfully if the only time she would feel secure and important to Alex was when he was in bed with her, satisfying his desire.

But why should she need more security? Hadn't she agreed to what Alex had termed 'a practical marriage'? She couldn't expect to move the goalposts now, mustn't start to look for the kind of affectionate extras that only came naturally with love. This was a male who gave flowers out of guilt. The beribboned baskets had not been the attempted romantic gesture that she had dimly and foolishly imagined them to be. Romance was out of the question too. Sex was in, sentiment was out.

He had been very honest about that. Alex valued that quality of emotional detachment in a relationship. And very possibly that was why he had married a woman in love with another man. Had it ever crossed his mind that that same woman might have fallen right back out of love again without even knowing it? Had it ever occurred to him that a woman who had been hurt and humiliated and then pursued by a fantastically handsome, sexy and strong male might find the image of her disappointing first love wholly obscured by his own?

For that, Sara registered dazedly, was what had happened. Brian's presence at their wedding had filled her with only a great deal of self-conscious embarrassment. She had felt no bitterness, no jealousy of Antonia and no regret. It had been Alex who'd consumed her thoughts. It had been Alex who'd taught her the meaning of desire, Alex who'd overshadowed Brian to such an extent that within the space of a day her former fiancé had inspired her with nothing but a need to run the other way.

But no, she wasn't foolish enough to start imagining that she was falling in love with Alex now. She was bound to feel *some* sort of attachment to him, she reasoned fiercely. After all, they were married; they were lovers. She understood perfectly what was happening inside her mind. A kind of natural bonding to Alex was taking place...only there had been nothing remotely bonding about the manner in which he had literally dumped her off him just now!

Her teeth clenched as she thrust her wildly tousled hair out of her flashing eyes. Her trophy husband indeed! Her perfect hero! He satisfied one appetite and immediately thought of the next. No, he needn't worry too much about inciting her to feelings of forbidden love and devotion!

'First love?'

Sara's nose wrinkled. 'You'll laugh...'

'I won't.'

'OK...I was fifteen. It was a crush, all that moony love-from-afar stuff,' Sara muttered dismissively. 'I saw him every day for weeks when I was walking home from school. He was part of the road gang who built the bypass. You said you *wouldn't* laugh!' In hot-cheeked reproach, Sara threw a grape at Alex, which he caught one-handed and crushed slowly between even white teeth while he endeavoured to silence his mirth. 'He was very fanciable when he took his shirt off.'

Alex tilted his tousled dark head back, a vibrant smile curing his sensual mouth. 'Beefcake appeal, *bella mia*? I'm surprised at you.'

'Are you really?' Widening dancing green eyes, Sara treated him to a slow, sweeping survey that started at his broad, bronzed shoulders, slid down over his magnificent torso to his narrow waist and finally ended at the muscular, darkly haired thigh half-exposed by the tangled bedsheets.

'Funny, I would say that in that department I haven't changed one bit.'

Alex reached out, knotted a punitive lean hand into her torrent of hair and drew her down to him. 'Vixen,' he reproved her softly, brushing his mouth provocatively across the swollen fullness of hers, and her heart skipped an entire beat, a familiar tide of immediate hunger washing over her, leaving her weak.

It didn't matter how often Alex made love to her. She had found that out over the past two weeks. Alex could awaken that wanting at will. She had stopped trying to fight it. The blood sang in her veins with a wanton anticipation that could still make her blush. As she curved into the hard heat of him, she felt the thrusting readiness of his arousal against her and the ache between her thighs intensified shamelessly. He kissed her breathless, then pinned her willing body under him with an earthy groan of satisfaction and sent her out of her mind with pleasure all over again.

'It's getting late!' Alex sprang out of bed, ruthlessly hauled the sheet from her warm, drowsy flesh. 'We're going out,' he reminded her mockingly.

Minutes later she stood under the shower trying to wake up again, envying Alex his electrifying energy. She looked dazedly back on days which had flown by in a whirl of constant activity. Alex seemed to need to busily fill every waking moment they shared. But why had she ever worried that she had made a mistake when she'd married him? she asked herself now.

Alex had the power to make her feel incredibly special. Alex had plunged her into a luxurious life of complete indulgence, and nobody had ever indulged Sara's wants and wishes before. Being spoilt, she had discovered, took a lot of getting used to but it had certainly done wonders for her shaky self-esteem. She had reeled dizzily through day after wonderful day of Alex's exclusive attention.

First he had taken her shopping. Now she had a wardrobe

stuffed with gorgeous designer clothes, most of them outfits that she wouldn't have dared even to look at had not Alex insisted, and for the first time Sara found herself taking a real pride in her appearance. 'Such a shame that Sara's so plain,' she had heard her grandmother complain once after fondly admiring her other grandchild's blue-eyed blonde prettiness. Sara had never felt beautiful in her life until Alex had said that she was, and, secure in the conviction that in *his* eyes she was not unattractive, she was beginning to see herself in a very different light.

He took so much interest in her, in every tiny thing about her. He had had to dig through all the layers of her conviction that she was a deeply boring person to get her to open out without apology or embarrassment. But he had persisted and he had listened. Was he always like this with her sex—a stunningly charismatic male who was highly attuned to the female psyche, who knew exactly what it took to make a woman feel not only desirable but also fascinating? Or was this current intensity more typical of Alex at the start of a new affair…before the boredom set in? She hurriedly squashed that pessimistic thought flat.

'Wear the gold dress,' Alex suggested.

'Won't it be a bit…flashy?'

'I like flashy on you. And you owe me,' Alex drawled teasingly.

'For what?'

'For destroying my appreciation of beauty with a year of ugly navy and brown suits.'

She laughed, caught the reflection of her own smile in a mirror as she dressed. There were stars in her eyes, and she had a crazy, irrepressible feeling of happiness that was becoming more and more familiar with every day that passed. Quickly she looked away again. But there was no avoiding what was going on inside her heart. Her head had nothing at all to do with it. Intelligence couldn't stop her pulses jumping every time Alex came within ten feet of her.

And if she was falling head over heels in love with her own husband it was not *her* fault, it was his. When a man made a woman feel this wonderful, what did he expect to earn in response? Cold, polite detachment? No doubt Alex wanted to make up for the rocky start of their marriage but, even so, he really did seem to care about her. He had to have cared to have asked her to marry him so quickly. He had to have wanted her an awful lot. It disconcerted Sara to realise that the manipulation that she had been so shocked by on their wedding day had now become something she hugged to herself as proof of the depth of Alex's desire for her.

'You look incredibly sexy...'

She turned. Cut on the bias, the fluid, simple lines of the gold shoestring-strapped dress accentuated the slender perfection of her figure. The gorgeous fabric shimmered seductively with her every movement.

'But rather bare...' Alex turned her back to the mirror and brushed her hair out of his path. He slid a slender diamond necklace round her throat, his cool, deft fingers brushing the nape of her neck as he fastened it. 'I bought earrings as well,' he murmured huskily. 'But they won't do. Your ears aren't pierced. *Not* very observant of me.'

Her fingertips shyly brushed the glittering jewels and her eyes suddenly stung. 'It's gorgeous, Alex... Thank you.'

'It's been an incredible two weeks, *bella mia*. I believe the pleasure has all been mine.' Alex let his lips feather briefly, caressingly across one bare shoulder and then he drew lithely back and enveloped her in a soft velvet evening jacket.

Grasping his hand, Sara stepped uncertainly onto the motor-launch, not quite accustomed as yet to the wholly frivolous height of her strappy sandals. They dined out almost every evening but the enchantment of Venice by night could not fade. The splendid faç ades of the *palazzo* along the Grand

Canal were floodlit, and against the rich indigo backdrop of the night sky and the dark, reflective water the sight was a magical one.

As the launch moved off, illuminated by the dazzling lights that framed the Rialto Bridge, Sara watched Alex with compulsive intensity. Sometimes she wanted so badly to get inside that sleek dark head and root around for answers that made sense. *Why me?* she wanted to ask suddenly. What was so special about me? She was an ordinary girl from an ordinary background and Alex was an immensely wealthy male with a blue-blooded pedigree that could be traced back centuries. He could have married any woman, yet he had chosen to marry her.

Was it utter madness or shocking vanity for her to wonder if Alex could be just a *little* in love with her? Maybe it was the shock of being treated with such incredible consideration and generosity which was encouraging her to cherish so wild a hope. No womaniser ever got successful by being less than charming, she reminded herself doggedly. He knows women inside out. Turning your head is probably just an ego-trip for him. Six months from now maybe he'll be treating you like a piece of furniture, any thrill you ever had for him staled by familiarity…so enjoy the Rolls-Royce treatment while it lasts.

'What's the matter with you?' Alex enquired as he handed her out of the launch onto solid ground again.

Sara tensed. 'Nothing.'

'You're very quiet.' Alex slanted a grim dark scrutiny over her taut profile. 'I suppose it was too much to hope that you would forget…'

'Forget what?' Sara queried, dismayed by the speed with which Alex's mood could change.

'Don't play games, *cara*. This is, after all, the day when you expected to drift blissfully up the aisle into Shorter's waiting arms!'

Sara was shocked by the unwelcome reminder. She

turned pale, thinking that Alex only had to mention Brian
and it was like having a freezer door slammed in her face.
It was little wonder that she went out of her way to ensure
that she never accidentally referred to the man who had
been a big part of her life for almost two years.

'No, I did not think you were unaware of the fact,' Alex
said very drily. 'You've put on quite an act today but it's
beginning to wear thin.'

'Is it?' Sara gazed up at him, anxious green eyes clinging
to the starkly handsome lines of his dark features, a distinctly strained smile curving her tense mouth. 'Alex, I'd
actually forgotten that this was the day.'

His brilliant eyes hardened. He said something in
Italian—something derisively suggestive of disbelief.

'I *had*!'

'I know that certain look on your face.' Alex thrust open
the door of the exclusive restaurant.

'No, you don't,' Sara protested, suddenly angry at being
unfairly accused.

The conversation came to a frustrating halt as the *maître
d'* surged forward with alacrity. He was showing them to
their table when a silver-haired older man thrust his chair
noisily back nearby and rose with an exclamation. 'Alex?'
The rest was in volatile Italian.

'Sara…' Alex drew her smoothly forward. 'Tony
Bargani, a family friend.'

'You must join us.' Tony snapped his fingers imperiously
to call up more chairs and settled her down firmly in his
own seat. 'Alex knows everyone. My wife, Claudia.' He
patted the shoulder of the stunning silver-blonde beside
Sara with distinct pride of possession. 'Guy Chilton and his
wife, Denise…'

Guy Chilton was already up, enthusiastically shaking
hands. Tony was calling for drinks. His wife, who must
have been a good twenty years his junior, was too busy
competing for Alex's attention to take account of Sara. The

American woman, Denise, sighed with a wry smile. 'I believe this is your honeymoon, Sara. You should have avoided us. The men will be talking business for the rest of the evening.'

Claudia dropped down into her seat again and sent Sara a flickering glance of amusement. 'I'm quite sure Sara knows the score, Denise. She used to work for Alex, and with Alex business always come first and last. I remember my time with him well.'

'You used to work for Alex?' Sara smiled.

Claudia widened her eyes and uttered a sharp little laugh. 'Darling, do I really look as though I ever worked nine to five in some menial little office job? How frightfully uncomplimentary!'

Faint colour stained Sara's cheeks as the upper-class English accent cut through her. 'I'm sorry. I misunderstood.'

'Hardly surprising.' Claudia turned hostile blue eyes on her. 'I expect you're feeling rather out of your depth in this milieu.'

With difficulty, Sara kept her apologetic smile in place. 'I'm learning all the time.'

Tony toasted them with champagne, his natural warmth in strong contrast to his wife's air of dismissive boredom. 'I'm surprised the two of you aren't on the yacht,' he commented.

'Sara gets seasick,' Alex returned casually.

Her dark head shot up, surprise etched in her eyes. 'Who told you that?'

'Your aunt.' Across the table, rich dark eyes locked with hers, amusement shimmering in their depths. 'At the reception. The news necessitated a decidedly last-minute change of destination—'

'You mean you didn't know?' Tony's portly frame shook with mirth.

Sara hadn't known either. And if she could have got hold of her aunt at that instant she would have strangled her!

One sickly day trip to France while she had still been at school was scarcely sufficient evidence on which to base such an assumption.

'How very inconvenient.' Claudia oozed sympathy. 'Will you be selling *Sea Spring* now?'

'Certainly not for my benefit. My aunt tends to exaggerate,' Sara interposed ruefully.

'Venice has to be the most romantic city in the world,' Denise Chilton commented warmly. 'I can't think of anywhere more wonderful to spend your honeymoon.'

'But then you didn't grow up here…Alex did,' Tony's wife slotted in sweetly.

A near-overpowering desire to empty her glass over Claudia's head assailed Sara as the first course was delivered.

The meal progressed. Alex smoothly engaged Tony in conversation. Sara's cheeks stopped burning. Their hostess was one of Alex's exes, Sara gathered grimly, dumped with the roses and the diamonds and still simmering over the blow to her ego. She would have to develop a thicker skin for such encounters.

'You know, the resemblance *is* really quite remarkable,' Claudia murmured very quietly over the coffee-cups when Denise had disappeared off to the cloakroom.

Sara lifted her head. 'Sorry?'

'Alex's father and Tony are old friends. We dined with them in London last week. Apparently Sandro was staggered the first time he saw you,' Claudia continued very softly.

'I'm afraid I don't follow…'

'You're the living image of Alex's one and only true love.' Claudia's eyes were bright with spiteful amusement. 'Sandro got a shock when he saw you coming down the aisle. For a moment he thought you *were* Elissa. Silly, of course…she'd be twenty years older than you now…but don't they say that everyone has a double somewhere?'

A creeping veil of coldness was slowly enclosing Sara. Her brain was in a fog. She could not seem to absorb what Claudia was telling her.

'I never actually met her,' Claudia confided. 'But when Tony and I got home I dug out some old family photo albums to satisfy my curiosity.'

'Family albums?' Sara questioned with a frown.

'Elissa was married to Tony's cousin at the time she took off with Alex...didn't you know that?'

Sara's tongue snaked out to moisten her dry lower lip. 'His cousin?' she said weakly, shooting an involuntary glance at the three men on the other side of the table, who were enjoying an animated, friendly conversation. Elissa had been married when Alex met her?

'You do have a lot to learn. Everyone blamed *her*, even Tony. Alex was only a boy and she was one devastating lady. Very petite, hourglass figure, long black hair just like you. Alex never did get over her. She turned him into a cold bastard. But then you're something special, aren't you?' Claudia touched her glass against the rim of Sara's in a mocking toast. 'Only with you can Alex relive his fantasy...and he doesn't even need to switch off the light!'

CHAPTER EIGHT

'I FEEL like a bath…' Sara mumbled, heading for the *en suite* bathroom like a homing pigeon seeking sanctuary.

'Sara, did Claudia say something to upset you?'

Sara paused, her slim back rigid, and then turned her dark head. 'What on earth could she have said?' she managed with apparent blankness.

Alex loosened his tie and surveyed her with intent dark eyes that were sharp enough to strip paint. 'Five years ago I met her at a wedding and invited her to a dinner party. She amused herself by shredding the looks and reputation of every other woman present. She's poisonous. I didn't see her again, nor did I sleep with her.'

Hot colour had drenched Sara's former pallor. 'You don't need to explain that to me,' she told him uncomfortably.

'Because you really don't care either way, do you, *cara*?' A tiny muscle pulled taut at the corner of Alex's compressed mouth, his narrowed eyes more slivers of glittering gold intensity as he stared back at her.

'It's not like that…I mean, I'm not an idiot,' she muttered, her head pounding with so much tension that she was beginning to feel physically sick. 'I know you have a past…obviously.'

'And a wife who doesn't have a jealous, possessive bone in her body. I am so fortunate,' Alex breathed with the suggestion of gritted teeth.

Sara looked back at him, bewildered by a dialogue which barely a tenth of her brain could concentrate on. 'Alex…I'm not feeling very well,' she whispered strickenly, her stomach twisting more than ever with the tension in the room.

'You don't need to make excuses and you don't need to hide in the bathroom either,' Alex delivered in a slashing undertone. 'I have no desire to share the same bed with you tonight!'

Bewilderment seized Sara as he strode out of the room. Her wretched tummy heaved. She fled into the bathroom and was very much preoccupied for some minutes. Finally, she rested her perspiring forehead against the cold surround of the bath and slowly got a grip on herself again before she began to undress. Claudia Bargani was vindictive. Alex had said it, Sara *knew* it for a fact. Normally she wouldn't have given credence to anything such a woman told her. But Claudia's revelation had still plunged Sara into deep shock. Why? Because taken in tandem with Sara's sudden marriage that revelation threatened to make a terrifying kind of sense.

Could Alex have wanted her only because she reminded him of Elissa? Did Alex even realise what might have attracted him to her? Or could the similarity be so striking that he had immediately recognised it? Whichever, she was left with the degrading possibility that she might well owe her present position as Alex's wife to something as agonisingly superficial as her face and her body. Not to mention being left at the mercy of a lot of really creepy, utterly degrading thoughts, she reflected in a tempest of angry pain.

Everyone had been stunned when Alex had married her. Sara had been stunned too when he'd proposed. She had been equally shaken by the discovery that Alex had been wildly attracted to her for the entire year that she had worked for him. But if she reminded Alex of the woman he had loved and lost, the woman he had never forgotten, what made her worthy of such obsessive desirability now seemed obvious. Was it possible that she owed everything they had shared since their marriage to the memory of another woman? The intensity of his interest, the exclusive attention, the extraordinary passion…?

She knew that she was tearing herself apart—in short, doing exactly what Claudia had wanted her to do—but she couldn't seem to stop doing it. But maybe Claudia had simply made it all up; maybe Claudia had a wildly inventive imagination. Sara curled up in a tight ball in a bed that felt horribly big, cold and empty. She was so tense that her muscles hurt, but it didn't really matter because it seemed to her that every fibre of her being was in agony.

She loved Alex…but suddenly she hated him too—for having the power to put her through such mental hoops of fire. Wild images of revenge swept her imagination. In every one of them Alex stood looking totally defeated while she packed her bags with frigid dignity and disdain and left him flat, publicly deserted him after two weeks of marriage. The door opened. She sat up with a jerk, switched on the bedside lights.

Alex was already standing beside the bed, quite magnificently nude and characteristically unconcerned by the fact.

'What do you want?' she demanded fierily.

'You,' Alex said succinctly.

Anger gleamed like a hurricane warning in his golden gaze and her engrossing revenge scenario sagged like a sofa bereft of its stuffing. Alex was a long way from total defeat. Aggression emanated from every line of his lithe, sunbronzed body as he slid into bed and reached for her with hands far too strong to be easily evaded. In one smooth movement he forced her down and flat again, anchoring her furious body into stillness with his own.

Her teeth clenched in disbelief. 'If you don't get off me, Alex, I'll hit you!'

Alex propped his chin on the heel of one hand, his tawny eyes ablaze with very male provocation. 'Be my guest,' he challenged.

Her hands bunched into fists. He lowered his glossy dark head and took her mouth with a raw heat that scorched. A splintering shard of answering passion pierced her, overpowering every other sense. He bruised her lips and yet still her hands opened out and clutched at him with a hunger she couldn't deny. Indeed the hunger felt sharper, stronger, more desperate than ever before, leaving her utterly defenceless. He leant back from her when she was breathless, her heartbeat racing fast enough to choke her, every skin cell and pulse thrumming with wild response.

As she struggled to focus on his intent dark profile, he closed hard fingers over the fragile silk screening her heaving breasts and quite coolly ripped it away, the sound of the rending fabric preternaturally loud in the throbbing silence. Momentarily Sara went stiff with fright, and then she watched his hand curve round the pouting swell of her own naked flesh, his thumb grazing across a straining pink nipple, and a hot, deep melting started inside her, reducing her to boneless, quivering collusion.

He let his tongue flick over the achingly sensitive peak and a strangled whimper escaped her as her whole body pushed up to him in an unstoppable wave of response. He lifted his head again, glittering gold eyes sweeping over her as he wrenched her free of the tangled remnants of silk confining her legs. He ran a sure hand back up the tightening length of one slender thigh and discovered the moist warmth of her most delicate flesh, and the spiralling excitement that he could evoke with the tiniest caress sent her ever more violently out of control.

'No, I didn't think you would hit me…' Alex murmured softly, chillingly.

She fought through the wanton layers of her own suffocating pleasure and struggled to think again. 'What…?' she mumbled, relocating her voice an equal challenge.

'I touch you and you wouldn't hear a fire alarm. I touch you at any time of the day or the night and it's instant surrender. You've taught me that in two short weeks. All the sex that I want, whenever I want.'

'A-Alex, what are you—?'

'Saying?' Smouldering golden eyes locked with hers with icy precision. '*Dio*…I am not complaining, *bella mia*. But what a waste of a year. I was needlessly cautious to a degree that now embarrasses me. Sexually harassing you between the filing cabinets would have been a hugely entertaining exercise… You can't keep your hands off me even in the middle of a fight! So if you have to languish over the pretty blond boy you lost, why should I be offended? Between the sheets you're still incredibly willing to satisfy my most basic needs…*and* your own.'

Eyes wide, Sara was rigid with shock until it belatedly dawned on her for the very first time that Alex might actually be jealous—a suspicion that made his verbal offensive wash over her. 'I wasn't thinking about Brian,' she said quietly, intently, wanting to convince him, and she would have said a great deal more with very little encouragement.

But she didn't get the encouragement. In coolly insolent response, Alex scanned the length of her naked body, so trustingly open to his gaze, before he met her anxious eyes again. 'Not right now, no,' he conceded with a pointed derision that was like a slap in the face. 'But, you see, I expect your full attention *out* of bed too. Feel free to agonise as much as you like over Shorter…but from now on I suggest you indulge your sentiments in private. Your tragedy-queen mood with its accompanying deathly silence sets my teeth on edge.'

And Sara shrank inside herself, the illusion that he might have been becoming jealous of that former love brutally, instantaneously dissolved. Her struggle to hide her growing distress earlier had meant only one thing to Alex once she had denied that Claudia had played any part in her change of mood. He had assumed that Brian was behind her withdrawal—a belief that had provoked not jealousy but coldly sardonic impatience and reproof. Love him all you like, was the message she'd received. Just don't bore me to death with your silly emotionalism.

And *that* was when Sara felt unbearably, hideously humiliated. She read the other message that Alex was giving her too: her undeniable ability to behave like a wanton slut in bed was just about the only thing he did appreciate about her! With a frantic hand she snatched at the sheet and dragged it clumsily over bared skin that now shamed her. She curved defensively away from him, her flesh clammy. Alex used her own body like a weapon against her. He made her feel cheap. 'Cold and detached,' Pete had said. She stared strickenly into those stunningly golden but frighteningly unreadable eyes and shivered compulsively, as if she were looking into the jaws of death, repulsed by her own vulnerability.

Alex frowned, muttered something fierce in Italian and tugged her firmly back against his warm, muscular length. In bitter pain, she felt the familiar surge of her own body against his and knew that he could make her want him no matter what he did, and that chilled and mortified her even more. She froze in instinctive rejection. 'Don't touch me.'

His strong muscles clenched hard. 'Sara...I'm finding out that I can't live with being the consolation prize. If you want to stay married to me, you have to put the love of your life behind you,' he spelt out with hard emphasis.

Reacting to the part of that threat which related to their marriage, Sara turned white. 'As you did with Elissa?' she whispered feverishly.

His ebony brows drew together. '*Madre di Dio*... what—?'

'Because you can't say you put her behind you, can you?' Sara suddenly launched at him an entire octave higher.

'Elissa doesn't come into this!' Alex dismissed with raw, stinging impatience.

Sara turned her head away, her heart thumping at the foot of her throat. 'I heard someone say…at our wedding…that I looked like her…'

The words lay there between them. The pulsing silence seemed to stretch endlessly. She was holding her breath. 'Alex?' she finally prompted very, very tautly.

There was slight movement beside her and the lights went out.

'No comment,' Alex murmured without any expression at all.

The response stunned Sara. She lay there rigid in the darkness but Alex made no further move towards her. However, there was nothing tense about the drowsy sigh of positively indolent satisfaction that escaped him as he shifted against the fine linen sheets and then lay with the stillness of complete relaxation—a reality soon borne out by the deep, even sound of his breathing as he fell asleep…while Sara lay awake.

The honeymoon was over.

Alex dealt her a measuring look in the limousine carrying them across London. 'You look tired. You should go straight back to bed.'

'I'm fine. I have to unpack—'

'The staff will do the unpacking. You might as well rest. I'll be late tonight,' he told her.

Sara stiffened. 'Then I'll go down to Ladymead, see how the work is going.'

'I should check out the workforce first,' Alex murmured with lazy mockery, dark eyes flicking over her strained face. 'If a brawny plasterer takes off his shirt in your radius, I might be history before I know it.'

'Very funny, Alex.' Flames of colour burnished in her pallor.

'I never did tell you who my first love was—'

'You mean your memory goes back that far?'

Alex smiled, his mood infuriatingly buoyant. 'I was twelve. She was thirteen. I lied about my age. She blushed every time she looked at me. She had skin like a peach, black curly hair and braces on her teeth. For the whole of one week I was enraptured.'

'The longevity of your affections is remarkable.'

Alex laughed appreciatively, his dark, flashing eyes colliding with hers. 'When she found out I was younger, she cut me dead!'

An involuntary smile crept across the tense line of her mouth, a giant wave of love surging up inside her. She veiled her shadowed eyes immediately but she was angry with herself now for lying awake all night brooding. Alex had never promised to love her, had he? He had said that he could make her happy and he had, but he had also shattered her illusion that she could somehow have more. Maybe she had needed that lesson. It had been very foolish of her to imagine that simply because she had fallen in love Alex might have too.

So she *did* remind him of Elissa…but it was a well-known fact that people were often attracted by the same particular physical type in human relationships. Why should it be anything more sinister than that? That resemblance might initially have drawn Alex's attention to her but he was far too strong a character to have married her to live out some ridiculous fantasy. Any male who would go to such lengths would be obsessed to a degree that suggested male instability. For goodness' sake, the woman had disappeared out of Alex's life thirteen years ago, turned him off love, *hurt* him! Elissa had to be more of a bad memory for Alex than a good one.

An hour later she stood in the same bedroom where she had awakened in a bower of flowers almost two months earlier. As she recalled her panic and horror that morning, it didn't seem possible that she was the same person any more. She was changing, she acknowledged; she *had* changed. In a cheval-glass, she saw a woman sheathed in an elegant Christian Lacroix dress—a woman who looked rich and exclusive and who held her head high. But the alteration was more than one of appearance and self-image. When she was with Alex, Sara realised, she felt extraordinarily free simply to be herself.

And wasn't it time that she cleared up his misapprehensions about Brian? If only Alex had not witnessed her shock and distress that day! He had seen too much, got too close. It wasn't that surprising that he should still believe that she loved Brian. Not one single thing had she done to convince him otherwise. And no, Alex was not comfortable with the belief that he was the consolation prize. A rueful smile curved her lips. She didn't blame him for lashing out at her last night. They would have to talk.

Ladymead was festooned with scaffolding and satisfyingly alive with noise and activity. The repairs and renovation work were moving right on target. There had been no major problems, nothing the architect in charge had not been able to handle. But when the current phase was over there would still be a million things to do, including decorating and furnishing. The size of the project made her head spin but Sara could hardly wait to face the challenge.

She was wandering around the kitchen when one of the workmen put his head round the door. 'There's a woman looking for you out front, Mrs Rossini!'

It was Alex's sister, Donatella. Sara stilled in momentary surprise and then walked forward smiling. 'I had no idea you were still here.'

'By the time I did my shopping, wandered round the galleries and caught up with old friends, my one-week stay easily ran over two,' Donatella admitted cheerfully. 'I saw Alex at the office and when he said you were down here I decided to join you… You don't mind?'

'I'm delighted to have the company.'

'I was dying to see it. I still can't believe my eyes. It's a wonderful old house, gloriously picturesque,' Donatella sighed appreciatively as they strolled slowly indoors. 'When Papà said that Alex had bought a ruin, we all laughed because Alex cannot bear to be uncomfortable on the domestic front. He is very spoilt that way. This dust, this dirt, this frantic upheaval would drive him crazy…but what a declaration of love that he should close his eyes to all the imperfections and buy it anyway!'

'Alex knows what I like very well.' Sara's eyes suddenly gleamed with secret amusement. Alex really hadn't needed to hedge his bets with Ladymead the day he'd proposed. She still would have married him. Perhaps it was time she told him that too. 'And he can hardly have been unaware of what was required here. The *palazzo* must require fairly constant maintenance.'

'But that's different. For Alex that is the home of his earliest memories. He uses it most. Papà rarely goes to Venice now,' Donatella said as they strolled round the echoing ground floor. 'He has never liked the *palazzo* since Alex's mother died there.'

'Did he love her so much?'

Donatella looked wry. 'He would tell you he did but then they were only together three years. I'm more cynical. With every wife but Francine he fathered another child, found his attention straying and got divorced again. I think he simply likes women too much, but he does like to think of himself as a family man.'

'His children do seem to be surprisingly close.'

'We have Alex to thank for that. He kept us all in contact with each other as we grew up…yet he had the toughest childhood. He had had three stepmothers by the time he was in his teens, none of them substitute mothers.' Donatella grimaced. 'Unfortunately for Alex, he was always very much Papà's favourite. Even my own mother resented

Alex, which was sad. He was only a baby when his mother died. It was not his fault that each new wife felt insecure and then decided that her child was being passed over in his favour.'

'Maybe…maybe that's why he fell for an older woman,' Sara muttered abruptly, abstractedly. Understanding what drove Alex in all his complexity did not come easily to her. Yet she so badly wanted to know what made him the way he was: capable of such immense warmth and sensitivity and then such paradoxical and chilling coldness.

'As a mother figure?' Donatella uttered a reluctant laugh and shook her head. 'I don't think so, Sara. Elissa clung to Alex. She leant on *him*. He was by far the stronger personality.'

'What was she like?'

'As a family friend, we all liked her… That is, until she became involved with Alex.' His sister compressed her lips. 'Everyone knew she was in a lousy marriage. Her husband wasn't the faithful type and she couldn't have children. I suppose she must have been very unhappy but she never complained. She worked tirelessly for charity. She was very well-known for her good works.'

'You're describing a saint.'

'A lot of people saw her in that light, so you can imagine the shocking scandal it caused when she took off with Alex. Nobody could believe it at first but I had seen her with him…' Donatella's eyes were rueful. 'He was very mature for his age, and with Alex she was a different person. It shone out of her. She couldn't hide her love. We were all very surprised when she left Alex after her husband divorced her, but to be truthful…equally relieved.'

'Why? The age difference?'

Donatella hesitated and then sighed. 'Please don't take offence…but talking about Elissa makes me feel uncomfortable. In any case, I can only repeat gossip and my own impressions as a rather judgemental teenager. Alex has never discussed Elissa with any of us.'

Sara grimaced. 'I'm sorry…my curiosity was running away with me.'

'Why?' her companion asked bluntly. 'Why concern yourself? It was a long time ago, an episode we were all glad to forget.'

Put like that, her own insecurities seemed neurotic.

'And you have been good for my brother, Sara. I saw a change in Alex today. He's more relaxed, less distant, not so driven as he used to be. You don't seem to be aware of the miracle you have worked. None of us ever really expected Alex to marry. When you grow up as we all did in divided households, it is very hard to have faith in marriage.'

But Alex didn't have faith in marriage. Oh, he had mustered impressive enthusiasm for the institution when he'd proposed but Sara reckoned that that had been for her benefit. No, for Alex this marriage was an experiment, with Ladymead the selected site for a home-making field test. But he would not be at all surprised if the experiment failed and he would probably be equally quick to cut his losses if their relationship hit one too many obstacles. The knowledge made Sara suppress a shiver.

Alex strolled into the drawing room of the town house shortly after midnight to find Sara curled up in the corner of a sofa, surrounded by a pile of magazines. 'I thought you would be in bed. You waited up for me…'

An irrepressible grin slanted her mouth. 'Alex, you suggested I rested this afternoon so that I *wouldn't* be too tired to wait up! Or did I misinterpret my instructions?'

The faintest colour highlighted the hard slant of his cheekbones and then he laughed. 'I didn't realise I was so transparent.'

'You aren't as a rule,' she said consolingly, her softened

gaze roaming over his vibrantly handsome features. 'Would you like something to eat?'

'Nothing.' He surveyed her with an intensity that made her heartbeat quicken. 'So bring me up to date on the bricks and mortar rescue mission,' he invited.

'Everything's going like clockwork.'

'When do we move?'

'That depends on how quickly I can furnish and decorate.'

'I'm amazed that you're not putting us under canvas on that field that the agent had the gross pretension to call a lawn.'

'Somehow I can't see you under canvas.' She swallowed hard and held his gaze. 'And if you don't want to live there you can sell the house when the work's finished…no hard feelings,' she asserted.

An ebony brow was elevated. 'Why?'

'I didn't decide to marry you because you promised to buy it—'

'But it helped…'

'When I was walking round Ladymead that day, I had no idea that you were about to ask me to marry you or that there was ever likely to be any possibility of it becoming my home.'

A slow smile curved his mobile mouth. 'But at least admit that you pictured some glossy magazine image of wholesome family domesticity: log fires, dogs and cats, children…'

'It seems to me that you must have been tuned into pretty much the same wavelength,' Sara protested.

'*Your* wavelength. I see smoke billowing out from inefficient chimneys, cats that scratch and dogs that bark. But that's not important if you're content. *Where* I live isn't important to me,' Alex returned with wry emphasis. 'As a child I learnt not to put down roots because whenever I did Sandro and I were on the move again. The abandoned wives and kids always got what was euphemistically termed the marital home. Becoming too comfortable or too attached to the roof over my head was never a good idea.'

The sheer physical upheaval of separation and divorce had not occurred to Sara before. Now she felt guilty. She should have appreciated that Alex had lived in many different houses throughout his childhood, never in one secure home. Had each new wife insisted on a new roof? And every time Sandro had opted for another divorce Alex's world would have been thrown into chaos again.

'While you, on the other hand…' Alex studied her with keen dark eyes. 'You grew up in a house where you were made to feel like an intruder, where nothing was ever really yours and where you felt you did not belong but where you tried very hard to fit. I can understand now why you dream of making a home that is entirely your own and why that need should be so important to you. But I have to confess that I didn't understand all that a month ago.'

And it's at times like this that *I* understand why I love you, Sara thought. Her throat had thickened. She slid upright and covered the distance between them in seconds. Alex's arms came round her and she breathed in deep. 'If the chimneys smoke, I'll get them fixed, and we'll start out with only one small pet—'

'That would be stretching self-denial too far, *cara*. The mice in that house require an army of cats.'

'Pest control, Alex…and they've already been…*three* times,' she admitted ruefully.

With a husky laugh, Alex pulled her close and looked down at her beautiful face. 'Only one warning, *bella mia*…if you ever bring a wallpaper book to bed—'

'You'll put the house on the market again?' she teased as he lifted her off her feet.

'I couldn't do that. Ladymead is yours.'

'Mine?' she said blankly.

'It's in your name. Think of it as a wedding present.'

'Are you selling this place?' she mumbled in a daze.

'Why? It's useful when I want to entertain.'

Abandoned wives always got the marital home... Was she getting hers in advance? And Alex was retaining the town house for his own use, ensuring that if they broke up he would suffer minimal inconvenience. Was it crazy of her to think like that? While she was wondering, Alex bent his dark head and exacted a long, lingering kiss that made her toes curl in wild anticipation.

Much later, lying in a wonderful tangle of peaceful satiation, Sara rubbed her cheek lovingly against a smooth brown shoulder and thought about the chaotic, insecure childhood Alex must have had. 'You're really close to your brother and sisters, aren't you?'

'It astonishes me when I think of what a whiny little brat Marco was, always throwing tantrums and telling tales,' he mused lazily. 'Donatella, now...she was very quiet and serious. She used to follow me everywhere. The twins...they were born shortly before I opted out of my father's tangled love life. Their mother was convinced I had to be pathologically jealous of them. *Dio*...she panicked if I went near them!'

'Bitch,' Sara said feelingly.

Alex vented a wry laugh. 'She's not like that now. She hasn't remarried and she hates Francine, so if there's a problem with Cara or Lucilla it lands in my lap.'

'Why not their father's?'

'Sandro will use any excuse not to get involved, and his excuse is generally Francine. She rules him with a rod of iron. She's very conscious that she's survived longer than any of her predecessors. She's hard as nails but occasionally I feel a little sorry for her. She's thirty-seven and I strongly suspect she would like a child but she's convinced that a baby would land her in the divorce court, and, going on previous form, she's very probably right,' Alex conceded. 'Like me, Francine worked out a long time ago that Sandro finds a wife who is also a mother a decided turn-off.'

Sara had tensed. 'But you're not like that.'

'I'd be very stupid to tell you if I was,' Alex mocked.

'Alex…be serious.'

'Why? Any prospect of us having a child is a very long way off,' he returned flatly.

Sara frowned, astonished that he could think that she had no right to the smallest input on the subject. 'How long…is *very* long?'

Alex exhaled on an impatient hiss. 'Let me put it this way, *cara*—I have no plans to compete with your former fiancé in the fertility stakes!'

'I beg your pardon?' Sara gasped, thoroughly disconcerted by that response as she lifted herself up to look at him.

'Nor have I any intention of changing my mind in the near future.' Alex surveyed her with hard dark eyes. 'It's not a topic open to debate. Why do you think I take responsibility for birth control? I saw this threat clouding my horizon weeks ago!'

Threat? Her cheeks flamed. 'Did you indeed?'

'*Sì*…the same second you told me that your cousin was pregnant,' Alex drawled softly. 'You are not in competition with her.'

'What on earth are you talking about? I asked a simple question,' Sara gritted defensively.

'And I gave you a simple answer. No,' Alex said emphatically. 'Sublimate your maternal urges in cats and dogs.'

Sara shifted across the bed as if she had been bitten by a rattlesnake. 'I have no idea why you had to drag Antonia into this!' Her voice shook with angry incomprehension and hurt.

Alex dimmed the lights. 'Go to sleep.'

'Don't treat me like a child!' she protested incredulously.

'I refuse to argue with you about this.'

'You're like your father, aren't you?' she condemned wildly.

'*Madre di Dio*…if I'd been like Sandro, *cara*, you would have been dumped before the ink was dry on the marriage licence!'

In the darkness Sara went rigid with shocked disbelief. He played really dirty in a fight… And you're *surprised*? an inner voice carolled drily. 'So why didn't you just do that?' she demanded.

'Don't ask me in the mood I'm in.'

'I want to know!'

'It's like there's a piece of elastic which keeps on hauling me back…but at this moment, *bella mia*, it's stretched very taut!' And the fact that he didn't like the feeling at all lanced clear as a bell through every splintering syllable.

'Help yourself to a pair of scissors!' Sara suggested painfully, sick and tired of the frequency with which Alex implied that their marriage might not have a future. Every time she stood up to him, he unleashed that threat.

Alex bit out a raw, exasperated imprecation in Italian. Sara pinned her tremulous mouth shut with enormous effort. There was a volcano of injustice boiling up inside her. One little question, casually asked, innocently meant—for, believe it or not, she was *not* gasping to become pregnant right at this moment—and she wouldn't have minded if Alex had merely said he would prefer to wait a year or two. Yes, she wanted Alex's baby but only when she felt secure in their relationship and only when he felt the same way. So what on earth did Antonia have to do with it? Did he really think that she would try to keep up with her cousin in such an utterly stupid way?

Or was Alex being almost too clever for his own good? she wondered painfully. Throwing up a red herring to conceal the fact that *he* didn't want children and certainly wouldn't risk an accidental pregnancy when he couldn't see their marriage lasting very long…was that what he had been doing? And she remembered, with bitter clarity, thinking that a woman in love with a man who did not love her might well become insecure, over-sensitive and anxious. And now she knew it to be the case, Sara reflected with stricken insight.

CHAPTER NINE

'IM SORRY,' the polite female voice responded when Sara reached for the phone at almost the same moment that she woke up in bed alone. 'Mr Rossini is in conference.'

'I'm sorry,' the same infuriatingly detached tone told her an hour later. 'Mr Rossini is not presently available.

'I am so sorry,' Sara was informed shortly before lunch-time and this time the voice sounded reprovingly weary. 'Mr Rossini is airborne.'

Airborne? Staving off a ludicrous image of Alex in free flight round the office, Sara cast aside the phone. It had finally dawned on her that he hadn't put his wife's name on the shortlist of approved callers allowed instant access to him...surely a deliberate oversight? How much enough was enough? A slow, steady anger was escalating inside Sara. She had done nothing to deserve such treatment.

He phoned from Paris at eight that evening. 'Things are hotting up here. I won't be back tonight,' he imparted. 'Everything OK?'

'Great,' Sara said in a stifled tone, for her anger had turned cold and heavy inside her.

'It might take me a couple of days to tie the loose ends up.'

'I understand.'

'I need a copy of a document on my desk in the library. Could you fax it to me?' He passed on the details in exactly the same tone that he had always utilised when she had been a humble employee. And she made a discovery there and then. Alex fell back behind that detachment instinctively when anything was wrong between them. He held her at a distance, forestalling argument or indeed any form of intimacy. No longer did she wonder why she had felt so damnably awkward with Alex on the phone before their marriage. That chill, silent disapproval could come down the line like a blast of polar snow.

Early the next morning Sara reached a very tough decision. No, Alex wasn't going to do this to her—blowing hot, blowing cold, making her feel that the smallest disagreement or displeasure might lead to the breakdown of their marriage. It was like being forced to live on a knife-edge. The more she took of it, the worse it would get. She packed a case with casual clothing. It would mean roughing it but she intended to stay at Ladymead. All she really needed for tonight was food…and a bed. So she would go shopping on the way down.

She faxed a message to Alex before she climbed into the limousine.

'Dear Alex,' it ran, 'waiting to be abandoned is bad for my nerves, so I've taken care of the problem for you. I am abandoning you.'

The builders' foreman greeted her at the door of the manor house. 'The phone has been ringing off the hook for you for the past two hours, Mrs Rossini. Somebody called Pete.'

'So, you are *there*,' Pete muttered frantically when she answered the next time the phone rang. 'What the heck was in that fax? Alex went through the roof and he was in a bad enough mood even before it arrived!'

'Did he tell you to track me down?'

'Obviously. This bid is at a crucial stage. He's very busy with the French negotiators,' Pete stressed with audible incredulity, that she should require such an explanation. 'Have you had bad news or something? Can't you handle it on your own? You know Alex doesn't like to be disturbed when he's—'

'I don't work for Alex any more,' she reminded him. 'Just tell him I was too busy to come to the phone.'

'I can't tell Alex *that*!' he spluttered in horror.

'But then Alex shouldn't have asked you to deal with this.'

In the background, she heard a deeper masculine voice intrude. There was a short silence and then, without warning, her eardrums were seared. 'What the bloody hell are you playing at?' Alex launched down the line at her full volume. 'How dare you send me a message like that?'

'That kind of blackmail doesn't exactly make your day, does it?' Sara pointed out gently.

Alex wasn't listening. 'I want you back in London by tonight!'

'No, Alex—'

'If you don't stop this insanity right now, I'll—'

'Save your breath. I know the options. Either you make a commitment to our marriage or you let me go, and since I really don't think you have the guts to do the first I'm placing my bets on the second,' Sara murmured tightly.

She replaced the receiver, her face white and stiff with strain. Then she straightened her shoulders and slowly released her breath. Now she had to wait. The next move was his to make. What she really needed, she conceded tautly, was nerves of steel, and what nerve she did have was petering out fast. She was risking so much...but *not* for so little. Would Alex come down to Ladymead? How long would it take him to come? Was she mad to have thrown down the gauntlet so blatantly?

She had taken Alex by surprise. You had to knock him off balance to make him listen. And if he left her here, chose to take her at her word—well, she was only ending what would have ended anyway, she told herself unhappily. She had to know whether or not he intended to give their marriage a chance. From the outside it didn't look as though he did. If she crossed him, he closed her out and put as much distance between them as he could. And maybe if he had loved her she could have handled that better, practised patience and hoped that time would take care of the problem.

But Alex didn't love her. Even worse he disliked the idea that she had any sort of power over him, even if it was only the far from cerebral power of sex. All the control had to be on his side…just as it had been in Venice. The expert lover and the amateur. Alex had controlled everything they'd shared. She sensed that it had always been like that for him with women. He had to call every shot. He didn't compromise. And he didn't trust her either.

By mid-afternoon the bed that she had purchased had been delivered. For the first time in her life, Sara had employed cash as an inducement to better service. She couldn't say that she was proud of herself but she could live with it when the alternative was sleeping on the floor. Ladymead was empty by four. The workforce downed tools and took off. Sara was left alone, free to wander silent rooms and wonder how she would furnish them, but the moment she appreciated that Alex might never share the house with her any interest she might have had drained away.

Almost as quickly she began to doubt and question her own actions. Wasn't it very probable that Alex would see her behaviour as a selfish, immature demand for attention? Suddenly she could not picture him responding to her change of abode with anything other than exasperated silence. Give her enough rope and let her hang herself with it—she could imagine Alex thinking like that. She had been the one to walk out; let her be the one to dig herself out of the tight corner she had put herself in. And that was assuming that Alex didn't decide just to let her go…

Suddenly she saw that, while she had very real concerns about their relationship, challenging Alex to such a degree had been needlessly provocative. Shouldn't she have tried harder to cut across those barriers of his to tell him without anger that they had to talk openly and honestly?

It was getting dark when she made herself sandwiches and then looked at them without appetite. The rain had come on slowly in a soft mist that dampened and blurred the windows. Now hailstones were lashing the panes. The electricity was only on in part of the house. As the shadows lengthened, she negotiated the magnificent main staircase with care, grateful that she had bought a torch. She crossed creaking floorboards in the bedroom that she had selected because it was next to the one functioning bathroom. Eventually she stopped pacing and wished that she had brought something to read with her. Shortly after ten she climbed into bed to keep warm while she listened to the rain and the wind battering the house.

A distant thumping noise woke her up at some timeless stage of the night. For a minute she was completely disorientated and then recall returned, making her spring out of her bed, breathlessly locate the light switch and lift the torch. It was almost two in the morning. From the top of the stairs, she could see the sturdy front door shuddering in complaint on its wrought-iron hinges and hurried down.

'What did I do in my last life to deserve this?' Alex splintered savagely as he rammed the door back in his eagerness to get over the threshold and out of the howling wind and rain.

Sara fell back, momentarily astonished by his appearance. He was soaked to the skin, his suit plastered to every muscular line of his powerful frame. He looked as if he had been swimming fully clothed, but he was not only very wet, he was also very dirty: mud was caked on his shoes and trousers and the front of a once pristine white shirt where he had clearly wiped his hands.

'If this is country life, you can bloody well keep it!' he blistered, fixing outraged golden eyes on her. 'The Bugatti died in a flood down that hellish mud track!'

'Oh, dear…' Sara said in a wobbly undertone, watching him rake a shaking hand through his wet, curling hair, pushing it back off his forehead as he stood there dripping, and she had a truly terrifying urge to put both arms round him and soothe him as if he were a furious, frustrated little boy who had just discovered the awful truth that life didn't always go his way.

'I need a bath and a drink.'

'Oh, dear…' Sara said again helplessly, knowing that neither was available and not quite sure how to break such bad news.

'My case is still in the car!' Alex delivered between clenched teeth.

'Oh, dear…' It was hard to think of anything more positive to say.

'*Madre di Dio*…if you say that once more…!' he exploded, but at the same time he shivered convulsively.

And it was the shiver that unfroze Sara. 'You need to get out of those clothes. Come upstairs.'

'The helicopter couldn't fly in the storm,' Alex grated, still boiling with rage as he followed her up the stairs. 'The jet was delayed. And there's not even electric light here. Have you any idea how long I've been banging at that door?'

Sara threw open the door of the bathroom, switching on the mercifully working light with a flourish. 'There's no hot water but everything else functions,' she told him encouragingly.

'No hot water?' Alex whispered in stunned disbelief.

Sara gave him a gentle push over the threshold and closed the door on him. Then she thought fast. In minutes she was fully dressed again. Lifting the torch and pulling on a jacket, she left the house.

It was a wild night and the sky was as black as pitch. The drive, with its potholes the size of craters, was a disaster zone for anyone forced to negotiate it without light. Alex's car had died near the very foot where the drive disappeared altogether as it dipped suddenly beneath a large, dark, uninviting expanse of water. Thankfully, Alex hadn't locked his car as he should have done. She waded in and located his leather case, searched for the keys and assumed that he had taken them with him. It was a good half-mile trudge back to the house but the rain was slackening off and the wind was dying down.

Alex had come. Alex had actually made a big effort to come. She hadn't expected him tonight, not so soon. And she certainly hadn't expected him to show up in the early hours, wet and filthy, a far cry from his usual immaculately groomed self. She had wanted very badly to laugh once the shock had worn off but amusement would have been cruel when Alex was so clearly at the end of his tether. A lukewarm shower would be equally cruel, she reflected. Maybe she should have offered to boil the kettle for him... What a shame she had switched the heater off earlier when she couldn't quite work out how to set the time switch.

When she found the bathroom deserted, she thrust the case through the bedroom door like a sneak thief. She didn't look in. 'I'll make you some coffee!' she called winningly, and hurriedly escaped again.

She carefully washed the beaker that she had used earlier and wished that she hadn't been quite so ridiculously sparing in what she had brought for her own needs. She could offer him a biscuit, a cup of instant coffee and banana sandwiches—not exactly a feast for a male with a healthy appetite.

'You shouldn't have gone back to the car for me...but thanks. The gesture was appreciated.'

Sara spun round. Alex was standing in the doorway wearing a black Armani sweater and well-cut linen trousers. He looked heart-stoppingly gorgeous. Her ribcage felt constrained. 'It was the least I could do. Anyway I had a torch.'

'This place is a hell-hole. And it's a judgement on me,' Alex mused fatalistically, scanning the vast, comfortless kitchen with a barely concealed shudder. 'I knew what I was doing. I disobeyed my own instincts—'

'Coffee?' Sara suggested, setting the beaker on the long, scrubbed table. 'Banana sandwiches are all I can offer in the way of food, I'm afraid.'

Alex didn't move. He exhaled sharply and surveyed her in grim silence for a long moment. 'Maybe you'd like to tell me what the hell all this is about…?'

Sara flushed uncomfortably. His anger vented, he now sounded coolly reasonable. 'I'm sorry you had such a rough time getting here—'

'Stick to the point.'

Sara stiffened. 'I had no idea you would come here tonight.'

'I very nearly didn't,' Alex admitted. 'Intelligence told me to leave you here to stew.'

'But you didn't…'

'No, rage blew me in with the storm. There was also the natural concern that something had happened that I didn't know about…some highly mysterious event which would miraculously justify your behaviour.' Alex regarded her with hard challenge. 'And if you can't come up with that miracle I'm calling a car and going back to London.'

'You see? You're doing it again,' Sara responded tautly. 'You're threatening me; you do it all the time—'

'I don't threaten you,' Alex countered fiercely.

'Maybe you don't even realise you're doing it, maybe it's second nature.' Beneath her bright, anxious eyes, her cheeks were taut with stress. 'But you do it. If I annoy you, Alex, you immediately close me out and start telling me that our marriage is on borrowed time if I continue. You enforce conversational no-go areas—'

'That is nonsense,' Alex interposed in flat rebuttal.

She was holding herself so rigid that her muscles ached with strain. 'No, it isn't—'

'*Dio*…' Shimmering eyes whipped over her with scorch-

ing incredulity. 'You *fax* me the news that you're leaving
me! You drag me all the way from Paris on a fool's errand
by crying wolf and then think you can tell me I deserved
this childish charade?'

'I wanted you to know what emotional blackmail feels
like,' Sara admitted with helpless honesty. 'You use it on
me and it makes me angry too. I don't like having my
strings pulled either. I don't like the fact that you make me
scared to talk about things we need to talk about. I don't
like being judged and refused the right to defend myself...'

Suddenly his glittering gaze pierced her like an arrow
finding its target. '*Madre di Dio*...you did *all* this purely
because I refused to consider allowing you to become pregnant?' he demanded in outrage.

Sara flinched in disbelief and then her chin came up, her
hands knotting into frustrated fists as her temper rose to the
fore. 'I think I'd have to be a mental case to want your
baby, Alex! Not only would you not want the child, I would
undoubtedly be left to raise it on my own, and believe me,
at twenty-three, with my whole life ahead of me, I have no
plans to shoot myself in the foot! No intelligent woman
would choose to bring a child into an unstable relationship,
most especially not when her partner has made his negative
attitude resoundingly clear—'

'We do not have an unstable relationship, and I'm not
your partner. I'm your husband,' Alex grated with an ir-
relevance which merely increased her anger.

'Furthermore, I bitterly resent the suggestion that I
couldn't be trusted not to become *accidentally* pregnant!
How dare you compare me to Antonia?' Sara asked him
furiously, well into her stride now. 'I wouldn't trick any
man like that—'

'You wanted *his* child,' Alex interposed icily.

Her head swam. Nothing that she was trying to spell out
seemed to be getting through. Alex was missing the
point...or possibly she was missing his, but what mattered

most to Sara at that moment was that Alex should understand that he had misjudged her and, in so doing, caused her a great deal of pain. 'That was different…'

'Patently.'

Momentarily Sara closed her eyes, needing to get a grip on her anger, knowing that this was not the discussion she had planned. Slowly she breathed in. 'It was a different sort of relationship,' she proffered. 'Brian and I…we were more friends than lovers. We shared a lot of interests. We had the same goals. Brian likes to feel secure, so do I. We agreed about so many things—'

'How touching.'

'What I'm trying to explain is that wanting children was just part of that.' Sara shrugged a shoulder and was briefly silent while she thought back. 'We had our whole future mapped out and it felt very safe, and maybe we both got a bit smug about how well matched we were…and maybe I did get so carried away organising everything that I wouldn't have noticed if he had six Antonias on the side!'

'You loved him,' Alex murmured harshly.

Sara lowered her head and wondered. Had she ever really loved Brian? She believed that she had been very, very fond of him but Brian had never had the power to tear her heart out as Alex did. There had been no highs, no lows, no soul-stirring fear or excitement. Two lonely people had met and formed a mutual support system which they had called love for want of a better word. 'Not as much as I thought I did. You were right about that,' she conceded wryly, her face pensive. 'Three years ago Brian wanted Antonia but she wasn't interested then—'

'He didn't belong to you.'

'No, it wasn't only that.' Sara wanted to be fair to her cousin. 'Back then, Antonia's modelling career looked like it was heading straight to the top. She was mixing with a lot of exciting people, travelling the world, having a fabulous time. She was only twenty-one, too. My uncle and aunt may have spoilt her to death but they also landed her with a whole set of gilt-edged expectations to live up to. She was the family star. They expected her to become a supermodel and marry someone…' her soft mouth curved with rueful amusement '…someone like you. I don't think I can blame her for not noticing Brian in those days.'

'What a very generous outlook you have.' Alex's dark gaze rested intently on her taut profile.

'No, I don't. I confess to feeling secretly pleased when her modelling career slid downhill again. She's very good at putting people's backs up. When she got into debt last year, she had to sell her apartment and her parents naturally assumed I would share my flat with her. When I think about it, Antonia's had a tough time, yet Brian was always sniping at her, running her down because she hurt his ego. I should have seen that, recognised it for what it was—'

'Fatal attraction,' Alex interposed flatly. 'There whether you want it to be or not.'

She wanted to be brave enough to ask if that was how Alex felt about her but she couldn't bring herself to plunge that deep. It wasn't a good idea to ask a question if you thought you might crumble when you got the answer, she thought strickenly. 'Brian thought he couldn't have her, so he settled for me.' She swallowed hard in the throbbing silence. 'I don't love him any more, Alex.'

His strong dark features were harshly set. 'You don't need to say that, Sara.'

'You see?' she demanded abruptly, her eyes flaring. 'You're doing it again. You're refusing to accept what I say. Perhaps there's a part of you which feels happier thinking I'm still in love with Brian!'

'That's a ridiculous suggestion—'

'Is it? I'm not so sure. Out of bed,' Sara framed tightly, 'you like a certain safe, emotional distance, don't you? All the boundaries are yours. You can barely mention the fact that we're married without implying that it's not likely to last…but that it's going to be all my fault if it doesn't!'

A dark rise of blood stained his hard cheekbones.

'It makes me feel like I'm waiting for a redundancy notice, and when I phone you at the office and I can't even get to speak to you I feel like I've already been dumped!'

'What are you talking about?'

'You didn't put my name on the list, did you?' Sara accused him.

'*Dio*…of course I didn't—you're my wife!' Alex gritted. 'Are you telling me that that stupid girl didn't put your calls through?'

Sara's mouth opened and shut again. It had never occurred to her that her inability to get Alex at the end of a phone line might simply be the result of human error.

'So I have her to thank for that fax!' Alex was visibly enraged by the idea.

'I assumed that she was doing what she had been told to do.'

'I am such an ignorant boor that I would tell an employee that I will not take calls from my own wife?'

Sara reddened hotly. 'Well, no, but—'

'*Grazie, cara*…what a wonderful light I appear to you in!'

'You can't blame me for assuming—' she began defensively.

'Can't I?' Alex shot her a look of derision. 'Was it totally beyond your power to insist on speaking to me? Is it my fault you let yourself be repulsed by a little office girl?'

Sara's cat-green eyes glittered. 'Probably. On the phone you treat me as if I'm *still* "a little office girl". I wouldn't have been too sure of my ground had I chosen to insist. The impression I receive is…' she hesitated and then forced herself on '…is that marriage was a step too far for you.'

Alex's facial muscles had clenched hard. 'I never thought you would force a confrontation like this.'

'You didn't leave me with much choice. I'm not like you,' Sara confided shakily. 'I can't shove things under the carpet and pretend they didn't happen the way you do. I can't behave normally when you freeze me off. I get angry and I get hurt. I've never known anyone who can be so warm…and then so cold…'

Alex was very still and very pale beneath his year-round tan.

'I mean—' Sara gulped, her throat closing over, knowing that she had dived into deeper waters than she had ever envisaged, but somehow unable to stop herself. 'When you called me from Paris, Alex…I knew you were just delighted to be away from me—'

'It wasn't like that,' he countered fiercely, his graceful hands restively clenching and then digging into the pockets of his tailored trousers, pulling the fine fabric taut over his long, powerful thighs.

But he still wasn't going to tell her how it *had* been, she registered painfully. 'What I'm trying to ask is, did you ever plan for this marriage to be a real one…or was it just a manipulative game which got out of hand? You knew exactly what you had to say to persuade me to marry you but how much of it did you actually mean? If you're having regrets already, it would be kinder simply to be honest.'

Alex released his breath in a sudden hiss. He looked like someone being subjected to some highly sophisticated form of invisible torture. 'I don't have any regrets—'

'But you don't trust me.'

'I've never trusted any woman!' he bit out.

Her throat constricted. 'Alex, I'd need lessons to be one tenth as naturally devious as you are. What have you got to worry about?'

He stared back at her with fathomless eyes as dark as ebony. 'I don't want to lose you. You're very important to me, *cara*.'

It was the most complimentary thing that Alex had ever

said to her that did not relate to sex. She breathed again, a wave of dizziness which she recognised as intense relief sweeping over her, leaving her light-headed.

'I wasn't aware that I was making you feel threatened,' he conceded in a driven undertone. 'But this kind of communication doesn't come easily to me. In fact, the more I feel, the less I want to talk about it.'

As her gaze collided with his rather grim half-smile of self-awareness, her heart flipped a somersault behind her breastbone. She wanted to be in his arms but instead she turned away and asked him prosaically if he wanted anything to eat.

And suddenly Alex was laughing and the tension, still humming uneasily in the atmosphere, evaporated simultaneously. 'You know, *bella mia*, if I'd arrived here to candlelight and a champagne reception, I'd have been outraged.'

'You would have felt set up.'

'But there is such a thing as a happy medium,' Alex imparted with the unevenness of amusement tugging at his dark deep voice.

'Like a hot bath and a drink?'

'Banana sandwiches?' He repeated her earlier offer, shaking his darkly handsome head. 'I haven't had them since I was a child. Marcella used to make them for me.'

And while she made the sandwiches he talked about the *palazzo* housekeeper with a warmth that eventually made her eyes burn. She had noticed Alex's fondness for the older woman in Venice, hadn't really thought about it much. But now she saw a lonely, loving little boy, starved of affection by a succession of indifferent stepmothers, and with a father who was very charming and no doubt very proud of his eldest son but far too selfish to have made any attempt to give him a stable home life. Alex knew far more than she did about feeling like an outsider. That was why he had so easily understood her own insecurities.

Dawn was breaking when they finally made it to bed. 'I need to get the Bugatti moved,' Alex groaned.

'It's Saturday,' she reminded him. 'It won't matter if the drive's blocked but you should have locked it up.'

'What with? I fell getting out of the car. I dropped the keys and my mobile phone in that filthy water!'

'Oh, dear.' But she giggled this time when she said it.

Alex hauled her down on top of him. 'You are the only woman I ever got my feet dirty for.'

'And you looked so funny!'

'And never felt less like laughing,' he admitted. 'It was not quite the entrance I had planned.'

'But I was terribly impressed by it all the same. I was struck dumb.'

Alex curved a hungry hand round the pouting swell of one bare breast, centring every nerve-ending in her thrumming body on one hot spot, and she ran out of oxygen all in one go, shaken by the sheer intensity of her response. 'I'm feeling very encouraged, *bella mia*. This is another first. No nightgown,' he teased.

Perhaps not so strange an oversight. It was wonderful what increased security did for your confidence, Sara mused. Only now did she see that their marriage was as real and as important to Alex as it had always been to her.

'Yours?' From the doorstep, Janice Dalton scrutinised the cream Jaguar with its scarlet leather upholstery and her mouth compressed. 'Very ostentatious...'

Sara reddened slightly. 'Alex bought it for my birthday. I was disappointed that you couldn't join us for dinner.'

'I'm afraid we'd already made other arrangements.'

Sara was shown into the lounge. Her determined smile revealed nothing of her uneasiness. Over the past month the Daltons had turned down her every invitation to visit. She had been relieved when her aunt had phoned her and asked her over but there was a marked coolness in the older woman's manner. What on earth was wrong? Sara wondered anxiously.

'I might as well get right to the heart of the matter,' her aunt told her stiffly. 'Antonia and Brian have split up.'

Sara tensed. 'I'm sorry.'

'I wonder if you really are?' A flush had mottled the older woman's cheeks.

'Yes,' Sara said quietly. 'I am sorry.'

Her aunt gave her an angry look. 'Of course you can afford to be gracious. You've done very well out of all this. Heaven knows, I never thought to see *you* swanning up in a brand-new Jaguar, dressed like Princess Diana!'

'Alex likes me to look smart.' And I will not tell him about this when I go home, she reflected painfully. It was uncanny how often Alex was right about people. Her aunt couldn't hide her resentment that Sara had married a very rich and powerful man, while her adored daughter had married a relatively ordinary one.

'Brian's been very cruel to Antonia.'

'I don't think this is any of my business.'

'That's the trouble…it's very much your business!' Janice Dalton condemned. 'Brian told Antonia that he's still in love with you!'

Sara was taken aback by the angry assurance until it occurred to her that it was probably something that Brian had thrown out in an argument. She had known that her cousin and her former fiancé would have a stormy relationship. Brian had very fixed ideas about the sort of wife he wanted and by no stretch of the imagination was Antonia likely to fulfil a stay-at-home role. Antonia didn't cook, didn't clean and sulked if she sat in more than one night a week.

'I don't believe for one minute that Brian still loves me,' Sara retorted. 'In fact I doubt that he ever did.'

'Antonia's had a terrible time.' Visibly mollified by Sara's assurance, her aunt began spilling out a highly coloured account of Antonia's sufferings—how Brian had demanded that they live in the house which *Sara* had furnished, how mean he was with money, how selfish, how insensitive…

'In fact what Brian badly needs is someone to talk some sense into him!' her aunt completed, tight-mouthed. 'He wouldn't listen to me but he might listen to you.'

Sara froze. '*Me*…talk to Brian?' she whispered in disbelief.

'Brian and you were always good friends. Why shouldn't you speak to him?'

'But I—'

'After all, Brian and Antonia only had a harmless little flirtation and then *you* rushed off and got involved with Alex Rossini. Let's face it, you weren't interested in having Brian back then! You couldn't have cared less. It's time that Brian heard that from you and stopped throwing you up to Antonia! Believe me, I don't like having to ask you for help,' the older woman informed her bitterly, resentfully, 'but I think you could get through to Brian where nobody else can.'

'I'm sorry, but I don't want to interfere and Antonia would be furious, and rightfully so, if I did.' Sara stood up.

'You're being very selfish, Sara. You wouldn't be where you are now if it hadn't been for this family's generosity!' Janice Dalton shot at her in furious reproach. 'I wonder how much interest Alex Rossini would have had in you if you'd been brought up in some council home?'

Sara had lost all her natural colour. It shook her that her aunt could cruelly throw that debt in her face. Over the years Sara had always shown her gratitude. But maybe she *was* being selfish. All that crossed her mind was that to meet Brian she would have to lie to Alex because Alex would never agree to such a meeting. Alex was extremely possessive…

'You owe it to me to do whatever you can to help,' the older woman spelt out harshly. 'Antonia need never know.'

'And then I melt back out of your lives again…right?'

For the first time Janice Dalton looked embarrassed.

'That's all right. Alex is all the family I need.'

'Sara…'

But Sara walked away, knowing that she would never walk willingly back into that house again. She wasn't wanted there. The little orphaned niece whom the Daltons had so generously taken into their home had committed the unforgivable sin of obscuring the family star in terms of material advancement. Sara felt slightly sick.

Further down the street she parked the car and lifted the mobile phone. Get this over with, she urged herself when she hesitated. What Alex doesn't know about won't hurt him. This isn't going to *hurt* anyone. Aunt Janice is right. If there is any possibility that you could help, you should try. She called Brian at work.

'What do you want?' he snapped.

A wry smile touched her strained mouth. Hardly the response of a man in love, she thought.

'You've heard about Toni and me, haven't you?' he assumed peevishly.

'Do you want to talk about it?'

'Why should you care?' Brian demanded bitterly.

'Once we were good friends. It might help if we talked.'

'I don't see how…but why not?' he muttered in a self-pitying tone.

She agreed to meet him after work at the house. Evidently her cousin had refused to live there and Brian had moved in alone. She was sitting in a traffic jam when Alex phoned.

'How did it go with your aunt?' he enquired straight off.

Her stomach twisted with guilt when she thought of the lie she was about to tell. Shakily she breathed in. 'I'll be back late. I've actually just popped out for a few messages.

My aunt's invited over some friends and I promised to stay for the evening,' she said stiltedly.

There was a long pause.

'No problems, then?'

She bit her lower lip and tasted blood. 'Well, my aunt's a bit cool—'

'The friends don't include Brian, do they?'

Sara almost choked. 'Of course not!'

'Just checking, *bella mia*. You sound upset. Why don't you develop a headache and bow out? I was planning to finish early tonight.'

Her eyes burned. 'I'll be home as soon as I can.'

'You stay under the speed limit. No racing,' Alex warned. 'I want you back all in one healthy piece, Signora Rossini.'

The constrictions in her throat ballooned. 'Yes… Sorry, the traffic's very heavy. I have to go now…'

Damn Brian and Antonia, she reflected with sudden, desperate resentment. It was one thing to wish them well, quite another to get involved to the extent of being forced to lie to Alex. But then she should have told the truth and faced the music. She was a lousy liar. And Alex was so attuned to her emotions now that he picked up on her tensions. She had this awful feeling that she was going to have to tell him anyway. And that would cause trouble. Lying had only made it worse, she saw now, and writhed with guilt.

Brian was waiting for her. Sara tried not to stare at the wallpaper half-ripped off the wall in the hall. 'Toni,' Brian said succinctly.

'You can't blame her for not wanting to live here. In every way that matters, I made this *my* house.'

'I blame her for everything.'

'It takes two people to have an affair.'

'But it only takes one liar to force an affair into a shotgun marriage!' Brian stabbed back bitterly. 'She told me she was pregnant…she's not! She was lying and I was the mug who believed her!'

Sara sank down on a sofa in the small sitting room and suddenly understood a great deal. For the second time that day she was forced to listen to a catalogue of woes, this time from Brian's side of the fence. She had some sympathy for him but she didn't let it show. She let him vent the worst of his spleen, knowing that it would cool him down. 'Had it ever occurred to you that she must love you an awful lot?' she asked when he'd finally finished.

'The only person Toni loves is herself.'

'She deceived you and that was wrong but she must have been desperate for you to marry her.'

'You would never have done anything like that.'

'Brian…Antonia and I are chalk and cheese and always will be, but don't forget that it was Antonia you really wanted.'

'That's not true…'

'Be honest with yourself. She didn't suit you as well as I did but you never stopped being attracted to her. Reminding her of me isn't fair. Where is she now?'

'Staying with a friend. I told her I wanted a divorce…'

'But you don't want one, do you? You only want to punish her,' Sara guessed, and watched him redden. 'Don't you think you could give her another chance?'

'Why should I?'

'It's up to you. But Antonia won't wait forever and she won't crawl. She was very hurt when you didn't stand by her after I found the two of you together. That was the time when you should have admitted how you really felt about her. She was afraid that you and I would get back together again. I'm sure that's the only reason she lied and pretended to be pregnant.'

Well over an hour later Sara climbed back into her car. She was exhausted and she had talked herself hoarse but only time would tell whether she had done any good. At least Brian had been a lot less bitter when she'd left him.

It was a long drive back down to Ladymead. She thought about Alex all the way and hoped that he wouldn't lose his temper when she admitted that she had been with Brian.

The manor house was all lit up. Alex's chauffeur was putting a case in the boot of the limousine. Sara frowned slightly. She found Alex in the spacious library which he used as an office. He was slinging files into a box. She paused on the threshold. 'What are you doing?'

Alex lifted his dark head, ice-cold eyes landing on her in glancing assault. His strong features clenched cruelly hard, his mouth flattening. 'I'm leaving you,' he said.

CHAPTER TEN

DEVASTATED by the announcement, Sara stared back at him in wide-eyed disbelief.

'In pursuit of points for being a supportive husband, I decided to join the surprise family gathering you mentioned,' Alex drawled with lethal effect.

Sara turned white with shock.

'Your uncle told me *when* you had left and while we were having a cosy little chat on the doorstep he also passed on the news that the other marriage in the family had broken up and that your aunt was upset. He hoped I would understand that he couldn't invite me indoors.'

Sara was trembling, her family's rudeness to Alex only another thorn in her shrinking flesh. She licked her dry lips. 'Alex, I can explain—'

'I know where you've been. You've been with *him* all evening,' Alex delivered with seething bite. 'The minute you found out that he was free again you betrayed yourself!'

'It wasn't like that!' she protested shakily. 'My aunt asked me to—'

'You lied to me.'

'Yes…but—'

'Did you actually make it into bed with him?' Alex demanded, a vicious edge to the sudden, slashing demand as his shimmering golden eyes cut into her. '*Dio* did I transform you into a sexually confident woman for *his* benefit?'

'Don't be disgusting!' Sara gasped.

'I find it even more disgusting that you've most probably been sitting holding hands and mumbling sweet nothings! That turns my stomach!' Alex roared back at her full-blast. 'I could understand a sexual obsession even if I couldn't condone it…but this nauseating sentimental attachment of yours makes my flesh creep—especially when I think of what you were doing with *me* in bed last night!'

Hectic pink brightened her pallor. 'You've got it all wrong!' She heard the pure panic fracturing her own voice. 'My aunt asked me to talk to Brian. I knew you wouldn't want me to and I didn't want to either but I didn't have the guts to say no when she put the pressure on. I don't feel anything for Brian any more…honestly I don't! Nothing happened, not a word was said which you could object to!'

'You lied to me—'

'I'm sorry but I was a coward. I thought I could see Brian without you ever knowing about it,' she admitted in a desperate rush. 'I just didn't want to spoil things. We've been so happy and I couldn't face another argument over him.'

'You're wasting your breath, Sara.' Alex sent her a look of cold hatred and contempt which made her reel back from him in shock. 'I'm still leaving.'

'Please listen to me…please, Alex! Brian means nothing to me—'

'No, obviously all this means slightly more to you than he does.' Alex indicated the Gothic magnificence of the room, his hard mouth twisting with bitter scorn. 'Why else would you have lied to protect yourself?'

'Because I *love* you!'

Alex gave a harsh laugh of incredulity. 'You bitch,' he breathed rawly, sweeping up the box in one powerful hand and striding past her.

Sara chased after him in despair. 'I mean it. I do love you!' she shouted after him, the words echoing through the great hall and coming back to her with an eerie resonance.

Alex swung back, his cheekbones fiercely prominent, the pallor beneath his sun-bronzed skin accentuating the cold austerity of his dark eyes. 'You don't know the first thing about love, *cara*. You never did,' he derided in a sudden savage undertone. He flung her a scorching look of violent threat. 'There's no way I'll agree to a divorce. I'll keep you tied to me for years and if you ever dare to bring him into this house I'll beat the hell out of the snivelling little jerk!'

Late the next morning, Sara woke up from an uneasy doze, stiff and cold. She was lying face down on the bed, still fully dressed. She focused on the crumpled white shirt lying half beneath her. Alex's shirt, still redolent of him, retrieved from the laundry like some comforting but empty talisman. Her throat ached more than ever. She faced reality. It was all her own fault, she conceded wretchedly. How could she have been that stupid!

Until yesterday she had existed in a blissful glow of contentment. They had moved into Ladymead a fortnight ago in spite of the fact that work was still continuing in various corners. Alex had taken the inconvenience in his stride. He had begun to take a tentative interest in the improvements being made, occasionally making his own suggestions. He had twice accompanied her to Sotheby's to buy furniture. They had spent last weekend on the yacht and she had discovered that she liked sailing and didn't get sick. Indeed the only time she ever felt tense with Alex was when she found herself having to swallow back words of love.

So what had she thought she would achieve by telling him that she loved him last night? Right at the beginning, Alex had made it clear that he didn't want her love…but after their wedding he had made it even more clear that he could not stand the idea of Brian having her love either. In fact, he couldn't even tolerate the mention of Brian's name without becoming aggressive, derisive or broodingly silent. Jealousy, she thought dazedly—rampant, murderous jealousy, not just arrogant male possessiveness, not just hostility to the idea that her loyalties might be divided. In Venice she should have had greater faith in her own suspicions. Had she understood, would she have been more honest last night?

In lying she had dug her own grave with Alex. She had lied on impulse, choosing what had seemed an easy way out of a difficult situation. Her primary motivation had been the need not to cause trouble in her own marriage. But how on earth could she persuade Alex to trust her again after what she had done? How could she ever convince him that she loved and needed *him*, not his wealth or any other man? Well, certainly not by sitting feeling sorry for herself in yesterday's clothes with eyes as red as overripe tomatoes! came back the answer.

When she went downstairs, she looked into the library, for the first time really taking in the devastation which Alex had wreaked the previous night. Filing drawers and cupboard doors hung open. Books and papers were tumbled across the desktop, with many more on the floor. Alex was a formidably tidy individual in any working environment. And yet last night he had torn this immaculately organised room apart and ended up only removing a single, half-empty box.

Had she arrived home earlier than he had expected? Something told her that had she returned a couple of hours later Alex would by then have swept the boards of Ladymead so clean of his presence that she would have had trouble finding evidence that he had *ever* lived here with her. It was a chilling thought, emphasising the frightening speed with which Alex had decided to walk out on their marriage. An instantaneous decision, immediately acted upon.

Instinctively she began to return the library carefully to

order, and then slowly her hands fell still again. *Alex wasn't coming back.* Alex wasn't coming back unless she kidnapped him. She had given him the true story last night and he hadn't believed her. She had told him that she loved him and he hadn't believed that either. The best she could do now was to face him again and repeat exactly the same things. So why was she wasting time cleaning up?

'Don't bother to ring ahead and warn him,' Sara told Gina, the receptionist, pleasantly on her way past. 'I want to surprise him.'

'Hello, Sara…' Pete stopped dead on the threshold of his office. 'Is Alex expecting you?'

'Do I need an appointment now, Pete?' Fevered tension made Sara sharp. She flushed. 'Sorry. Is anyone with him?'

'No, but the helicopter's waiting to take him up north.'

'I won't keep him long.'

She walked into Alex's office on the power of one long, pent-up breath.

He was standing by the windows. He spun lithely round and stilled, his strong features freezing into impassivity. Cold dark eyes settled on her without any perceptible emotion. That scared her, wiped out her prepared speech.

'Now *this* I didn't expect,' Alex drawled reflectively. 'I assumed you would have too much pride to create a scene here.'

'I'm not going to create any kind of scene…' Her heartbeat thundered in her ears as she stared back at him with a compulsive intensity that she couldn't control. Already she felt as though he had left her at least a month ago. An agonising sense of loss engulfed her without warning.

'But you shouldn't be here. I made my wishes very clear last night. Go home. You can have nothing to say that I am prepared to listen to.'

'But you *have* to listen,' Sara protested.

'Why? I don't want you anywhere near me.'

Her colour receded. On the drive up to London she had not prepared herself for this level of cruelty. Had Alex still been seething with anger, she could have borne it better, but rejection couched in cold detachment was infinitely more final. 'Alex…haven't you ever done anything you're ashamed of "on the spur of the moment"?' she prompted in desperation.

'Married you.'

Sara flinched as if he had struck her. 'Don't do this to us. Once you said to me, "Nobody's perfect," and I know that you have a right to be angry—'

'I am not angry.' But for an instant she saw a flash of stark, bitter pain in his narrowed gaze before he screened it. 'And you're embarrassing me,' he continued with cutting precision.

In a numb motion, Sara shook her head, wondering if she had imagined that pain. 'Alex?'

He shrugged back a white shirt-cuff to scrutinse his watch. 'I haven't got time for this—'

'If you say one more word, I may well hate you for the rest of my life,' Sara told him strickenly.

'Anything you feel you have to say, share it with your lawyer, not with me.' Alex strode past her to the door.

'I thought you didn't want a divorce,' she muttered unsteadily.

'I've changed my mind,' he imparted without turning round. 'I want you out of my life.'

As the door closed Sara was in such a daze that she slid down on the nearest seat, her stomach cramping up. Oh, you really made him listen, didn't you? Oh, you were really convincing, weren't you? she derided herself. But it had been as though Alex had retreated somewhere where she couldn't reach him.

'Sara?'

She glanced up to find Marco standing several feet away. She hadn't even heard the door open.

'What did you do to my brother?' he enquired with unhidden aggression.

'Where did you come from?' she mumbled.

'I was calling in to see how he was but I appear to have missed him. So what did you do?' he demanded again fiercely. 'He came round to my apartment last night and sat there like he'd been hit by a truck!'

'Did he?' She realised how low she had sunk when she experienced a flicker of hope.

'I could see he was hurting but not a blasted word could I get out of the stubborn bastard!' Marco complained. 'So what's going on?'

'I told him a lie about something and he assumed the worst and walked out.'

'And you're surprised?'

She sighed. 'You couldn't say anything to me that would make me feel any worse than I already feel…OK?'

'I don't like seeing my brother upset like that. It would be much more healthy if he got drunk and punched walls instead of walking about like the living dead!'

Sara took a deep breath. 'Could you find out where he's gone?'

Marco walked to the door and bawled, 'Pete!'

'The Lake District,' Pete supplied cheerfully, walking in, obviously having been listening.

'What the blazes is he doing there?' Marco enquired.

'Visiting friends, I assume. He goes up there maybe twice a year. I've never gone along.'

'So?' Marco pressed impatiently. 'Who are they?'

'I spoke to the woman once. Her name's Elissa,' Pete informed them helpfully. 'I don't think I ever got her surname.'

Marco looked stunned. *'Elissa?'* he repeated. 'Are you sure?'

The roof had fallen in round Sara's head. Shock was roaring through her in waves. Pete frowned in bemusement at them both as he walked back out again.

'Did you know about this?' Marco asked her sharply. 'That Alex was in touch with her again...I mean that he even knew where she was?'

'No.'

'Elissa living in England,' he muttered, still struggling with his own incredulity. 'And he never said a word.'

'I understood she was always too special to talk about.' Sara's voice quivered.

'If you're thinking that Alex is keeping a mistress he only sees twice a year, your head's away!'

'Is it?' She studied her feverishly linked hands through a blinding blur of tears.

'Alex is nuts about you—'

'He's never said so.'

'So he's a bit tight with the words!' Marco conceded in frustration. 'But he married you. He's living in a freezing cold house with one bathroom for your benefit. He's doing weird things like buying furniture and taking off out of the office in the middle of the day... This is not Alex as we have known him for the past thirty-four years!'

'No?'

'Sara, he's so sickeningly happy with you that he throws your name into every other sentence. Pete can't keep him in the office after five. This is a guy who cannot wait to get home to his wife every night. I ask you, is it likely he's doing a line with some old doll from his past?'

'I think I'd like to meet that old doll before I commit myself,' Sara admitted as she slowly got to her feet. Although she was still pale, her mouth was firmly set.

'What do you want to meet her for?' Marco regarded her in open dismay.

'Are you scared of what I might find? So am I...but it

would be much more scary to sit at home wondering,' she confided.

It was already the middle of the afternoon. It was over two hundred miles to the small village where Elissa lived but Sara climbed into the Jag with unassailable determination. Alex might well have gone by the time she arrived...well, so be it. It was Elissa whom Sara needed to meet. She did not want to see Alex with the wretched woman. Such an encounter required a certain discretion, didn't it?

The further north Sara got, the more tense she became. Suddenly she doubted her own sanity, the need to *know* which had blanked out every other prompting. Alex had kept his continuing acquaintance with Elissa a secret even from his family...for how many years? And how did she know that he only saw Elissa twice a year? Pete would only be aware of those visits when Alex went directly from the office. And Elissa was discreet, wasn't she? Pete had only *once* spoken to her on the phone. The perfect mistress...?

She stopped for a meal at a motorway service station. She was exhausted and she forced herself to eat and drink simply to keep going. It was much later than she had hoped when she finally came upon the old stone farmhouse which lay about a mile outside the village on a steep, narrow road. There wasn't a single glimmer of life or light about Elissa's home. Sara stopped the car and rested her aching head back. So what now?

Was he in there with her? The idea totally wiped Sara out. Two long-time lovers entangled in the comfort of an adulterous bed... In silent agony she shut her eyes. Elissa had betrayed her first husband—why should she think twice about betraying a woman she had never even met? Why hadn't Alex married her? Why had she left him in the first place? Why hadn't he told Sara the truth? But no, he hadn't lied except by omission. So what was the secret of Elissa's enduring appeal? If he still loved her, wouldn't he have married her?

And then finally Sara grasped wearily at an explanation for behaviour which struck her as incomprehensible. Only last night Alex had told her that he could understand a sexual obsession. Was that Elissa's continuing attraction after all these years? Was it possible that Alex had married her to try and break free of that affair? And was it possible that she had driven him straight back into Elissa's waiting arms again?

Sara hit her lowest ebb then. Alex *had* been happy with her. She wouldn't have had the courage to put her pride on the line today had she not been clinging to that awareness. Only Alex had not responded...Alex had been implacably cold and unimpressed.

Why had she come up here? What had she hoped to achieve by confronting a woman who probably knew Alex so much better than she did? Forcing herself on Elissa would be demeaning and pointless. It sunk in on Sara then that Alex really was gone, that it would be pathetic to pursue him one more step, that he had left her with nothing to do but retire in defeat. Her whole world fell in pieces around her the minute she reached that conclusion. She covered her convulsing face with her hands, a choked sob of despair ripped from her working throat.

Suddenly someone tapped on the windscreen and she was in such a state that she didn't even jump. She looked up and saw a woman in an incongruous pink dressing gown hovering. Gulping, she buzzed down the window a few inches.

'Sara?' the woman said uncertainly. 'You are Sara, aren't you? I looked out when I heard a car stop. Alex described this car to me. Would you like to come in?'

'In?' Sara echoed, blinking at the lights now illuminating the previously dark house.

'I'm going to look really daft if a car comes along,' the woman pointed out gently. 'And it's beginning to rain.'

'You're…Elissa?' The soft Scottish accent was equally disconcerting. Sara had simply assumed that Elissa was Italian.

'Everyone but Alex calls me Liz now.'

Sara snatched in a steadying breath and climbed out of the Jag, trying not to stare.

'I'm afraid you've missed him. I assume that's why you're here…but he hardly ever stays over. Still, I'm glad you came,' Elissa asserted, as if Sara's unannounced arrival were perfectly normal. 'I hate being on my own at night. John took the kids up to his mother's this evening and he won't be back until morning.'

'John?'

'My husband.' Elissa thrust wide the door of her home and Sara saw her properly for the first time.

She wasn't exactly seduction personified, in a pink towelling robe and fluffy mules. Not my double either, Sara registered, still staring. She had wide blue eyes, very curly, short dark brown hair and a figure that verged more on the plump than the petite. But she had a beautiful face and the sort of vivacious warmth that just leapt out and grabbed you.

Elissa was looking Sara over with equal fascination. 'I've been dying to meet you but Alex didn't think it was a good idea.'

'Didn't he?'

'He didn't say so.' Elissa grimaced, pushing open the door of a cosy, cluttered kitchen. 'Alex can be very tactful when he wants to be but I could see him bristling the way he does when you put your feet in it…which I always do around Alex. He's not at all like John. John is wonderfully easy to live with… *Sorry*!' Like a dismayed child who had dropped a brick, Elissa clapped a hand to her mouth.

'You don't need to apologise,' Sara assured her with a

glimmer of slowly awakening amusement. 'Actually, I came up here thinking you were having an affair with Alex.'

Elissa frowned in astonishment. 'But why?'

'Alex had neglected to mention the fact that he was still in touch with you.'

'I did ask him not to tell anyone. I left my old life behind and I don't want it to catch up with me again. John knows all about it, of course, but I would hate Alex's family to know we're still in touch. They really hate me,' she sighed. 'But Alex has done so much for us since our first business went bankrupt. We couldn't have gotten through that without him. He helped us get back on our feet and then start up again. Good grief…an affair,' she repeated, as if Sara's words were only now sinking in.

She swept a pile of laundry off a chair while Sara studied a montage of photos on a pinboard. 'Your children?'

'Well, technically John's. He was a widower with three children under five when we met up ten years ago. A match made in heaven,' Elissa joked. 'This was my fresh start.' She hesitated. 'I got in touch with Alex a couple of years after we broke up because I still felt guilty. I mean, I just ran out on him, which was pretty hateful after the way he'd stood by me.'

'Why did you leave?' Sara murmured.

Elissa gave her a wry look. 'I was making a mess of his life, Sara. He wasn't happy with me. He wouldn't admit it but I could feel it. I owed him so much. Without Alex's support, I would never have had the courage to leave Sal… My first husband was a very violent man,' she said tautly. 'Alex felt sorry for me. I started depending on him and the rest you can probably guess.'

'Yes,' Sara said with sympathy. 'I'm sorry I landed on your doorstep like this—'

'But how brave when you thought what you did.' Elissa

surveyed her with amused but frank admiration. 'My lack of guts always got on Alex's nerves.'

'Can I ask you why Alex came up here today?'

'He owns the majority of our business, Sara. We import terracotta from Italy,' Elissa explained cheerfully. 'He refinanced us when we couldn't get a loan after going bust the first time. John isn't terribly good with money and Alex keeps an eye on things. Well, to be honest, he watches us like a hawk so that we don't overextend ourselves again. He doesn't make much of a profit out of us either. He's been a very generous friend.'

Sara smothered an embarrassing yawn.

Elissa laughed. 'You can't possibly get back behind that wheel again. Will you stay the night?'

Alex hadn't even confided in Elissa, Sara thought as she drove back home by easy stages the next day. Elissa had thought that he was a little quiet, but had noticed nothing else apart from the fact that he'd appeared to be in a distinct hurry to leave again. 'A very generous friend', she had said. But was there something more on Alex's side? Was that why he had chosen not to tell her that he still saw the other woman? And what did it matter now anyway? she asked herself despondently as she turned up the drive to Ladymead. Nothing she had found out made the slightest difference really. Alex had left her. Yesterday his attitude to her had hardened even more. He had told her that he wanted a divorce.

In the frame of mind that she was in, it was a heck of a shock when the first thing she saw as she got out of her car was Alex striding towards her.

'*Dio*, where the hell have you been?' he demanded explosively. 'I've been up all night worrying myself sick. I was going to ring the police again!'

Sara blinked in bewilderment at this astonishing transformation. Her tongue cleaved to the roof of her dry mouth. Alex closed his arms round her with such force that he very nearly knocked her off her feet. 'It doesn't matter where you have been,' he groaned then, releasing his breath with unconcealed relief. 'You've come home.'

Wide-eyed, she gazed up at him, taking in the tousled hair, the heavy blue shadow of stubble on his usually clean-shaven jawline, the shadows beneath his feverish dark eyes. 'Alex—'

'Please don't ever do this to me again.' With an obvious effort he loosened a grip that was threatening to crack her ribs and grasped her hands tautly in his. 'I have now lived through the worst forty-eight hours of my life. I know I asked for it, but shout at me the next time, don't disappear! Not that there'll be a *next* time,' he hurried to assure her emphatically. 'I'll never take a risk like that with you again!'

Alex had come home. Alex was practically on his knees with gratitude that she had come home. Her head swam. Obviously he hadn't been in touch with Marco... Either that or Marco had decided to keep quiet. In a daze she looked at the glossy black head bent over their linked hands. 'We're not on the brink of a divorce any more?' she asked, just to check.

His head flew up, stark guilt and discomfiture clenching his vibrantly handsome features. 'I was sick with jealousy and bitterness, *cara*. I wanted to hit back and yet the whole time you were standing there I was cutting myself in two as well.'

'You were like the iceman,' Sara whispered reflectively with a shiver.

'I didn't want you to know how much you had hurt me,' he muttered gruffly.

'When did you come back?'

'Yesterday...as soon as I could. I assumed you'd be here...and then I called everywhere I could think of and panic set in. I was afraid you had had an accident. I checked with the police.'

'I went up north to meet Elissa.'

In the act of walking her into the house, Alex spun his dark head to her at speed. 'You…*what*?'

'I spent the night there. I liked her—'

'You spent the night?'

Sara relished his stunned reaction. 'When I heard that name, I thought I had discovered a secret mistress. I decided to confront her—'

'*Dio*…' Alex had paled. 'So that is where you have been all this time.'

'But I soon realised I had nothing to worry about. I don't know where anyone got the idea that Elissa and I look alike…'

'Sandro started that nonsense at the wedding,' Alex admitted grudgingly, his arm tightening round her as if he feared that she might pull away. 'Elissa once had long dark hair, but that was the only real similarity between you. Sandro has very poor eyesight but he's too vain to wear spectacles. I doubt if he even remembers Elissa that well.'

'Yet Claudia told me I was Elissa's double.'

Alex vented an angry imprecation in his own language.

Sara smiled sweetly. 'And I don't recall you denying it when I mentioned the idea. Do you think you could explain that, Alex?'

A slight darkening of colour had highlighted his hard cheekbones.

'Stuck for a ready excuse?' she probed in mock disbelief. 'I don't believe it.'

He released his breath in a hiss. 'I thought a little jealousy might give your thoughts a new direction—'

'Back to you…and away from Brian,' Sara guessed. 'But then I wasn't thinking about Brian at the time.'

'Every time I saw your face cloud, every time you went

quiet, I assumed he was on your mind,' Alex confessed tautly. 'I couldn't stop doing it even though I realised I was being unreasonable. After all, I had married you knowing that you loved another man. I thought I could be patient but I found that a much tougher challenge than I had imagined.'

'You should have told me you were still in contact with Elissa.'

'My family have the very embarrassing habit of behaving as though Elissa was this great tragic love who wrecked my life and broke my heart and whom I never recovered from,' Alex said through decidedly gritted teeth. 'I didn't mind you wondering a little about that affair but I certainly didn't want you getting the same maudlin ideas fixed in your head.'

'Didn't you put them there in the first place?'

'The day I told you about her, I was attempting to empathise with you,' Alex admitted wryly. 'But I was very young when I met Elissa. It was first love and intense but I wasn't ready to make the kind of commitment she needed. She was right to leave before we ended up hating each other but at the time I felt she had just used me as an escape from a rotten marriage. Meeting up with her again a couple of years later put paid to that. We were both able to laugh about what a bad match we were once the romance wore off.'

'So you stayed friends?'

'No, we went our separate ways until three years ago when she phoned and asked me for financial advice. John had just been declared bankrupt. They were in a real mess. I was happy to help.'

'That was a kind thing to do.'

Alex shrugged. 'They're a pleasant couple, but hopeless in business.'

'Were you really worried sick about me last night?' Sara pressed.

'Panicking.' His deep voice fractured as his eyes collided with her searching gaze.

'So when did you decide to come home?'

'Five minutes after the helicopter took off.' Alex reached for her hands again. 'I know I was a real swine but I was hurting myself as much as I was hurting you. *Dio, cara*, I have loved you for so long…'

'How long?' she whispered shakily.

'The first month you started working for me,' Alex confided heavily.

In shock, Sara stared back at him. 'But you told me you didn't believe in love—'

'Sara, I would have told you the sky was pink if it would have impressed you. I would have done and said anything it took to persuade you that it was a good idea to marry me,' Alex admitted, scanning her shaken face with wry comprehension. 'If I had told you how I really felt, it might have frightened you off. You're so considerate about other people's feelings that you could have decided it wouldn't be fair to marry me.'

'So you offered me a marriage of convenience.'

'Non-threatening.'

'And didn't complain about anything until you had that ring on my finger,' Sara said, and she remembered him saying that he had expected too much from her and finally understood why. The knowledge that Alex had been in love with her for such a long time stunned her.

'I was terrified you would get cold feet.'

'But you smouldered in silence.'

'I thought I could be patient—'

'You're not the patient type,' she interposed absently.

'And when I heard that Brian and your cousin had split up and guessed where you had to be…' Alex paused, his dark eyes revealing lingering pain. 'And you'd lied to me. It was one hell of a shock. I went right off the rails—'

'Alex, I—' Sara began strickenly, distressed by what she read in his expressive gaze.

'But I still came back. I didn't believe your version of events for one moment, though. Then your aunt phoned this morning and asked me to tell you that she was grateful for a little favour you'd done for her and would I please pass on the message that Brian and Antonia were talking again. She had no idea that I knew what she was referring to...' Alex's troubled features clenched. 'Sara...I should have trusted you.'

'When people lie, trust can be very difficult,' she conceded softly.

'If you hadn't lied, you wouldn't have done any little favour,' Alex gritted. 'I'd have torn him limb from limb!'

'No, you might have felt sorry for him. Antonia faked being pregnant.'

Alex absorbed that with a complete lack of interest, his burning gaze engaged in roving over her. 'Did you mean it when you said you loved me?'

Sara lifted possessive hands to his broad shoulders and looked up at him with glowing eyes. 'What do you think?'

'I think I want you to say it at least once every five minutes.'

'I love you...'

His lean hands were unsteady as he cupped her cheeks. 'I don't know how you didn't *see* that I was madly in love with you, greedy for your attention, possessive of your every thought...'

His hungry mouth closed over hers and the aching emptiness was banished for ever as he hauled her up into his arms and carried her upstairs. 'Would you really have to be a mental case to want my baby?' he muttered between hot, drugging kisses that made her wildly responsive senses swim.

'Do we get to do this a lot in pursuit of the objective?'

'Do we need an excuse?'

They decided that they didn't and concentrated on the difficulties of getting undressed when neither of them was prepared to stop long enough to accomplish that feat. A long time later they lay entwined, so mutually entranced that even the sound of a not too distant workman's hammer didn't penetrate the heady sense of wonder they were both experiencing.

And then a stray thought occurred to Sara. 'Alex...do you think you could fix Brian up with a better job?'

As his dark eyes shimmered and tensed Sara rested a teasing fingertip against the compressed line of his mouth. 'I don't object to you helping Elissa and her family, do I?'

'No, but—'

'Brian and Antonia's marriage would have a much better chance of succeeding if he was earning a bit more.'

His tension evaporated as that sank in.

Sara smiled with sunny satisfaction at him. 'I'm learning how to think like you do, my love—you had better watch out.'

'All that jealousy stuff is behind me,' Alex asserted, fiercely on the defensive.

'Because now you know you didn't need to be jealous. I started falling for you the very first day; how could I have failed to do anything else?' Sara leant over him, tenderly amused that Alex could have his insecurities too. 'You're gorgeous, you're sexy, and sneaky only when it's in my best interests...and, by the way, Brian does not want to work in Alaska.'

'Dubai...currently doing very well in the tourist market? They would get a break from an interfering bunch of in-laws, a lively social life, sunshine and a maid to do the cooking.' Alex treated her to a slashing smile of megawatt intensity. 'What do you think?'

'I think you're going to keep me on my toes,' Sara

admitted, transfixed by the speed with which he had responded to the challenge.

'And *I* think that you are the best thing that ever happened to me, *bella mia*.' And with the aid of one passionate kiss Alex ensured that other people's problems were the very last thing on her mind. She gave herself up blissfully to sensation instead.

Jacqueline Baird began writing as a hobby when her family objected to the smell of her oil painting, and immediately became hooked on the romantic genre. She loves travelling and worked her way around the world from Europe to the Americas and Australia, returning to marry her teenage sweetheart. She lives in Ponteland, Northumbria, the county of her birth, and has two teenage sons. She enjoys playing badminton, and spends most weekends with husband Jim, sailing their Gp.14 around Derwent Reservoir.

Don't miss another *passionate playboy* in
WIFE: BOUGHT AND PAID FOR
by
Jacqueline Baird

In November 2002, Modern Romance™

MISTAKEN FOR A MISTRESS
by
Jacqueline Baird

CHAPTER ONE

To GO or not to go to Italy? That was the question. Marlene, her hand curved around a nasty weed, gave a vicious tug then paused dramatically, the weed half pulled out of the dry ground. To honour a dying man's last wish, or conveniently forget about it for her own peace of mind. She yanked the offending weed out completely, dropped it, then wiped her sweat-soaked brow with the back of her hand. She decided it was too hot to make a serious decision and instead collapsed flat on her back on the brown earth.

She gazed up through the fluttering canopy of bushy green leaves to the clear blue sky above and sighed. She loved the garden, and occasionally thoroughly enjoyed meeting the mixed bag of customers. The Johanson Herb Garden attracted, but weeding between row upon row of raspberry bushes on a hot July afternoon was not usually her idea of fun. Today, though, for some reason she had needed the hard physical labour to take her mind off her more pressing problems. In the distance the low murmur of voices floated on the summer air, but it did not disturb her reverie because the garden was closed to visitors on Mondays.

Strictly speaking, she mused, raspberries could hardly be classed as herbs, but because her grandfather had planted them years ago neither Marlene nor her late mother, for that matter, had ever had the heart to uproot the things.

At the thought of her mother, Marlene's golden eyes shadowed with sorrow. Two years had passed since a drunken driver had mown her mother down, and the memory only served to remind her of a more recent tragedy, almost as painful. Twenty months after the death of her mother, Paolo Rossi, her mother's lover, father of her brother Paul and a good friend and mentor to Marlene, had died suddenly of a massive heart attack, in March of this year.

She grimaced at her morbid thoughts, then frowned, nibbling on her full bottom lip in nervous indecision. For more than two months now the letter from a London firm of solicitors acting on behalf of their Italian associate company had lain unanswered on the dressing table in her bedroom. She knew she was going to have to answer it soon. But how? That was the problem. Judging by the personal revelations Paolo had shared with her just before his death, and the remarks he had made about his family in Italy during the eight years Marlene had known him, she was not at all sure she should subject young Paul to their influence—even if a fortune in property was involved. There were more things of value in life than money, as she knew to her cost…

At that moment it dawned on Marlene that the distant voices were a heck of a lot closer, and by an amazing coincidence the language they were using was Italian. Or was it her imagination running riot? She stiffened and would have stood up, but something made her stop.

It was a woman's voice, shrill and rapid.

'Honestly, Rocco, for Papà to take a mistress who digs in the dirt for a living is unbelievable—and to actually give her a percentage of the company and a seat on the board is just too much. He must have known my mother, the Contessa, would be forced to recognise the bitch. It simply beggars belief. You have got to persuade the woman to sell her holdings for a few thousand pounds and to disappear with her bastard child.'

Marlene turned scarlet with embarrassment and anger at the callous comments. Having studied Italian and French

as secondary subjects at university, she had understood
every hate-filled word. That this creature should presume
Marlene had been Paolo's mistress and mother of young
Paul was bad enough, when it had been her mother and
Paolo who had loved each other quite desperately and produced the darling little boy. But to call an innocent child a
bastard even if technically it was true was beyond the
pale...

Marlene guessed immediately who the woman was. It
could only be the late Paolo Rossi's legitimate daughter.
But she had more sense than to stand up and confront the
spiteful female. 'Know thine enemy,' she murmured under
her breath, and peered surreptitiously through the bushes.

A thin, fashionable, dark-haired woman of about her own
age—twenty-six—was picking her way along the narrow
path in stiletto-heeled white shoes. Dressed in a pink suit,
obviously designer label, she clung to the arm of her companion—and what a companion!

Marlene's eyes widened in awe and a tingling sensation
slid down her spine. She had limited experience with men
but even she could recognise that he was a fabulous example of the male species. About six feet four of sheer
masculine perfection. His cream pleated trousers clung lovingly to lean hips, and a cream- and brown-patterned tailored shirt, open at the neck, revealed the beginnings of
crisp black body hair and emphasised his broad chest. A
soft cream matching sweater draped elegantly over incredibly wide shoulders completed the ensemble.

The whole outfit screamed Armani. But this man would
have looked good in anything—or *nothing,* she thought
with sinful erotic delight. The image forming in her brain
of the man naked made her pulse race, and she swallowed
hard, fighting down a sudden total body blush!

The man was a hunk. He had it all. The way he moved,
the proud tilt of his head, even the sun catching the odd

strand of silver in the longer than fashionable black hair declared to the world at large that here was a dynamic, powerful man—a man who would bow to no one, a man who was used to the best and would not settle for anything less.

Marlene suddenly shivered. A man, moreover, who looked vaguely familiar. Did she know him? He was rather like Julian, she realised, remembering her one and only disastrous love affair. Julian had been a ruthless devil, trying to use her love for him to further his career at the expense of hers, until she had found out and ditched him.

This man had the same predatory look about him, but even more so. Maybe that was why she'd thought she recognised him, why her mouth was dry and her heart was pounding as if she were a teenager with a surfeit of hormones.

No, she could not possibly know him, she told herself firmly, dismissing the notion with a faint shake of her head. As for her body's instant reaction to him, well, she had probably been in the sun too long. She rationalised her behaviour and, never one to shirk a confrontation, she decided to challenge the arrogant pair and put them straight about Paolo's relationship with her mother. Until she heard a deep, conciliatory voice responding to the woman.

'Don't worry, Caterina. Leave it all to me. I have dealt with her kind of low-life before. The woman will not be a problem for long, I promise.'

Low-life. Marlene was almost apoplectic! How dared the swine refer to her in that way? She took a deep breath and remembered some good advice from Paolo: 'Don't get mad, get even'. And in that second her mind was made up. She would have some fun with the pair, and take them down a peg or two in the process, before getting down to business. They deserved it.

Rolling onto her knees, she stood up, her back to the

approaching couple, and, stretching to her full height of five feet nine, turned slowly. Acting for all she was worth, she feigned startled surprise at seeing two strangers in the garden. Pushing her tangled blonde hair from her face, then slowly rubbing mud-caked hands on the denim cut-offs that barely covered her hips, she stepped towards them.

'I'm sorry, sir, madam, but the garden is closed today.' Marlene concentrated her attention on the woman, searching for some trace of her beloved Paolo in the smooth features, but there was little resemblance. The eyes might have been the same, except where Paolo's had been rich chocolate-brown, twinkling with humour at life, this girl's were cold and hard.

'We do not buy. We…er…er—' The woman spoke in fractured English but the man interrupted.

'My companion does not speak very much English. Allow me to explain the reason for our intrusion, Miss Johanson. I can assure you it will be to your benefit.'

At the mention of her name Marlene was forced to confront the man. She had to tilt her head back to look up into his hard, autocratic face—unusual for her—and when she did her eyes widened in appalled recognition. She had seen him before. It had been at the lowest point of her life to date, and one she would never forget. In that instant she knew this man would never do anything for her benefit; the truth was quite the reverse. She could see it in his black eyes, in the flicker of grim animosity he could not quite disguise.

Unconsciously her gracefully arched eyebrows drew together in a concentrated frown, her mind spinning back to their last meeting. She had just been to the morgue to identify the shattered remains of her mother's body. Paolo had accompanied her, of course, but as he hadn't been technically a relation—although he had virtually lived with her mother for the past few years—he could not do the job for

Marlene. But his support had been a great comfort, and later, when he'd insisted they must try to eat, she had accompanied him to a small French restaurant in the centre of London.

Both emotionally distraught, they had been idly pushing the food around their plates when the man who stood before her now had walked into the restaurant with a glamorous red-headed woman on his arm. Spotting Paolo, he had forced an introduction from him.

Paolo, completely distracted, had simply introduced Marlene as his friend, Miss Johanson, and had made it very obvious that he did not want to make polite conversation. Marlene, even in her distress, had registered the cynical contempt in the man's eyes when he had responded abruptly.

'Charmed, Miss Johanson,' he had said, and his low-voiced murmur, 'And no doubt expensive…' had not hurt her at the time, because all her pain had been concentrated on the loss of her mother.

Now, however, it was a different matter. She could not remember his name. but she knew his type. Her golden eyes clashed with black and she saw the self-same contempt as before. And this time she resolved to make the arrogant swine pay for his attitude.

'Explain away,' she finally responded casually. 'But I can't imagine we have anything to discuss.' And, fluttering her long eyelashes flirtatiously, she added, lying, 'I'm sure I would remember *you* if I had met you before.'

'We have met once, briefly, but your attention was concentrated on your companion at the time.' The hard mouth twisted cynically. 'It is not surprising you do not remember me. Allow me to introduce myself again. I am Rocco Andretti and this—' he smiled briefly at the small woman at his side '—this is Caterina Rossi, the daughter of Paolo

Rossi—someone I believe you were extremely well acquainted with,' he said with thinly veiled disdain.

Marlene was left in no doubt as to his opinion of her and her relationship with the late Paolo, and she saw no reason to enlighten this stuck-up pair with the truth. Instead she merely looked blank and said, with the slightest shrug of her shoulders, 'Yes? So...' And she hid a secret smile as she registered the anger her casual response had ignited in the man's dark eyes.

'I'm sure you can guess why we are here. As I understand it, our London associates did write to you,' Rocco said curtly, 'but there seems to have been some delay or difficulty in your replying.'

'I was never much good at writing, I'm afraid.' Marlene excused her lapse with simpering false naïvety.

'So we gathered—hence our appearance here. We wish to reach some amicable agreement over Signor Rossi's will and the shares you hold in his company as soon as possible.'

Is that the royal 'we'? Marlene was tempted to snap back sarcastically, but common sense prevailed. Instead, ignoring the penetrating gaze of Rocco Andretti, and most of what he had said, she forced a smile to her lips and held out her hand to the other woman. After all, common human decency decreed that the woman was deserving of sympathy at the loss of her father, even if she did appear to be a grade A bitch.

'It is a pleasure to meet you, Caterina. Paolo was a lovely man—you must miss him greatly,' she murmured.

At the look of horror on Caterina's face Marlene glanced down at her very dirty extended hand, which Caterina had taken one look at and ignored. With a barely restrained grin, Marlene dropped her hand.

'You're right, of course—I am rather mucky. If you would like to follow me to the office...' Her gaze strayed to a tumbledown shed in one corner of the huge walled garden and an imp of mischief lit her wide golden eyes before she added, 'I'll wash my hands and we can talk there.'

Caterina turned to Rocco and burst into a torrent of Italian. 'My God, Rocco. Look at the woman. She can't be any more than a few years older than me, and so coarse—nothing more than a peasant. How could Papà?'

A few years older! In her dreams, Marlene thought, and had to fight the angry retort that sprang to her lips. She plastered a dumb, questioning smile on her lovely face and forced herself to stand still as Andretti's dark eyes swept her briefly clad body with slow and blatant masculine appraisal, taking in her flushed face, the tumble of thick blonde hair, her skimpy white cropped top, bare midriff and brief cut-offs, travelling down her long, long legs and then back to her face. And all the time he spoke in soft Italian.

'Enough, Caterina. She looks like a dumb blonde country yokel, but even so she might understand some of what we say. After all, she was your father's mistress for eight years—perhaps some of the pillow-talk rubbed off, if nothing else. We can't afford to take any chances.'

And when his eyes finally met Marlene's he smiled, a totally false twist of his lips, and raised his voice. *'Scusi, signorina, parla italiano?'*

Her face rosy with anger, which she hoped he would put down to embarrassment, not by a flicker of an eyelash did Marlene betray that she understood every word. Instead she gestured with her hand. 'The office shed is down here—if you've finished your chat?' She smiled questioningly back at the pair of them and almost chuckled as she saw the relieved glance that passed between them.

'Lead on, Miss Johanson. We are completely at your disposal,' Rocco said blandly. 'I'm sure you are as anxious as we are to get this little matter settled.'

Making no response—she could not, she was so incensed—she spun on her heel and strode along the narrow pebbled path. 'Little matter' indeed! she fumed. A twenty-four per cent share in a multi-million-pound business empire and a seat on the board of directors was hardly 'little' by anyone's standards. Never mind the added complication of a villa in Amalfi for young Paul, if she decided to take him there.

This couple obviously thought she was a complete idiot—a dead man's ex-mistress to be bought off with a few pounds. They had callously insulted her—and Paolo and her late mother too, for that matter. Well, they were in for a very rude awakening, Marlene vowed silently. If they had been even faintly polite, faintly compassionate about the recent death of a lovely man, she would have invited them to the house and listened to what they had to say. But as it was Ned's old shed was more than good enough for the arrogant, conceited jerks.

Reaching the shed, she opened the door, a spark of devilment in her eyes. The shed was more of a lean-to, built against the wall of the magnificent walled garden that was the home of The Johanson Herb Garden. She crossed the confined space, pushing past a battered old wooden chair and table so she could reach the cracked pottery sink set against the wall behind them. She turned on the rusty tap and proceeded to wash her filthy hands with a tiny sliver of old soap, taking her time about it.

Decades ago, as a young man, her grandfather had escaped during the Second World War from German-occupied Holland to England. He had found employment as a gardener at a stately home set in acres of rolling countryside in Sussex. The lady of the house, a Mrs Barker-Smythe, lost her son in the war and later, in the fifties, her husband. Meanwhile Grandpa Johanson had met and married an English girl and taken up residence in the old coach house alongside the stables and attached to the back of the walled garden. Marlene's mother had been born in the house and had delighted in telling her daughter the story.

Apparently Mrs Barker-Smythe had begun to find money in short supply, and with no family left had reached an agreement with Grandpa Johanson. She'd given him a hundred-year lease on the coach house and walled garden on the estate, to develop it into a money-making market garden, with two conditions. One, that he planted a rose garden in front of the massive iron gates set in the wall between the big house and the garden, so her view would not be spoilt by rows of vegetables, and secondly that he and his wife would look after Mrs Barker-Smythe for nothing until her death.

The shed had been the original office, donkey's years ago. Now there was a very smart one in the converted stableblock, along with a retail outlet and coffee-shop. Ned oversaw the actual planting, and the manager, John Watson, with a permanent staff of six, plus casual workers at the busiest times, made sure that both the wholesale and the retail side of the business ran smoothly.

After the death of her grandfather, when Marlene was still a baby, her mother had inherited the place, but with the influx of fruit and vegetables from all over the world becoming more and more common, and so reducing the profit on home-produced stock grown on a small scale, the business had been in difficulty by the time her own father had died when she was only three.

Marlene barely remembered him, but her mother had kept his memory alive with photographs and stories of when they were young. He had been a good man. A cousin from Marlene's grandfather's side of the family before he was a husband, and her mother had often joked about how her name had never changed when she had married.

Left with a three-year-old daughter to take care of, and

no other form of income, her mother had decided to concentrate on herbs, with the assumption that the work would be slightly less strenuous and that herbs were going to be the crop of the future. Her hunch had proved correct. It was now a very profitable business. One, moreover, that Marlene had very little to do with. Her expertise was in a completely different field.

A discreet cough broke Marlene's train of thought. She shook her head to dismiss the memories and, straightening up, turned off the tap. She reached up to take a piece of torn towel from a nail on the wall and dried her hands. She saw no reason to tell the two people behind her the truth. Let them think she was an empty-headed bimbo—it should be interesting!

'Sorry about this, but the muck does take a lot of shifting—especially from under the fingernails, I find,' she said blithely, turning around to face her visitors while dropping the scrap of towel strategically over the ancient order papers on the table, in case the shrewd Andretti saw them.

'I would ask you both to sit down, but as you see there is only one chair. We don't go much for office furniture.'

At that precise moment a huge spider fell from the rafters, suspended on a silken thread. Highlighted by a ray of sun slanting through the door, it spun inches from Caterina's face like a golden tarantula.

A high-pitched scream rent the air and a swirl of pink shot out of the door and off up the pebbled path as fast as white stilettos would allow.

Marlene spluttered, and with a hand to her mouth she tried to disguise her amusement with a fit of coughing. Not very successfully…

'You don't go much for good manners either, it would seem,' Rocco Andretti said bitingly, and, catching her by the arm, he hauled her hard against his tall body.

Too astonished to resist, Marlene looked up, all amusement vanishing at the sight of the venom she recognised in his narrowed black eyes.

'You dare to laugh at Caterina when you are not fit to kiss the feet of a lady like her, you gold-digging little whore. Be warned, it is me you have to deal with now, and I am nothing like the gullible old fool Paolo was. It takes more than a luscious body, a beautiful face and fluttering eyelashes to fool me. Try playing games with me, and I will make you sorry you were ever born—and that is a promise, Miss Johanson.'

It sounded more like a threat than a promise, Marlene thought cynically, while feeling oddly flattered that he had called her beautiful. Which just shows what a fool I am, she said to herself silently. The knives were out, she realised, and this man would carve her into little pieces given half a chance. But she refused to be intimidated. Four years as a foreign exchange dealer with a large firm of stockbrokers had taught her how to hold her own with any man.

'Worried, Miss Johanson?' the mocking voice drawled near her ear. 'You should be.'

It was the edge of triumph in his tone that really angered Marlene, and, ignoring the shiver of pleasure his breath against her cheek aroused, she finally asked the question she should have asked ten minutes ago.

'And who exactly are you, Signor Andretti?' she prompted insinuatingly, boldly holding his gaze. 'The immaculate Caterina's lover? Or perhaps her financial adviser, hoping to line your own pockets? Just who gave you the right to interfere in my affairs?' She felt his long fingers tighten angrily on her bare skin, and a jolt of something very like electricity shot up her arm, making her catch her breath in surprise.

'I would not touch your "affairs" with a barge-boat,' he drawled, the double meaning obvious.

Marlene's lips twitched slightly at the word 'boat'. It was

the first and only sign of weakness in his otherwise perfect English. But he made no mistake in the threat that followed.

'My father's law firm is responsible for administering Signor Rossi's estate. Paolo was clever, signing over the stock to you but still administering it himself. No one knew he was voting his mistress's shares along with his own. But he is not around to protect you any more. The Contessa and Caterina are long-time family friends, and anything I can do to stop you getting your grubby little hands on any more of his assets I will.'

So Signor Andretti was Paolo's lawyer, Marlene realised with a sinking heart. And he was obviously more loyal to the female members of the Rossi family than he was to the late Paolo Rossi. The shares he was talking about had been put in her mother's name years ago by Paolo, and when her mother had died the shares had passed to Marlene.

She stared up into his dark face. 'For a lawyer you're not too bright. I already have the shares,' she reminded him sarcastically, at the same time fighting to ignore the primitive attraction simply being so close to him aroused in her.

'Women like you should not be allowed to profit at the expense of legitimate family simply by spreading their legs,' Rocco declared scathingly.

Shocked rigid by the insult, Marlene felt her golden eyes widen at the look of cold determination on his hard face, and she knew she should have answered the letter from the English law firm when she'd had the chance, and so avoided this confrontation with a highly volatile Latin…

She dropped her gaze to the lips that were mouthing the threats. He had a nice mouth, a sensuous mouth—and what was that enticing scent? The lingering trace of some masculine cologne, or simply the man? she wondered. God! What was she thinking of? She jerked her arm out of his grasp, horrified at the erotic turn her mind had taken. She needed to get out of the shed, out of this man's presence—and quick.

'*Rocco, caro.*' A tremulous voice broke the tense silence and a second later Marlene was watching Andretti's broad back as he strode up the garden to the waiting Caterina.

Marlene hesitated for a moment in an attempt to regain her equilibrium and control of the situation. Perhaps Andretti was right. It had been stupid to play games with the couple, and she would have to be even more stupid to continue doing so having felt the full force of Rocco's powerful personality.

After all, it had been Paolo's one and only request of her in eight years. He had known he had not long to live well before the massive heart attack that had finally killed him. They had spent his last few weeks together, mostly in his London apartment, and it was then he had revealed to Marlene his worry that someone on the board of his multinational electronics firm was deliberately blackening the good name of Rossi. Consequently the share price was dropping dramatically for no real reason.

He had asked her to investigate for him, and she had half promised that she would go to Italy and try to find out what was going on, not wishing to upset him when he was so ill. It was only after he was dead that she had discovered a very personal letter from him, reminding her of her promise and a few other things.

Marlene sighed deeply, and reluctantly followed after her visitors, finally deciding to tell the truth, or at least some of it. She did not know if Rocco and Caterina were mixed up in the dodgy business in Italy, and until she did she would keep quiet on that front. But as for the rest, she was an intelligent, highly educated young woman. She spoke Italian and French, and she was also exceptionally successful, having made her first million by the tender age of twenty-four. It would do the arrogant Andretti no harm to realise she was a more than capable adversary. She had been taught by the best…

Rocco and Caterina were talking heatedly, their backs to her, and did not hear her approach. Marlene was a few feet away, about to make her presence known, when all her good intentions flew out of the window as she overheard their conversation yet again.

'All right. All right, Caterina, have it your way. Actually, having met the woman again, I am inclined to agree with you. I called her a whore and a gold-digger and she made no attempt to deny it. Even she can't be so dense as to put up with an insult like that unless it's true. We will try to buy her shares first. As for the rest, I believe the boy is young enough to be controlled. All we have to do is prove she is an unfit mother.'

'I knew you would see it my way, *caro.*I saw the way she looked at you in that hovel that passes for an office, Rocco. If we can't find an ex-lover here to blacken her name, a man of your undoubted skill could easily seduce her and expose her for the slut she is. She'll be putty in your hands.' And Caterina's own hand slid suggestively down his chest as she smiled up at him.

Her smile was reciprocated by the slow, knowing curl of Rocco's sensuous mouth as he placed his hand over Caterina's and casually removed it from his chest. 'I'm flattered by your faith in me,' and I think I might just be able to force myself to seduce her.'

In that moment Marlene came as near to exploding with rage as she ever had in her whole life. It was only with a superhuman effort of will that she made herself cover the few paces that separated them, and, ignoring Rocco completely, she looked directly at Caterina.

'I'm so sorry about the spider—I do hope you're all right. You must be suffering from shock. How awful for you.' She knew she was babbling but it stopped her having to face the hateful man, and, grabbing Caterina's arm, she urged her forward. 'Come along to the house. Hot, sweet tea is what you need.'

In reality what the arrogant, conniving couple needed was a swift kick in the butt and expulsion from the premises, Marlene silently fumed. They thought she was immoral and that Paul was her son, and they were quite prepared to do anything to get the boy away from her and under their control... They were in for a very rude awakening—but not yet, she vowed...

CHAPTER TWO

'MAR, Mar—I'm back.' The appearance of a small boy running across the garden stopped the Italian couple in their tracks.

But Marlene didn't notice as she let go of Caterina's arm and dashed off on a diagonal path to meet young Paul. Swooping down, she picked him up and swung him high in the air. 'Hello, darling,' she cried happily, and nuzzled the soft black curls of his head before lowering him to his feet and asking, 'How was playschool today? You were a good boy, I hope.'

Straightening up, she waved to her friend Jean who was standing at the entrance door set in the twelve-foot-high wall. They ran a rota to transport the children the ten miles to pre-school. Today had been Jean's turn. 'Thanks, Jean,' Marlene called. 'See you in the morning.'

The young mother grinned and shouted back, 'Thank God my stint is over for a couple of days. That Paul of yours takes more controlling than all the rest put together—and boy, can he *talk.*'

Marlene waved again and watched her friend leave, glad that Jean had referred to Paul as hers. It might help to prolong the belief of the other two in her motherhood. But she need not have worried. When she looked down for Paul she discovered that he was heading for the two visitors, a determined expression on his chubby face.

She shot after him in time to hear him demand inquisitively, 'Who are you? Why you here? Today is my Mar's holiday.'

The fact that he called her Mar reinforced the belief that

21

she was his mother. A tender smile curved Marlene's wide mouth. Paul sounded so like his father—macho-male and very protective. It was uncanny in a child not yet four years old. She reached down and rumpled his dark curls with a gentle hand.

'It's all right, Paul, they're…' she hesitated for a second '…friends.' And, looking across at Caterina and Rocco, she almost chuckled out loud at the look of distaste on the other woman's face.

Rocco glanced down at the child, then straight at Marlene. 'So this boy is your son?' he demanded, with evident disgust darkening his hard face.

A surge of anger almost made Marlene blurt out the truth, but she knew it would do neither Paul nor herself any good to lose control in front of this astute man. Her mind working fast, she realised it was to her advantage to let them think she was Paul's mother, and for once she blessed her young brother's habit of shortening her name to Mar.

'The boy is your son?' Rocco Andretti repeated his question curtly.

Equally curtly Marlene responded, not lying exactly— except perhaps by omission. 'The boy has a name. Paul— named after his father, Paolo Rossi—and I would thank you to use it. He also has ears,' she warned him sharply. Any discussion of Paul's parentage was not going to take place in front of him, if she could prevent it.

Paul, bored by even a minute's inactivity, chose that moment to acknowledge Caterina. 'You are a pretty pink lady, but not as big as Mar.'

'*Dio grazie,*' Caterina murmured insultingly.

But Rocco cut in before Marlene could retaliate. 'Hello, young man. Paul, is it?'

Marlene's eyes widened in astonishment as Rocco dropped to his haunches and smiled at the little boy. The smile transformed his harsh features into charming, almost boyish beauty, with just a hint of mischief and a subtle male bonding in his gleaming dark eyes.

He was really quite endearing, she thought, her own eyes lingering with rapt fascination on his tanned face. He was the most exquisite man she had ever seen, and for a long moment she simply stared, until Rocco flicked a glance her way, with a knowing, purely male grin twisting his sensuous mouth. Suddenly remembering he was the enemy, she hastily lowered her eyes from his too attractive face— but that was a mistake.

The fabric of his trousers was pulled tight across his knees and clung to his muscular thighs like a second skin, filling her head with wildly erotic thoughts that brought hot colour to her cheeks. She shook her head in confusion and, pushing back her hair from her brow, looked over the top of the two males at Caterina. The flash of sheer hatred in the other woman's eyes brought her back to her senses with a jolt. Just in time to tune in to the conversation going on at her feet.

Rocco's deep, melodious voice, his almost perfect command of English, had Paul enthralled. 'I knew your father very well, and you look very like him. I would have recognised you anywhere, Paul. I hope you don't mind me calling you Paul, and you must call me Rocco, as your daddy used to.'

'You knew my daddy?' Paul asked excitedly.

'Yes, he was a good friend of mine. When I was much younger he used to take me fishing and swimming, and we played all sorts of games together.'

'I have lots and lots of games, and when my daddy comes we play. You want to see, Rocco?' And trustingly Paul held out his hand to the man. 'They in the house.'

Rocco Andretti had said exactly the right thing to catch Paul's attention, Marlene thought rather sourly. Not only could he charm women, but children as well. Though she could not begrudge Paul the man's friendly advances. The boy had loved his father deeply, and missed him dreadfully. She had tried to explain, but Paul, at three, was a little too young to understand the finality of death. Recently he had been asking more and more if his daddy was coming back. It was a worry to Marlene, but she did not see what more she could do.

'You don't mind, do you, Ms Johanson?'

With a start Marlene looked up. Somehow Rocco Andretti was towering over her, and his eyes, lit with mocking triumph, caught and held hers.

She had been lost in her own thoughts. 'D-d-don't mind what?' she stuttered, struck anew by the overwhelming masculine appeal of the man standing only inches away from her. Luckily Paul came to her rescue.

'Roc can play with me, can't he, Mar?'

She looked down. Paul had already shortened the man's name to Roc, a habit of his, and was gazing up at her pleadingly, his small hand engulfed by the much larger one of his new-found friend. She tried to discourage him. 'You have to have your tea now, Paul.'

'Please, after tea. He can stay for tea. Please, Mar.'

'I'm sure Mr Andretti can't stay that long, and Caterina...' She trailed off helplessly as it suddenly hit her that Caterina and Paul were brother and sister. She glanced up at the man in the forlorn hope that he would back her up. But no such luck...

'We have plenty of time,' he said flatly, leaving the ball firmly in her court.

Marlene looked back down at the grinning child and, smothering a sigh, said, 'Yes, of course.'

'Come on, Roc!' Paul cried in glee, and set off up the path as fast as his chubby legs would take him, the man in tow.

Caterina followed quickly, and it was left to Marlene to bring up the rear. She watched them disappear through the door in the wall and, following on, she turned and took a large bunch of keys from her pocket. She locked the door securely behind her and noted that the other three were almost at the entrance porch of the mellow old stone house she had called home almost all her life. Inexplicably she shivered. She had a chilling premonition that unless she was very careful around Caterina Rossi and Rocco Andretti she might find herself in more trouble than she could handle, and possibly be shoved into the background of Paul's life for good. Over my dead body, she thought decisively.

'Hurry up, Mar. We're waiting!' Paul yelled.

Straightening her shoulders, she strolled across the gravel road to the house and, choosing another key from the bunch, unlocked the arched oak door and pushed it open.

'Welcome to our home,' she said politely, and if a trace of sarcasm echoed in the oak-panelled hall she didn't really care. She stood back and let the three of them walk past her. She took an apple from the bowl on the hall table and handed it to Paul. 'Take our friends through to the den and show them your toys. I'll give you a shout when tea is ready.' She badly needed some time alone to sort out her thoughts.

'Oh, no...!' Caterina began, obviously not wanting to play with Paul, but Rocco grabbed her arm and said something softly in his native language which Marlene did not catch, and they followed Paul along the hall to the back of the house.

With a sigh of relief Marlene took the first door on the left into the large farmhouse kitchen. She looked around at the familiar scrubbed pine furniture and the dried grasses and herbs hanging from the ceiling beams. She smiled and drew a deep, calming breath, then collapsed gratefully on the bentwood rocker set in front of the stone-mullioned window. She was just congratulating herself on getting rid of the Italian pair for a while when the door opened behind her.

She turned her head and once again was looking up into the harsh face of Rocco Andretti.

'I thought you were playing with Paul.'

'I told him I needed something from my car, but actually I want to speak to you in private.'

'Could it not wait until after we have tea?'

'No, there has been far too much delay in settling Paolo Rossi's affairs already. My own mother, who was a family friend of the Rossis, died only four months before him, and her estate is already wound up.'

'You have recently lost your mother?' Marlene asked softly, struck by the solemn tone of his deep voice.

'Yes, but to get back to the point,' Rocco said curtly, obviously not appreciating her sympathy, 'I think I can begin to understand why Paolo made the arrangements he did. In Italy the rule of law is closely connected to the church— an illegitimate child does not necessarily have the same rights as a child in England would. With you owning part of his company for so long he has obviously assured the financial independence of his son. That being the case, I'm sure I can persuade the family to come to a generous settlement over the shares and the property bequeathed in the will.'

He spoke as if he was doing her a favour, and she had to wonder why. Remembering the conversation she had overheard in the garden between Andretti and Caterina, Marlene tensed and rose to her feet. She looked into the dark, surprisingly compassionate face of Andretti, and wasn't fooled for a minute. Seduce her into compliance— get Paul and the villa that way? Fat Chance! she thought, and said bluntly, 'Young Paul was a much wanted and much loved son to his father, but he has absolutely nothing to do with you. And as for buying back the shares, I might not want to sell. They are mine… It is me you have to deal with.' She fixed him with her wide gold gaze. 'Me alone.'

They stared at each other, a tense silence stretching between them. Marlene refused to be the first to drop her gaze, and to her amazement Rocco suddenly smiled—a broad grin that took years off his age.

'You alone. I like that. But not here, not now. We cannot have a serious talk with the boy and Caterina around.'

'Rocco, where are you?' The demand, in Italian, echoed through the house, underlining his words.

'I think your lady-love has had enough of childminding,' Marlene said cynically. 'If you will excuse me…' She made to walk past him, but he stepped in front of her. His long fingers caught her chin and tipped her face up to his.

'She is not my lady-love; I am reserving that position for you,' he declared outrageously.

Marlene's gasp of surprise was swallowed by hard, firm lips closing over her mouth and a darting tongue flicking the heated interior with stunning expertise. It was over so quickly she wondered if she had imagined it, but the racing of her pulse and the scarlet burn of her cheeks let her know it was all too real. 'You—you…' she spluttered.

'Get a baby-sitter for tomorrow night. I will pick you up at seven-thirty. You and I have a lot to discuss.'

She wanted to deny it, but at that moment Paul dashed into the kitchen with a furious-looking Caterina behind him, and the conversation became general.

The tea that followed was a disaster, the only one doing any talking being young Paul. Caterina was obviously bored to tears, and Marlene was still reeling from the effect of a single kiss. But at least after tea Rocco kept his word and played with Paul in the den for half an hour.

Later, when the guests were long gone and Marlene was tossing restlessly in her wide bed, she decided that that was the only good thing to have come out of the whole afternoon. She could console herself with the fact that Paul had for a short time thoroughly enjoyed himself with a man to play with—something that had been sadly lacking in his life of late.

Paul was not the only one lacking male companionship. She hadn't been out on a date with a man since she'd split with Julian the Toad, she thought wryly, and that had been over two years ago. In all honesty she had never felt deprived until today, when Rocco Andretti had appeared in her life.

Instant attraction! Instant lust! Whatever name she put on it, there was no denying that Rocco had had an amazing effect on her usually dormant libido. Just lying in bed thinking about him, and the kiss he had snatched, made her breasts swell and her nipples tighten in sensual need. Why now? And why him? she pondered. The one man in the world who seemed destined to be her enemy, and who obviously despised the sort of woman he thought she was.

Hot and restless, she turned over to lie on her back and stare at the ceiling, her mind spinning like a windmill. If it hadn't been for the promise she had given Paolo, she could have told Rocco Andretti the truth, at least about her career, but until she discovered who the traitor was in the late Paolo's firm she did not dare. A deep sigh escaped her. Wheels within wheels did not begin to describe her predicament.

Her mind went back to the first time she had met Paolo Rossi. She had left school the week before and had been awaiting the results of her exams to confirm her place at university—she had been accepted by the London School of Economics to read Economics and Languages. Her mother had gone into the village to deliver some feverfew plants—an old-fashioned but potent remedy for migraine—to Dr Branton, a man who was not afraid to mix the old with the new. Marlene had been in the house on her own when someone had rung the bell, and she had answered the door.

It was a man she had never seen before. Middle-aged—about fifty, she had thought. Tall, with steel-grey hair and dark brown eyes. He had stood looking at her in open-mouthed amazement.

'Yes? Can I help you?' she enquired.

'Marlene? Is it you?' he whispered, with the trace of an accent. Then he added, 'No, it can't be—you have to be nearly forty.'

'I am eighteen, thank you very much,' she replied cheekily. 'I think it must be my mum you want. We share the same name and everyone says I am very like her.' And that was the start of a great change in the lives of all three of them.

Her mother returned home and fainted at the sight of Paolo Rossi, and then it all came out. They had known each other years ago, when Paolo had been setting up the London branch of his company, and her mother had worked as a secretary in London. They had parted when Paolo had returned to his native Italy and married and had a daughter. Her mother had returned to Sussex and married her cousin, the then manager of the market garden, and had given birth to the younger Marlene Johanson.

His reason for looking up her mother after so long was simple. He had recently had a minor heart attack and, heeding the warning, had taken a long, hard look at his life and hadn't liked what he saw. So he had decided to take time out from his hectic work schedule to look up his old friends, to 'smell the roses', before it was too late. Paolo now lived in his London apartment almost permanently, only visiting his native Italy when business demanded it.

He and Marlene's mother became lovers. At first Marlene was angry, and a bit wary of the new man in her

mother's life. With the idealism of youth she thought it was
wrong, but she could not deny that he made her mother
very happy. And, according to Paolo, his marriage had been
a sham for years. The Contessa had married him for his
money and he had married her because she was pregnant—
nothing else. She considered him to be beneath her in every
way, an ill-bred self-made man.

Finally, when young Paul was born, and although he was
Catholic, he asked his wife for a divorce. The Contessa
refused and went on refusing right up to Paolo's death.

Over the years he spent a lot of time at the Johanson
house in the country, and was instrumental in helping
Marlene through university and getting her her first job with
a city stockbroker. He was like a second father to her—
more, because she could barely remember her own father.
Paolo was there for Marlene when her one and only romance with the rat Julian broke up, and again when her
mother died.

When Paolo asked for her help in bringing up young Paul
she willingly gave up her job in the City and returned to
the country to look after her little brother. But the death of
her mother had had a disastrous effect on Paolo, and he
never really recovered.

By the time he realised someone was working against
him in Italy, trying to take control of his business, it was
too late for him to do much about it. He was too ill. Hence
the promise he elicited from Marlene to discover what was
going on and try to prevent the destruction of his good
name... Of course Marlene vowed to help all she could,
but secretly she thought when he died that it wasn't so
much a heart attack as a broken heart that had killed him.

Marlene yawned widely now and turned onto her side,
pulling the sheet up around her neck. Reliving the past did
no good, she thought sleepily. Tomorrow was for the living.
And she had finally reached a decision on the other promise

Paulo had extracted from her—to take his son to Italy for two months every year and let him get to know the land of his father's birth.

He had even gone so far as to leave young Paul the family villa in Amalfi in his will, according to the letter from the London firm of solicitors which had been lying on her dressing table for months. It still hurt her a little that Paolo had thought it necessary to make his request for his son to visit Italy official, as though he had not quite trusted her completely to carry out his wishes. But then again, she couldn't blame him. His view on the female sex's ability to be truthful had always been somewhat biased by the actions of his Italian wife and, in a way, of her own mother, she supposed.

School was due to finish this Friday, the twenty-sixth of July, for eight weeks. She could procrastinate no longer. The decision had really been taken for her, with the arrival of Rocco Andretti and Caterina. Even before that, really. With the arrival of the solicitor's letter, if she was honest. Tomorrow she would make the arrangements for Paul and herself to fly to Italy at the weekend. As for Rocco Andretti, she would have dinner with him tomorrow night, listen to his offer for her shares and, with Caterina's words in the forefront of her mind, beware of any attempt he might make to try and seduce her into parting with either them or Paul.

She had made it her business to know that an extraordinary general meeting of Rossi International had been called for Friday the second of August, to discuss the disappointing performance of the company and appoint a new MD. Marlene had been considering keeping a low profile and dealing with the problem through the London lawyers, but after meeting Caterina and Andretti, and after having been roundly insulted by both, she now determined to discover exactly what was going on and hopefully reveal the truth at the board meeting in August in person.

In fact, she quite relished the challenge. Andretti could not be that sharp, despite appearances, because he could quite simply have checked that the Ms M. Johanson on the present share certificate was not the same Mrs M. Johanson who had owned them earlier.

She loved her young brother, and did not regret living in the country for the past two years for his benefit. She found the occasional stint in the garden quite therapeutic, though her main interest was still finance—she did miss the cut and thrust of the dealing floor sometimes…

Another wide yawn, and minutes later she was asleep.

Marlene stretched her hands above her head in an attempt to get the crick out of her back and took one last look at the computer screen before switching it off. She had instituted a few lines of enquiry with friends in the City and on the international markets. Very soon she should have the information she sought.

If Andretti could see her now, she thought with a smile, he would get one hell of a shock. As she swivelled around in her chair, her glance skimmed the banks of machinery installed in the attic room she used as her office. She had not given up her career on the death of her mother. With all the high technology now available she simply worked from home as a consultant for numerous finance houses.

Pushing back her chair, she stood up and walked out of the room, locking the door behind her and quickly descending the narrow staircase to the first floor and her bedroom. Paul was all right. Jean had taken him to stay at her house for the night and she had the house to herself.

Stripping off her shirt and shorts, she crossed to the wardrobes that filled one wall and slid back a mirrored door. Her mouth twisted in a regretful grimace as she surveyed the Calvin Klein and Donna Karan suits, separates and dresses—her favourite designers and her usual choice.

Sliding back another door, she rummaged at the very end of the rail and finally found what she was looking for. A cotton frock she had not worn in years. Yes! Just the image she wanted to portray. Caterina and Andretti thought she was some kind of ignorant, immoral peasant. Who was she to disillusion them? She asked herself, a secret smile curling her wide mouth as she walked into the small but luxurious *ensuite* shower room.

Half an hour later, with her blonde hair washed and dried and left loose to flow in waves down her back almost to her waist, and with the minimum of make-up, she surveyed herself in the mirror and almost laughed out loud.

Physically she had been a late developer, and at eighteen she had been a lot smaller in the bust department. Now the autumnal-coloured Indian cotton dress barely caught her shoulders and strained across the full curves of her high breasts. The bodice buttoned down the front and cinched in at her waist, then swirled out over her hips to reach to mid-calf. Green espadrilles were tied around her ankles and she looked like a hippie from the sixties. Absolutely right for the part she was about to play, she told herself, and, with a casual flick at an errant strand of hair floating over her breast, she left the bedroom and went downstairs.

Marlene had barely reached the hall when the doorbell rang, not once but three times. Sharp and impatient, she thought, and was in no doubt as to who her caller was. Taking a deep, calming breath, she opened the door.

Her breath stopped in her chest and her eyes widened in helpless awe at the picture Rocco Andretti presented. Gone was the casually dressed man of yesterday afternoon, and in his place was a hard, sophisticated businessman. It showed in the dark blue three-piece suit, immaculately tailored to fit his large frame. The brilliant white shirt contrasted sharply with his bronzed features, and the Paisley silk tie in muted blues added just the right conservative touch. She could easily picture him in a court of law, dominant and dynamic.

Unconsciously she took a step backwards, her eyes lifting to the strong face, and she was caught in the hard glitter of his dark gaze. It would take a brave person to try and go against this man, was her immediate thought. Or a fool. Unable to tear her eyes away, she had the sinking sensation that she was the fool…

'Are you going to ask me in? Or stand here all night admiring the view?' he demanded, his predatory gaze roving over her body with undisguised sexual insolence.

'What? Yes—no. I'm ready,' she blustered and, taking a step forward, pulled the door closed behind her.

'Such punctuality in a woman. I am impressed,' Rocco declared, cupping her elbow with one large hand and staring down into her blushing face.

His smile was incredible—a flash of brilliant white teeth, eyes that gleamed with pleasure and something more…a blatant appreciation that set her pulse racing. He led her to a long, low-slung sports car and opened the door, watching her manoeuvre herself into the bucket seat and grinning broadly as her dress hitched up, revealing a length of bare, shapely leg. Then, closing the door, he swung around the front to the driver's seat and slid in beside her.

Marlene was speechless. For some reason he had the ability to make her behave like a love-sick teenager, and she did not like it. He angered her and attracted her both at the same time, and she seemed unable to do anything about it. The engine roared to life, the car shot down the long drive and out onto the road, and she still had not got her breath back.

'A quiet woman, as well as beautiful. Quite a combination,' Rocco said, flashing her a sidelong glance. 'They say the best courtesans in history all shared the same ability to be good listeners.' He smiled sardonically, his gaze dropping for a second to the soft curve of her breasts revealed by the scoop neck of her dress, before returning to the road ahead. 'Along with other, more earthy attributes, of course,' he added. 'Which I am sure you also have in abundance.'

If he had not been driving Marlene would have hit him for his scandalous remark, but at least it had the effect of bringing her out of her stupid fascination with the physical perfection of the man and back to reality. 'My attributes or lack of them are none of your affair,' she said curtly. 'This is supposed to be a business meeting and I will thank you to keep it that way.'

'For a country girl who has spent most of her adult life as an old man's mistress, your indignation seems a touch out of place, Marlene.'

'Ms Johanson to you,' she shot back. Hearing her name on his tongue seemed oddly intimate, and she needed all her wits about her for the next few hours.

'If you think I am going to call you Ms Johanson all night, forget it, Marlene. Given your occupation over the past few years, calling yourself Ms seems a bit of a cheek. As I understand it, that particular form of address is used for hard-hitting businesswomen—hardly suitable for an old man's mistress.'

'All right, Miss Johanson will be perfectly acceptable,' she conceded.

'Marlene, there is something you should know about me. I like my women malleable and I insist you call me Rocco. There is no way I am spending the next couple of months arguing with you over a name. Understood?'

'Two months?' she exclaimed in astonishment, the colour draining from her face. He could not possibly know she had decided to go to Italy. She had only decided herself last night. Was the man a mind-reader or what? 'You're staying in England that long?' she queried.

'I have a couple of months' vacation, and if you make

it worth my while I rather think I might,' he drawled throatily. 'What do you say, Marlene? You and me together.'

'Worth your while?' she snapped back, ignoring the breathless feeling the idea of spending time with Rocco gave her. 'I don't pay for men; I prefer it the other way round,' she said tartly. Then it hit her. Of course, Rocco knew the terms of the will and didn't want her to go to Italy. He was quite prepared to spend weeks in England playing the besotted lover if it stopped Marlene claiming young Paul's inheritance.

His deep shout of laughter broke into her muddled thoughts. 'I am beginning to see why Rossi was so enamoured of you, Marlene. You are quite a challenge.' And before she could ask him what he meant the car had stopped outside an imposing country house and Rocco was sliding out of the driver's seat.

Her door was opened with a flourish. 'Harlton Grange. I am informed it is a good place to eat. Shall we go?'

Marlene knew the Grange, and for a second she regretted her ancient summer dress. And then a bigger worry hit her.

'Yes.' She reluctantly murmured her assent and, stepping out of the car, meekly allowed Rocco to take her arm and usher her up the wide stone steps to the entrance hall. She had been here before—quite a few times, in fact—but never dressed like a charity shop reject!

Harlton Grange was the best restaurant in the county, and was often used by members of the business establishment not only locally but from the City as well. Besides that, The Johanson Herb Garden provided the restaurant with its products. She knew most of the staff, and it was quite possible that someone who knew her real career might inadvertently make a comment about it and blow her cover.

The prospect of keeping Rocco Andretti in the dark about her relationship with Paolo Rossi and young Paul, never mind her actual field of expertise, was looking remoter by the second. She could have kicked herself for not asking where he was taking her to dine. If she had not been so bowled over by the man's pure animal magnetism she might have done so. But it was too late now and, stifling a sigh, she casually flicked a swath of her long hair, seemingly artlessly, so that it fell down over her shoulder, hiding one side of her face.

As a disguise it failed dismally. A voice boomed out, 'Good evening, Miss Johanson. This is a pleasure.' Deep blue eyes set in a handsome face looked her over in puzzlement. Henry, the head waiter, could have been a double for Paul Newman, and she smiled back at him, knowing his surprise was at the state of her dress, though he was far too much of a gentleman to comment.

'Business doing well? Still rolling it in?' he asked with a grin.

'Oh, yes, yes.' She rushed to respond before Henry could put his foot in it completely and ask her for a tip on what shares to invest his money in—something he was prone to do every time he saw her. 'The Herb Garden is doing brilliantly. I hope the chef is still happy with the produce?'

'Yes, of course—best in the country, as ever. But—'

Luckily for Marlene, before Henry could go on Rocco cut in. 'I have a booking. Rocco Andretti,' he said curtly, his brows drawing together in an unsmiling look at the other man. 'And the lady is my guest.'

Henry glanced up at Rocco and straightened perceptibly, once more the immaculate *maître d'*. 'Yes, of course, sir. A table for two. This way, please.'

Marlene almost grinned. Poor Henry had been instantly quelled by the air of authority Rocco displayed. But one glance at Rocco's forbidding countenance and all thought of amusement left her.

Long fingers tightened perceptibly around her bare arm.

'You appear to be well known here, Marlene. Rossi brought you here, did he?'

'On occasions,' she said coolly as she was ushered through the large, ornately carved arched doors into the dining room. She glanced around quickly and sighed with relief. It was a Tuesday night and there were not many diners—and none she knew, thank God! With an upsurge of confidence, she continued casually, 'But we also supply the Grange with fresh herbs—they are old and valued customers. Henry and I are good friends.'

'It seems to me any man over fifty is your *good friend*. What is it? Looking for a father figure, are you? Or simply frightened a younger man might demand more than your sort can give?'

'You know absolutely nothing about my "sort", Mr Andretti, and if you intend to spend the evening insulting me we might as well leave now,' Marlene snapped back, and, freeing her arm from his hold, she would have walked out.

But Rocco grabbed her wrist and halted her in mid-stride. Bending his dark head towards her, he husked, 'Forgive me,' and brushed her brow with warm lips. 'I find I have difficulty accepting the thought of you in bed with Rossi. And watching the even older Henry ogle you does nothing for my temper.'

His apology and light kiss were so unexpected, and the implication of jealousy so surprising, that Marlene stared blankly up at him.

Urging her towards the table, Rocco said, 'Please sit down,' and, pulling out a chair before the waiter could reach it, he hovered over her until she obeyed.

Her skin still warm from the heat of his mouth, she nervously straightened the cutlery on the table, at the same time watching with wary eyes as Rocco took the chair opposite. Without realising what was happening she found one of her hands covered by his.

'Pax for the rest of the evening, hmm?' he drawled softly.

His large hand engulfing hers sent shivers up her spine, and the seemingly casual way his thumb rubbed her palm made her flesh tingle. Hastily pulling her hand free, she mumbled, 'All right,' and gratefully took the menu the waiter was holding out to her.

Pax? A feeling of peace was the last thing Rocco Andretti aroused in her! Quite the reverse, in fact. He had an uncanny ability to make her pulse go into overdrive and her knees go weak. Not a good way to feel about a man she was trying to deceive, she thought wryly, with a growing conviction that it was going to be a very fraught evening.

CHAPTER THREE

MARLENE held the menu in front of her face, apparently studying it, but in reality she didn't read a word; she simply needed a moment to recover her self-control.

'Typical female—can't make up her mind,' Rocco commented in a flippant aside to the hovering waiter as his hand once more covered Marlene's and lowered her menu down to the table. 'Allow me to order for you.'

'Typical male chauvinist,' she responded coolly, quickly withdrawing her hand. And, ignoring the gleam in her companion's dark eyes, she tilted her head back and bestowed a brilliant smile on the waiter. 'I'll have the melon with the almond trout to follow.'

'An excellent choice, and just to show you I am not the male chauvinist you imagine I will have the same,' Rocco responded, and, leaning back in his chair, his body at ease, he stunned her with a slow, dangerously sexy smile.

She blushed and looked away, glancing around the room—anywhere rather than at the man opposite, who seemed to radiate a lethal charm without even trying. She noticed the covetous glances cast in his direction by the other females present and knew exactly how they felt. No one man had the right to look so good, and if she felt a tinge of triumph because he was with her who could blame her? she thought smugly as, in her peripheral vision, she registered the arrival of the wine waiter and Rocco's casual order of a bottle of the best champagne.

'Until I know a woman's taste intimately, I find champagne is usually acceptable,' he opined, his dark eyes seeking hers. 'Don't you agree, Marlene?'

Ignoring the innuendo, she said, 'I'm not much of a drinker, but I'm sure you're right.'

'I am right about most things,' Rocco drawled. 'Bear that in mind when we get down to business later.'

'Why later?' she asked bluntly.

'Because I have no intention of spoiling a fine meal with business, so relax and enjoy,' he commanded as the waiter deftly uncorked the bottle with a reassuring pop and filled two glasses with the sparkling liquid.

Grasping her glass, Marlene raised it to her lips and took a hasty swallow. She needed it to shore up her dwindling confidence where Rocco was concerned. Was it just her, or could he possibly be feeling the same fierce physical attraction as she did? she puzzled, before responding, 'I am relaxed.' Then, meeting his dark gaze with slightly more self-confidence, she added, 'And I am quite capable of discussing business and eating at the same time.'

'I am sure you are capable of many interesting things.' A teasing smile curved his hard mouth. 'I hope to discover that for myself eventually.' He glanced down to where her full breasts strained against the fabric of her dress, making her tremble with awareness. He noted her reaction, his glittering eyes clashing with hers, and, raising his glass, he said, 'A toast to business and our closer association. May there be a successful conclusion to both.' He took a sip of the champagne before adding, 'But for now let us concentrate on eating... Other appetites can wait.'

If he did not stop this sexual innuendo she was liable to clock him one, but, perhaps luckily for Rocco, at that moment the first course arrived.

Surprisingly the meal passed with remarkable ease. When he set out to charm Rocco had no equal. They discussed neutral topics—the theatre, music, the opera—and he regaled her with stories of his travels in far-flung corners of the world that had Marlene laughing out loud. It did cross her mind that for a lawyer he did an awful lot of travelling, but she dismissed the thought.

They had finished their meal and the bottle of champagne and were sipping their coffee when the warning bells rang loud in Marlene's head. A head definitely hazy with champagne.

'Tell me,' Rocco demanded suddenly, 'how old are you?'

'Twenty-six... But don't you know it's an insult to ask a lady her age?' she quipped with a grin.

'Some lady!' His mouth twisted cynically. 'That makes you only eighteen when you took Rossi, a married man, as your lover.'

She looked up sharply, her golden eyes glinting with anger, and almost blurted out the truth—that Paolo had been her late mother's lover. But common sense prevailed. Perhaps the coffee had had a sobering effect as it hit her. Rocco had drunk very little champagne, she realised. She had quaffed the lion's share. Straightening in her seat, she responded with contrived flippancy. 'Eighteen is over the age of consent.'

'So young to be so mercenary,' he taunted savagely. 'Perhaps it is time we got down to business after all.'

'I could not agree more. Fire away.' She flashed him an insolent smile. 'But keep it simple. Remember I am a country girl, with a very tenuous grasp of financial matters.' She was lying through her teeth, but his callous comment on her character had stiffened her resolve. Plus the fact that she did not trust him an inch...

His hooded lids lowered over his black eyes, masking his expression, and his deep voice softened considerably. 'Yes, I suppose you are, and as such I should not judge you too harshly. It takes two to start an affair, and Rossi, at his age, should have had more sense than to seduce an innocent eighteen-year-old girl. You *were* innocent when you met him, I take it?'

He did not deserve an answer, but, in keeping with the character she was trying to portray, she decided to give him one. 'Certainly,' she shot back truthfully. 'I have only ever had one lover.' Again, it was the truth. The fact that the one lover had not been Paolo Rossi was her secret. 'And I really miss Paolo—he was so good to me. Which is why I must try to do what Paolo would have wanted with my shares in the company. It is a worry. The market garden is quite simple to run, but big business I don't understand too well.' Silently she hoped she had not laid it on too thick.

'I understand your feelings, Marlene, and you have nothing to worry about, I promise,' Rocco said, and to a casual observer his expression would have appeared to be one of sincere concern. 'I am here to help you.'

But Marlene was not fooled for a second. She wanted to laugh at the change in his manner, so obviously false! It was only by taking a sip of coffee that she managed to hide her grin. Pull the other one! she thought, but said nothing.

'I want to do what is best for you and your child,' Rocco assured her.

If she had not known better Marlene would have sworn the sincerity in his tone was genuine, and when his eyes met hers the compassion in his gaze had her marvelling at his acting ability. 'Thank you for that,' she gushed, no slouch in the acting department herself.

'I know it must be hard for you, losing your lover and being left with complex financial arrangements to deal with, but I intend to make it very simple.'

'Please do,' she encouraged huskily, gazing limply at his rugged face.

'As you know, Rossi put twenty-four per cent of his company shares in your name a few years ago. He voted them himself, of course, but since his death the London

office has, quite naturally, as you are the official owner of
the shares, sent information on the company to you.
Whether you read it or not, or understood it, I don't know.'
One dark brow arched quizzically, and Marlene did not
disappoint him.

'I glanced at a few letters, but I can't say I understood
too well,' she said, and once again she had to bite her lip
to stop the grin threatening to break out when she recognised the gleam of triumph in his eyes.

'To put it simply, Rossi International is in a bit of a
slump, and at the present time the share price is low. One
pound fifty at close of business today. Also, the majority
stockholders have called an extraordinary board meeting at
the beginning of August to try and rectify the situation.
Unfortunately until then, and until some salvage package
is arranged, the price is liable to drop a lot lower.

'Now, I know you won't want to get involved in the
technicalities. Your main interest must be to obtain the best
price and assure your son's financially secure future. That
is why I am here at the Contessa's request. Both she and
her daughter realise Paolo must have been very fond of the
boy, but he must also have known there was no way a
young woman like you would want to get involved in what
is basically still an Italian company. Worrying about finance and board meetings is not your style. They are quite
willing to buy the shares back, and have authorised me to
offer you…' Rocco paused, allowing a small smile to curve
his mouth.

Now we come to the nitty-gritty, Marlene thought drily.
'Offer me what?' she asked eagerly. She was silently thinking that the true market value of the company, as perceived
by the leading market gurus, was more like four pounds a
share. It was only the machinations in Italy that had brought
the price so low.

'They are prepared to be quite generous, because they

understand your position as an unmarried mother, and of course they want to make sure the company stays in the family as a tribute to Rossi's achievements. Therefore they will happily pay you two pounds a share.' Rocco leant back in his seat, confidence oozing from every pore. 'It is a brilliant offer, and you can be sure no one is trying to cheat you.'

Marlene watched as his hand slid into the breast pocket of his jacket and he withdrew a business card.

'This is a leading firm of stockbrokers in the City. Ring them tomorrow and check for yourself. They will confirm that the price I have quoted is the truth and that the Contessa's offer is truly generous, I assure you.' And then he mentioned the total amount in pounds sterling.

'So much!' she exclaimed, as he obviously expected, and responded to the self-satisfied if derisory smile he bestowed upon her with equal mock innocence.

'It will certainly keep you and your boy in the manner to which you are accustomed.'

This man could sell ice to eskimos, Marlene thought, her eyes roaming over his darkly attractive face. His oh, so concerned expression! Reaching out her hand, she took the card. Her fingers touched his, and a disturbing flash of awareness made her draw back quickly and glance down at the card in her hand to hide the sudden flush of colour to her cheeks. She recognised the name of the firm even as she battled with the unwanted emotions his slightest touch aroused.

'I'm sure you're right, and I will ring these people.' She waved the card in front of her face, which was red with a mixture of anger and arousal. 'First thing in the morning.'

'There is no great hurry for your answer,' Rocco drawled complacently, his chiselled mouth curving in a confident grin. 'How about I call for you at seven-thirty again on

Thursday? We can repeat this delightful meal over again, and you can give me your answer then.'

Once more he reached across the table and caught her hands in his, and, turning them both palm up, he added, 'As for the Will—the property in Italy—I'm sure the Contessa will come to some equitable agreement over that as well. You really have nothing to worry about.' And, bending his head, he lifted her cupped hands and pressed a kiss in each palm. Marlene felt the effect of his kisses right down to her toes, and could not have pulled her hands free even if she had wanted to. But at that precise moment she had no such inclination. Instead, she looked down at his bent head and had an overwhelming urge to run her fingers through his thick black hair. She shivered, and Rocco looked up at her through long black lashes, his dark eyes gleaming with sensuality.

'Rossi was a very lucky man, but he is dead. It is time you cut all ties with the past and moved on. I want you...' he drawled throatily.

She caught her breath, and in that second wanted Rocco more than any man she had ever met. Until he spoke again.

'I want you to let me help you do that.' He sat back, freeing her hands. 'Believe me, you and Paul need not visit Italy or meet the Contessa. I will arrange everything.'

Marlene had not blushed in years, but around this man she seemed to be doing it all the time, she thought with rising fury, knowing that he had deliberately played on her attraction to him, hesitating over his 'I want you' simply to tease her.

She looked across at him and her mouth tightened in a grim line. He looked like the cat that had swallowed the canary. In fact, she would not have been surprised if he had licked his lips, so confident was he that he had her exactly where he wanted her. It would have been funny except that she found little amusement in knowing that the only man she had been attracted to in years was trying to cheat her.

Obviously he thought that seducing her into staying in England and so forfeiting the property by the terms of the Will would be a whole lot easier than trying the same thing in Italy and then having to prove her an unfit mother. He was a devious swine. No mistake. But she had been deceived by a man before and had vowed never again. The self-knowledge gave her the courage to continue with her plan.

Wide-eyed, and forcing her expression into one of suitable awe, she simpered, 'It is kind of you to offer to help me. But I hardly know you. I really could not put you to so much trouble. I will check with this firm tomorrow, as you said—' she carefully placed the card in her purse '—but I don't think I should rush into anything.' And she meant it both ways. Business and pleasure.

Deliberately folding her arms beneath her bust, she rested on the table and leant towards Rocco, revealing an even greater amount of cleavage than her too small dress already allowed. She saw his eyes drop down and the gleam of lust in their darkening depths, and she hid a little smile before dropping her bombshell.

'You see, Rocco, Paolo asked me to take his son to Italy, to give the boy a taste of his father's birthplace, and he reaffirmed his request in his Will. I could not possibly defy the wishes of a dead man, so I have booked our seats and Paul and I fly out on Saturday. As I am going to be in Italy when the board meeting takes place I might as well go. And after that I might consider selling my shares, but not before.'

The confusion in his expression was a joy to behold. He did not know where to look—the ripe curve of her breast or her beautiful, seemingly innocent face. His lips compressed and temper flared briefly in his black eyes, then his gaze narrowed assessingly on her lovely face.

'Let me get this straight. Your flight is booked, you are leaving at the weekend and you intend turning up at the board meeting?'

'Yes.' Marlene sat back and, tilting her head to one side, added, 'It will be quite an adventure—a holiday in a foreign country. Paul and I are really looking forward to it.'

'But you don't even speak the language,' he grated, his exasperation showing.

'I've bought a phrase book,' Marlene shot back airily. 'We'll manage just fine. I believe Amalfi is lovely at this time of year.'

'You have been busy since yesterday.' His eyes narrowed acutely on her face, as if he was trying to read what was behind her bland smile. Then, abruptly pushing his chair back, he stood up. 'Let's get out of here,' he said, and, signalling to the waiter for the bill, glanced back down at Marlene.

'I am beginning to think there is more to you than meets the eye.' His gaze lingered on the soft swell of her firm breasts and rather daring cleavage. 'And god knows what *is* on show would tempt the Pope himself,' he declared, pure male frustration lacing his voice.

Marlene hid a grin as she meekly got to her feet. Smoothing down the skirt of her dress over her slim hips, she said, 'I thought you would be pleased, Rocco. You did imply you wanted to get to know me better,' she could not resist taunting.

He slanted her a black, flaring glance before dropping a handful of notes on the table, and then, taking her arm, urged her towards the door. 'So I did,' he murmured, almost to himself, as they walked out of the dining room. 'But I rather hoped to keep it discreet. And somehow, with you in Italy...' He shook his dark head and, turning, caught her by the shoulders and looked into her eyes. 'Are you sure you want to meet Rossi's legitimate family? Expose young Paul to what might be a negative experience? They have to suffer you as a shareholder, but they don't have to like it. Be sensible—let me arrange a deal with the Contessa for the villa, for everything.'

Marlene could feel the warmth of his hands on her shoulders, and the subtle male scent of him filled her nostrils. She felt dizzy, staring up into his tanned, attractive face, and for a second she wanted to agree to whatever he said. He looked so genuinely concerned for her and her young brother. A rush of cool air as someone entered the restaurant brought her back to her senses. 'No, it's all arranged,' she said, and, shrugging off his hands, she headed for the exit.

Sitting in the passenger seat of the car, she cast a sidelong glance at Rocco as he guided the vehicle expertly through the twisting back roads towards her home. His hawk-like profile, his long fingers curled loosely but in complete control around the steering wheel, the movement of the muscles in his thighs so close to her own as he shifted through the gears all had an unsettling effect on her brain, already overheated with champagne. She found herself imagining what his handsome features would look like taut with passion, what his hands would feel like controlling her... And then an uneasy thought struck her. He was a dynamic, powerful man and yet he had given up far too easily, with hardly a murmur...

Sensing her scrutiny, Rocco sent her a brief glance, one dark brow arched quizzically. She shook her head and, swallowing hard, looked away. He was remarkably quiet, and she could feel the sexual tension building between them with every mile they travelled. But perhaps it was just her over-fertile imagination, she told herself sternly, and made herself look out of the side window until they arrived at her home.

'Are you going to ask me in for coffee?' Rocco demanded as he held out a hand to help her out of the car.

Marlene put her hand in his and stood up. 'No' trembled on her tongue as her fingers curved around his, delighting in the sudden warmth of his grasp, but the sound that came out of her mouth was, 'Yes.' Hastily she pulled her hand free and darted for the door.

Her fingers fumbled with the big old key and Rocco's hand closed over hers again. He took the key from her unresisting fingers and opened the door. She stepped over the threshold with Rocco at her side. She had left a lamp lit on the hall table, and somehow the panelled hall suddenly seemed very intimate. She dropped her bag on the table as Rocco closed the door behind them.

'Welcoming,' Rocco murmured and, swinging her round to face him with a hand on her shoulder, he tilted her chin with his index finger. 'I wonder if the hostess is as welcoming?' His voice was a husky purr.

Marlene watched immobile, a prisoner of her own desire, as his dark head bent lower and his firm mouth settled softly over hers. The kiss was like no other she had experienced. His lips swept light as a butterfly wing, then withdrew, only to return and nibble at her full bottom lip. His tongue traced the outline of her mouth and her lips parted on a sigh as she leant into the hard warmth of his large body, her eyes closing as his tongue sought the inner secrets of her mouth.

She felt heat pool low in her stomach, and she knew she had been waiting for this all evening, however much she tried to deny it. She wanted his kiss, his taste and a whole lot more—everything he had to offer, she finally admitted, and surrendered to the pleasure he promised.

Her tongue started a voyage of discovery of its own. She

loved the warmth of his mouth and, lifting a slender hand, she cupped one side of his face, the slightly rough texture a tactile delight. She loved kissing him. His hard, firm lips were like no other man's in the universe, she was convinced. She delighted in the pressure of his hands on her shoulders, the way he deepened the kiss, probing and possessive. Her other arm snaked up around his neck and she threaded her fingers through the silky black hair of his head, something else she had been wanting to do all evening.

He lifted his mouth from hers, finally allowing her to catch her breath. His large hands slid from her shoulders— one to her waist, the other to cup her bottom—holding her hard against him, making her aware of his bulging masculine arousal. She looked up through her lashes into his brilliant black eyes, her heart racing, her lips swollen from his kisses, her mind blank.

'I knew it would be like this,' Rocco drawled huskily, and with a brief, fierce hug he eased her away from him. 'But not yet, my sexy siren.'

Marlene was not sure she liked 'sexy siren'. A moment later she knew she did not as slowly she regained her senses. She could not help being aware that Rocco, with a brief, bland smile at her flushed face, had recovered from their passionate interlude remarkably quickly, while she was still shaken and totally mortified by her spineless surrender.

'This time business first,' he said, and, brushing past her, he opened the door into the kitchen. 'You make the coffee and then we will put all our cards on the table.'

Following him into her own kitchen, Marlene battled to recover her former poise. If looks could have killed he would have had a dagger in his back.

'Agreed, Marlene?' he prompted.

'I don't know what you mean.' Was he suspicious? 'All our cards on the table' sounded ominous, but still she added coolly, 'I already have.' And, crossing the kitchen floor on none too steady legs, she set about making the coffee—without looking at Rocco.

'I think not.'

Ignoring his comment, she took two cups from the cupboard above her head and the milk from the refrigerator; the sugar bowl was standing on the bench.

'Amazing—so much activity for a cup of coffee.' Rocco's cynically voiced comment scraped over her frayed nerves. 'One could almost believe you were nervous. Now, why is that, I wonder? You're hardly the shrinking violet type, afraid to be alone with a man.'

Slowly she turned around and leant against the bench for support. He was sitting with legs astride one of the pine chairs, his arms folded on the high back, propping up his dark head, looking incredibly sexy with his black hair ruffled from her earlier ministrations. 'You said you wanted coffee, and that is all you are getting,' she snapped, resenting the way he had made her feel with a simple kiss. Well, not so simple! she admitted in her mind. But seeing him sitting there so at ease when her insides were still churning was infuriating.

'What are you so afraid of, Marlene?' he asked silkily. 'Surely not of me? I'm simply your basic man, and we both know your experience in that department.'

'Nothing—I'm not afraid of anything at all.' Turning back to the percolator, she quickly filled two cups with the steaming brew. Basic in his desires, certainly, but there was nothing in the least simple about Rocco Andretti, she reminded herself forcibly, before asking, 'Black or white?'

'Black, no sugar—and come and sit down. You're hovering there like a humming-bird poised for flight.'

Marlene stirred sugar and milk into her own cup with obsessive determination, until finally she could delay no longer without melting the spoon! Taking a deep breath, she picked up both cups and turned around. She carefully placed a cup in front of Rocco on the scrubbed table, before crossing to the opposite side of the table and sitting down. She cradled her cup in her hands and looked at him over the top of it. He lifted his to his mouth and drained it in one go.

'Now that's out of the way. Not bad coffee for an Englishwoman, actually,' he murmured, and swinging back round on the chair, he leant his elbows on the table and fixed her with dark, intent eyes. 'I am going to be honest with you, Marlene.'

That will be a first! She took a deep swallow of her coffee, thinking for a horrible moment that she had spoken out loud. But Rocco was still speaking, so obviously she had not. Thank God! She needed all her wits about her to deal with him… No easy task, when a simple look from his deep brown eyes had the power to make her skin burn.

'The offer I made on behalf of the Contessa for the shares was perfectly fair, as you will find out when you check tomorrow. But as for the villa, and the conditions set out in Rossi's will, it must be obvious to you the whole idea is ridiculous.'

'Ridiculous?' She tilted her head to one side, studying him curiously. 'Why ridiculous? It seems perfectly straightforward to me, but no doubt you, with your superior intellect, know better,' she drawled sarcastically.

He had to be the most casual lawyer she had ever met. His firm had drawn up the will; if it was so ridiculous he should have advised his client at the time, not come here after the man was dead and try to negate it. But then maybe Italian lawyers were like that! What did she know? As a student she had visited Italy twice, once to Florence and once to Venice, and she had spent most of her time in the art galleries. She knew next to nothing about Italian law.

'We both know your sudden desire to fulfil Rossi's wish

for your son to spend two months at the villa in Amalfi every year for the next five years is simply so you can claim the property for Paul. True, it is the condition laid down in the will. But even you cannot be that mercenary.'

'Maybe I am,' she said, stung by his insult. Actually, she had no idea how much the villa was worth and cared even less. She was going to Italy to fulfil her own promise to Paolo Rossi. She had more than enough money of her own, but Rocco didn't know that…

'What kind of mother are you?' His tone was biting, cynical. 'Have you thought of the harm it might do the boy? The unpleasantness that will ensue? The Contessa will make sure everyone knows the boy is a bastard and the family will certainly not recognise him, even while they make sure you adhere to the absolute letter of the will.'

'She would do that?' Marlene exclaimed in disgust.

'And worse,' Rocco said flatly. 'Southern Italy is nothing like England. Unmarried mothers are still frowned on. The Contessa is a leader in society; she can make it very difficult for you and the boy, if not downright impossible. You seem to love the boy, but two months can seem a very long time with only a child to talk to. Surely you can see it would be much easier for everyone involved if you took the Contessa's offer for your shares, and I'm sure I can persuade her to reach monetary solution—compensation— in the question of the villa as well. You need never set foot in Italy.'

Stunned by his duplicity, Marlene drained her coffee-cup and replaced it on the table, not daring to look at him. It saddened her to think that the man sitting opposite her, the man she was undeniably seriously attracted to, was so lacking in any sense of loyalty. He was Rossi's lawyer, and by his own admission a friend. Yet he cared nothing for his late client's wishes and would quite happily betray them to please the Contessa. Even going so far as to try and buy

Marlene's shares in the company for half of what they were worth. It was despicable behaviour, and if it wasn't illegal it ought to be…

'Well, have we a basis for a deal?' Rocco's deep voice broke the lengthening silence.

Marlene shook her head in disbelief. She was beginning to see why Paolo had spent most of his time in England, as far away from his estranged wife as he could get. The woman was obviously a first-class manipulator. She had to be to have persuaded a man like Rocco Andretti to go against his lawyer's training and do her bidding.

'Was that shake of your head a no?' Rocco demanded sharply.

'I haven't decided yet.' Her lips twisted in a cynical smile. 'I need to know more about the family first. Tell me…' She pinned him with a gimlet gaze. 'The aristocracy has been defunct in Italy for years. Why did Signora Rossi insist on retaining her title of Contessa?' And, disgusted by the whole sordid mess, Marlene shoved back her chair and got to her feet, not bothering to hide her anger. 'Descendant of Lucretia Borgia, was she? She certainly sounds like it.'

Rocco looked up into her glittering gold eyes, his own lit with amusement, then he chuckled. 'Nasty, Marlene.'

'Humph,' she snorted inelegantly, crossing to the kitchen sink with her empty cup. 'But probably true, from what I have heard.'

'Your snide comments are not going to deter me, Marlene—and, let's face it, you are hardly in a position to judge the woman.' He had joined her at the sink and, catching her by the arm, he swung her around to face him. 'Let's not pretend you are the injured party in all this. You have done very well out of Rossi over the years. We both know exactly what kind of woman you are. You want money, and I am prepared to see you get a fair settlement.'

His hands slid up her arms and tightened on her shoulders. His closeness, the masculine warmth of him tantalised her senses even as anger at his misguided assumptions about her coloured her cheeks. She glanced helplessly up into his hard face, unable to find a cutting response. His hands caressed her bare arms, raising goosebumps on her over-sensitive skin. She wanted to break away, but her feet seemed glued to the floor. His mouth descended and she waited for his kiss, but instead he continued talking.

'And I can see you get a lot more if you like,' he declared huskily, his mouth brushing her brow. 'I'm also quite prepared to take up where Paolo left off, and keep you as my mistress.' For a stunned moment she was mesmerised by the sensuous invitation in his dark eyes. 'You will find me a very generous lover,' he drawled seductively as his other hand cupped her chin and tilted her head back. 'Both financially and physically, I promise. What do you say?'

Erotic images of his large body, naked and poised over her own, filled Marlene's imagination. She swayed towards him. Then she recognised the triumphant curl of his lip and at the same moment realised that he was going to kiss her. If she let herself be caught in the sexual web the man spun so easily around her she would be no better than what he said she was!

It took every ounce of will-power she possessed to jerk her head free of his hand and take a swift sideways step. Ignoring his crude proposition, she shot across to the door. She turned and leant against the doorframe; she needed the support because her legs were shaking. 'I think you'd better leave, Signor Andretti,' she said bluntly.

'Not the response I expected. But maybe you're right. Best to get all you can from the last love before taking on a new one,' he offered cynically, and in a few lithe strides he had covered the space between them. 'I will call on Thursday for your answer on the shares.'

'You can have it now. No, no and no again.'

'So adamant and so foolish.' His hard eyes sought hers. 'You realise the Rossi family have every right to contest the will in court and stop you getting the villa? They don't have to win—they can tie you up in litigation for years and cost you a fortune. You could end up with nothing at all. Maybe even lose this little business.'

Bravely she held his gaze. 'And you would advise the Contessa to do that, of course.'

'Maybe... Dare you take the chance?' he demanded silkily, giving nothing away.

Perhaps she *was* being foolish. But there was no way she was allowing this man to intimidate her into breaking her promise to Paolo. She had a very personal reason and it was not just for Paul; it was her own private secret.

'Maybe,' she parroted sarcastically. 'But I have no intention of changing my mind. I think we have said all we need to say, so, if you don't mind, I'm tired.' And, turning her back on him, she walked into the hall, intent on getting rid of him.

'But I do mind,' Rocco drawled, and, clasping her around her waist, he spun her to face him. 'I never leave my dates without a goodnight kiss.'

Before Marlene could object, his dark head swooped down and his hard mouth covered hers in a long, drugging kiss. He's doing it again, was her last coherent thought for some time.

'As I thought.' His deep voice rumbled in her ear.

She raised dazed eyes to his. She could feel the pressure of his linked hands at the base of her spine, and a different kind of strictly masculine pressure on her stomach. She licked her lips and felt the swollen contours of her mouth. She should have been disgusted, fighting him off, but all she could feel was the heat of his huge body, the pounding of her blood through her veins, the quivering of every nerve-end under her skin.

'As you thought, what?' she muttered, her passion-clouded eyes drowning in Rocco's glittering black gaze.

'It gets better and better between us with every kiss, every touch. The chemistry is dynamite.' He moved his hips suggestively against her and Marlene bit back a groan. 'We both know it, Marlene. Why deny ourselves?' His lips teased her cheek and one strong hand slid over her hip and down her thigh.

'Deny what?' she mumbled inanely.

'The pleasure we can give each other.' His mouth dropped lower and fastened on her softly parted lips. His tongue traced their swollen fullness with slow eroticism and Marlene's hands linked behind his head as she gave herself up once more to the wonder of his kiss. 'You want me,' he husked against her mouth. 'You ache to feel me buried deep inside you, and I ache to be there.'

In some deep recess of her brain Marlene knew she should deny him, but her body had other ideas. She felt his hand on her naked thigh and the trembling started deep inside her. She felt his long fingers inching higher. She had no idea when he had lifted up her skirt, and didn't really care—until what he was saying registered...

CHAPTER FOUR

'FORGET about the past.' His lips trailed kisses around the curve of her jaw. 'Forget about business.' His lips found her neck. 'Forget about the will.' His tongue licked the pulse beating out of control in the hollow of her throat. 'I will take care of everything and make sure you don't lose by it. But first, Marlene—' his dark head lifted '—show me the way to your bedroom, sweetheart.'

An icy tendril of reality pierced her fuddled brain and Marlene tensed in his arms, suddenly aware of the intimacy she was inviting, encouraging a man like Rocco when they were alone in the house. The sensual mist cleared from her golden eyes and she really studied his passion-darkened features.

His jet-black eyes gleamed with lust and a tinge of male triumph. He looked like some big, sleek jungle predator that had just cornered its prey and was anticipating the delight that was to follow. Her arms fell from his neck and she grasped the first thing she could find for protection— the china fruit bowl on the table beside her. Lifting it in her hand, she held it shoulder-high like a shield, apples and oranges cascading around them.

'Let go of me, you great brute, or I'll brain you!' she cried.

An apple bounced off his chest. Rocco automatically let go of her to catch it. He missed!

Marlene had an insane desire to laugh, but choked back the chuckle rising in her throat.

Rocco stepped back, the puzzlement in his eyes a treat to see. He looked at her set face, down at the fruit rolling around the floor, then back to her face. 'You are joking. Yes?' He shook his head in amazement. 'You have to be. You were with me every step of the way.'

'No.' Forcing down the turbulent emotions flowing through her body and thinking furiously, Marlene continued, 'I simply wanted to see how far you would go to help your clients. It seems even as far as using your body.' The memory of Rocco and Caterina in the garden, planning for him to seduce her, came back to her and gave her the strength to keep her voice reasonably calm. 'Is there a name for a male prostitute?' she queried lightly, while inside she was still shaking.

His black eyes glittered with fury. His face turned red, his big hands reached towards her, curled into fists, then dropped to clench and unclench at his sides. He swore long and violently in his own language—curses that would have made a Naples docker blush.

Marlene had to stifle a gasp of outrage. She dared not let him know she understood. Not yet! Not until she had unravelled the mystery of the crooked share dealings, she told herself firmly. Instead she waited until he finally stopped to draw breath, then commanded bluntly, 'Please just go.'

'Don't worry, I will,' he snarled. 'If you were a man I would have knocked you flat on your back for that insult. But then I should have expected as much from a woman who is only one step up from a prostitute herself.'

'Now who is insulting whom?' Marlene queried cynically.

'Your kind cannot be insulted, and as for helping you with the Contessa—forget I ever said it. Do whatever the hell you want. A bitch like you hasn't a hope of winning against a real lady.' And, swinging on his heel, he pulled open the heavy oak door. 'See you in court!' he flung over his shoulder as he stepped out into the cool night air.

'Italy, yes. Court, never!' Marlene yelled back, unable to contain her anger any longer, and slammed the door behind him.

Trudging upstairs to bed, Marlene couldn't decide whether it was the word 'bedroom' or 'sweetheart' which had brought her back to her senses earlier. Or perhaps, more honestly, the fact that his long fingers had reached the edge of her lace panties had made her panic. She sighed as she walked into her bedroom. Whatever it had been, she doubted she would ever have to fight off the forceful Rocco Andretti's advances again.

Somehow the thought did not give her any satisfaction. She traced her swollen lips with one finger; she could still feel the touch of his mouth on hers. She sighed again with regret. Rocco would be a fantastic lover; the pity of it was she was not likely to find out just how fantastic after to-night's episode…

The captain of the aircraft had kindly allowed the only youngster on the plane to visit the flight deck. Marlene looked up from her magazine and grinned as Paul came running back down the aisle of the aircraft, a stewardess a few steps behind him.

The doubts she had suffered at the thought of Paul's first flight had been dispelled the minute they had reached the airport. The boy had hardly been able to contain his excitement, and a million questions had tumbled from his mouth before they'd even got on the plane. And now, to top it all off, he had actually met the pilot. Her grin broke into a chuckle as he threw himself over her knees to reach his seat by the window, chattering nineteen to the dozen.

'Mar, it was huge—and all lights and sticks and knobs and everything. And I met the pilot and the navi… naval…navig…' The word defeated him. 'And I'm going to be a pilot, Mar.'

Still smiling, Marlene gave him a swift hug. 'I'm sure you will one day, darling.' Reaching across his small body, she fastened his seat belt, and her own. 'But for now, my pet, content yourself with looking out of the window and watching the plane land. We're almost there.'

She had to appear calm and in control for Paul's sake, but inside her stomach was churning with nerves. It wasn't the flight making her nervous, she acknowledged wryly; she actually liked flying; it was the thought of what she had to do in the next few weeks.

The day after her last encounter with Rocco Andretti she had taken a short trip to London and talked to a business associate. The information she had learned was invaluable, and the steps she had put in motion for further information should very quickly succeed.

The following day an official-looking airmail envelope had arrived at her home. Inside had been a rather long-winded letter from the Italian law firm of Andretti, but basically all it had said was that the Contessa would not contest young Paul's right to the villa in Amalfi providing he adhered to the conditions laid down. Paul had to spend two months in Amalfi every year for five years.

But what worried Marlene was the fact that underneath all the legal terminology lay the implication that in return Marlene was to give the Contessa first option on buying her shares in Rossi International and also on buying the villa, if, as Paul's guardian, Marlene decided it would be in his best interest to sell. Also included with the letter had been a map and directions on how to reach the villa, plus the information that the caretaker and his wife would be expecting them.

All very civilised, so why did she have a sneaky suspicion that it was a little *too* civilised? Perhaps the hired help were a pair of psychopaths employed to make their visit so horrible she would be more than grateful to sell the house or, worse, decide never to return to the place, and so the villa would automatically return to the Contessa.

God! She was getting paranoid! Marlene sighed and glanced tenderly down at the small dark head of her brother. In fact, yesterday she had said as much to her own solicitor, and had queried whether it was really worth the bother. She was a wealthy woman in her own right, and of course she would always provide for Paul. But her solicitor had been horrified, and had mentioned the value of the real estate involved as being over two million. His advice was to accept immediately as a prelude to securing young Paul's future.

The seat belt warning lit up in the cabin and Marlene adjusted first Paul's and then her own. The plane was preparing to land. Well, there was no turning back now, she thought resignedly. Let battle commence!

Andretti had been clever and covered all the bases, Marlene thought cynically as the plane touched down, but whether or not he and his friends could disguise the fraud in the Rossi empire so easily remained to be seen. The more she knew of the man, the more convinced she became that Andretti had something to do with the trouble in the late Paolo Rossi's company, and she was determined to find out. Even if it did mean she had to act like a woolly-headed bimbo for a while.

She looked out of the window, her eyes squinting at the glare from the midday sun. So this was southern Italy, she thought wryly, her gaze flickering over Naples airport. She had never been to this part of Italy before. When her mother was alive, Paolo had never wanted to subject her to the animosity of his family here, and had rarely mentioned the place. It had only been after the death of her mother, and with his own health failing, that he had begun to talk about his young son seeing the country of his father's birth.

Marlene smiled as she carried Paul down the aircraft

steps, but her golden eyes were hazed with sorrow and she murmured a prayer under her breath. 'Well, Paolo, we're here, Paul and I, as I promised you, and I will try and rescue your company and your good name. May you rest in peace.'

Half an hour later, she walked hand in hand with Paul through the exit gate at Naples airport, and stopped abruptly, her eyes clashing with deep, glittering brown.

'Welcome to Italy, Marlene.' The dark, sexy voice was all too familiar.

She had not been expecting a reception committee, but three feet in front of her stood Rocco Andretti, casually attired in white trousers and a short-sleeved, open-necked silk-knit shirt. There was a sort of dynamic power about him—a vitality that jolted Marlene to the depths of her soul every time she saw him.

Ignoring the frisson of fear—or was it excitement?—that travelled down her spine, and the inexplicable urge to run, she forced her gaze away from him and to the man standing by his side, a very much older man, small, dark and wizened, wearing what looked like a chauffeur's uniform. Her hand tightened on Paul's. Pride and determination to get the better of Andretti gave her the strength to reply in a cool voice.

'Thank you. But there was no need to meet us. The directions were quite explicit.' She straightened her shoulders, adjusting the strap of her bag with her free hand. 'Even I could understand them,' she added with veiled sarcasm. At the same time she was glad she had chosen to wear a plain blue denim skirt and a cropped top for the flight; they reinforced the unsophisticated image she wanted to portray.

'Roc! Roc!' Paul cried. 'I've been on a plane—a huge plane.' And, pulling his hand free of Marlene's, the little boy dashed to the man's side, tugging at his trouser-leg for his attention.

Rocco swooped down and picked Paul up in his arms. 'I know, young man, and judging by the smile on your face you enjoyed it. You can tell me all about the flight in a moment, but first let's get your mum's luggage and get out of here.'

After swinging Paul around once, he deposited him back on the ground. Straightening to his full height, he looked at Marlene, and so missed the puzzled look on the little boy's face and his murmured, 'Mum? But—'

Marlene didn't! She burst into speech. 'Very kind of you, Mr Andretti. So unexpected. Please introduce me to your friend.' And, turning to the little man, she flashed him a brilliant smile. 'I am Marlene Johanson, and this is Paul. Happy to meet you.'

She was gushing but she didn't care. Paul had almost betrayed the fact that she was not his mother, and that was a secret she desperately needed to keep. Italian law was still a mystery to her and, although she was Paul's guardian, his sister Caterina was equally related to him. She was taking no chances on the Rossi family taking Paul over.

The little man broke into a torrent of Italian, all of which Marlene understood perfectly, and she could feel the colour rising in her cheeks at his effusive compliments on her beauty and her marvellous young son. She held out her hand and grasped his nut-brown fingers, and simply continued smiling.

'This is Aldo, the chauffeur-gardener-handyman. His wife is the housekeeper at the villa. Unfortunately neither of them speak much English,' Rocco said smoothly. 'Try saying, *Piacere, Aldo*. That will suffice.' His dark gaze intent on her smiling face, he added, 'Though the way you smiled at him has probably made him your slave for life already. You can't resist ensnaring old men, can you?'

Ignoring Rocco's barbed comment, she slowly repeated the Italian salutation, and was rewarded by a gap-toothed grin from Aldo.

'Let's get in the car before the old fool salivates at your feet,' Rocco said curtly, before instructing Aldo to collect the luggage and meet them outside. Then, catching Marlene by the elbow, and grasping young Paul with his other hand, he almost frogmarched them out of the airport.

The touch of his long fingers on her bare flesh had the same disturbing effect on Marlene as always, and she wanted to pull free. But she thought better of it when she saw the bustle outside. The heat was stifling and the air rang with the sound of arguing and gesticulating Italians. Taxis darted all over, and row upon row of tour buses were lined up, with hundreds of tourists either alighting or embarking.

'Gosh, it's hot, Mar!' Paul exclaimed, his eyes, huge as saucers, darting all over, trying to take in so many new sights and sounds at once.

'It will be much cooler once we get in the car,' Rocco answered him. 'It is air-conditioned.'

As if on cue, a long white Mercedes drew up in front of them with Aldo at the wheel. How had he managed to collect the luggage and fight his way through the traffic in barely five minutes? Marlene could not begin to understand. And as she slid into the back seat of the car, and Rocco slammed the door behind her, she had a sinking sensation that there was an awful lot about the present situation she did not understand. And she was never likely to, if Rocco had his way.

The two-hour car journey was a nightmare. Aldo appeared to be the proof of every bad joke about Italian drivers. He shot out of the car park with a squeal of rubber and Marlene was thrown against Paul, who thought it was hilarious. To Marlene's mind, the only saving grace about the journey was the fact that at least she didn't have to sit beside Rocco. He had taken the front passenger seat and left the back for herself and Paul.

The scenery was magnificent as the road wound around the coast towards Sorrento—cliffs on one side and the deep blue of the Mediterranean on the other. She might have appreciated it, and the couple of gems of information Rocco imparted—pointing out the great health spa hotel and the original Bikini Beach, with its tiny artificial island with one palm tree, equally artificial—except for the fact that Aldo never seemed to have two hands on the wheel at any one time. For some reason he drove in the middle of the road, swerving from every approaching car. On top of that he carried on a non-stop conversation with Rocco on the relative merits of Italian football teams.

When they hit the final leg of the journey along the notorious Amalfi coast road, it took all of Marlene's willpower not to yell at Aldo to slow down. Meanwhile, Paul thought it was brilliant. His nose pressed to the window with childish delight, totally without fear, he described the sheer cliffs falling hundreds of feet to the sea. To Marlene's horror he declared that he felt like a bird and was sure he could fly off them!

It was with a sigh of relief that she recognised they were slowly getting nearer the sea, and when the road finally wound down into Amalfi, and they drove along the harbour of the small port, she finally began to breathe easily again, but not for long...

'Why have we stopped here?' she asked, looking around with interest. There was a small rocky beach and a harbour, where a ferry was just arriving, and on the opposite side of the road were a few shops and terraced houses. 'I don't see a villa here.'

Rocco swung around in his seat, one arm over the back,

and grinned. 'The villa is not here. But you need a drink before going any further.'

'Drink? What for?' But she was talking to fresh air. Rocco was out of the car and holding open the door for her.

'Hurry up, Marlene. We'll grab a drink at a café in the square. But we do want to arrive before dark.'

She slid out of the car with more haste than elegance and, leaning back in, lifted Paul out and onto his feet. Keeping a firm grasp on his little hand, she faced up to Rocco.

'What do you mean, *we* have to arrive before dark? Just what are you playing at, Signor Andretti? As far as I am concerned there is no valid reason for you to accompany us at all. And I certainly do not need a drink.' Marlene looked at him coldly, summoning all her strength to meet his dark eyes, and his lips twisted wryly.

'You will! There is a reception committee waiting to meet you, and I thought I'd better give you a few pointers on what is expected of you.'

'What?' she exclaimed in horror. According to the letter she had received, the villa was solely for her and Paul. Now Rocco was saying something quite different.

'Let me explain. The house is about another ten minutes from here, but I thought it would be better for you and Paul if we broke the journey for a while. Aldo can take Paul along the pier to watch the boats dock and we can talk in private over a drink. The Contessa and Caterina are at the villa awaiting your arrival. The Contessa, being the lady she is, decided it was only polite to meet you both and make sure you are comfortable as guests in what is still her house.'

'How very civilised,' Marlene said drily. 'But that still does not explain your presence.'

'As neither of them speaks very good English and you

speak no Italian, I will act as interpreter. Break the ice, as I believe you say. Satisfied?' And he smiled, that slow, sexy smile she had seen so many times before.

Marlene was caught by her own deceit. He was right, she thought, swallowing hard. She did need a drink before meeting the female members of the Rossi family. Why did they want to meet her and Paul? In the letter she had received with the directions there had been no mention of the Contessa or Caterina visiting the villa at the same time as herself. It was worrying. Was this their first step in trying to gain control of Paul? Plus, she could not admit to understanding Italian—not yet. So she would have to suffer Rocco's company. Not something she relished, when she only had to look at him to go weak at the knees.

She stared dumbly up at him, noting the glinting triumph behind his grin. She felt trapped, like a mouse by a big cat, tension in every line of her slender body at this new threat. Then suddenly his smile broadened in real humour. His white teeth sparkled against the tanned skin of his face and he reached out to brush a stray tendril of hair from her brow. She shivered and the hard lips quirked.

'I frighten you, Marlene, and I don't see why. I am not threatening to kidnap you, but simply to take you for a drink, give you time to freshen up and then continue our ride.' His deep voice softened. 'And if a different kind of ride appeals to you you only have to ask. I'm your man.'

'You are disgusting,' she said, her face scarlet.

His large hand reached out and caught her slender wrist. 'No, merely stating the obvious when confronted by a beautiful woman.' His lips quirked again. 'Plus, I love teasing you. But come on, we can continue this debate over a glass of wine—or something stronger if you prefer.' And, dropping to his haunches, he ruffled Paul's hair. 'What say you, Paul? Will you go with Aldo to watch the ferry arrive while

I talk to your mother? Aldo will buy you an ice cream, OK?'

Paul looked up at Marlene. 'Why does—?'

She just knew he was going to ask, 'Why does he call you my mother?' and, bending down, she did the only thing she could think of to shut him up. She kissed him quickly. 'Do as Rocco says, please, Paul, and we will be back here in…' She glanced sideways at Rocco, who was standing again, and watching her with a rather odd look in his dark eyes.

'Twenty minutes should do it,' Rocco offered.

'See you in twenty minutes,' she said, and, standing up herself, she waited as Rocco explained the arrangement to Aldo. Marlene heaved a sigh of relief when Paul quite happily put his little hand in Aldo's.

Sitting at the roadside café in the centre of Amalfi, she sipped a glass of mellow red wine and gazed in pleasure at the sight before her. On the opposite side of the steeply rising road stood a church, and in keeping with the hilly contours of the place the approach to it was up a vast stone stairway. The steps must run into the hundreds, she mused, and then gasped in delight as the church doors at the top were opened and out came a wedding party.

The stream of guests were all in their very best clothes, the men in dark suits and ties that looked alien to their tanned, weatherbeaten features. The bride was a local girl— Marlene had gathered as much from the conversation of the waiters. The girl looked impossibly young and innocent, dressed in yards and yards of floating white lace, her black hair entwined with flowers and her long veil off her face and trailing behind her as she descended the steps with her new husband.

'Poor fool,' Rocco remarked, with a cynical twist to his hard mouth.

'Why? They make a lovely couple and they look very happy.'

'Surely you're not advocating marriage, Marlene?' he drawled mockingly. 'With your record.'

She shot him an angry glance and took a deep drink of the red wine. What would he know? she thought bitterly. He was the sort of man who took what he wanted where women were concerned, but kept the same hoary old double standard. Showing only contempt for women who did the same. He was such a male chauvinist, and, draining her glass, she could not resist goading him.

'Certainly. I think it's a marvellous institution, and I am actively looking for a husband.' Suddenly she saw an opportunity to put Rocco off pursuing her for good. Let him think she was trawling for a husband and he'd run a mile. So, modifying his words of earlier with 'marriage' instead of 'ride', she continued, 'And if marriage appeals to you you only have to ask.' She licked her full bottom lip with the tip of her tongue and leant slightly towards him. 'I'm your woman.'

He got the connection immediately. '*Touché*, Marlene! But no way!' he shot back.

'Shame.' She sighed in mock sorrow. 'And here was I thinking what excellent husband material you would make—a wealthy lawyer, and you're kind to children and ladies in distress.'

'I doubt you have ever been in distress in your life. The more I see of you, the less I believe you are the blonde airhead you portray. You're much too mercenary and much too good at it,' Rocco opined cynically, his dark eyes narrowing on her lovely face.

Warning bells rang in Marlene's head. She did not like his intense scrutiny or the speculative gleam in his eyes. 'I'm glad to know you think I'm good at something,' she said lightly, and slanted him a flirtatious smile, hoping to divert him. She succeeded...

'Oh, I know very well your best attribute, Marlene—warming a man's bed. And, as I have mentioned before, I'd be more than happy to make you my mistress—a straightforward, honest relationship. But wife—never. I have yet to see a happy marriage. My own father always had a mistress, and I hate to disillusion you about Rossi, but he had many mistresses before you.'

Marlene knew why, but she was not about to tell Rocco. 'Maybe,' she said, with a negligent toss of her blonde head, and, dropping her voice to a husky murmur, she added outrageously, 'But you have to admit he did save the best till last.' And, pursing her lips, she mouthed a kiss to him.

'God! You're shameless,' Rocco said sternly, but she saw his lips twitch in amusement and the brown eyes glint with humour.

'Unless I miss my guess, exactly how you like your women,' she shot back teasingly.

'And you are *going* to be my woman, Marlene.' He reached across the table and ran a long finger down the soft curve of her cheek, then casually flicked her under the chin. 'And you're going to love every minute—and that's a promise.' His dark eyes met and held hers.

She wanted to deny his comment, but somehow the words would not come. She watched as he raised the glass in his hand and drained the wine, without ever breaking eye contact with her. He held her mesmerised by the sheer force of his piercing gaze. The noise and bustle around them faded into nothing; she was aware only of Rocco—aware with every atom of her being. It was uncanny, magic, and it was only when he placed the glass on the table and turned to signal to the passing waiter that she was able to break free from his sensual spell.

She was frightened... For the first time in her life she

felt frightened—not of the man, but of herself. She hardly registered his words.

'Now to business. As I told you, the Contessa and Caterina are staying at the villa for a night or two. Until the five years are up, and the villa belongs outright to young Paul, they are perfectly entitled to use it. They are both fine ladies and expect a certain standard of behaviour. The Contessa is being very brave and generous in even meeting you, considering your position in her late husband's life, so I expect you to try and behave like a lady.'

That did register. 'Behave like a lady'? Of all the cheek. Marlene could not believe what she was hearing. Her would-be Latin lover of a minute ago was actually lecturing her on how to behave.

'I know you're not used to this sort of society, but really all you need to remember is basic good manners.'

If Marlene had not been sitting down she would have fallen down. So this was what he'd meant by giving her 'a few pointers', she thought, suddenly furious. 'You mean like not eating off my knife or slurping the soup or—horror of horrors—blowing my nose on my napkin,' she snarled, and, pushing her chair back, got to her feet. 'Keep your pointers, buster. It will be a cold day in hell before I need a lecherous lout like you to teach me manners.' And, shooting him a vitriolic look, she added, 'I'm going to find Paul. As for you—you can go to hell.'

She only managed half a dozen steps before Rocco grabbed her arm and spun her around to face him.

'That is just the kind of behaviour I was trying to warn you about. I don't give a damn how you eat, you stupid bitch,' he grated in a low, hard voice, 'but you will treat the Contessa and Caterina with the respect they deserve. Got that?' He shook her arm, as if to reinforce his command. His brown eyes glittered angrily down into hers. 'And if you have any sense at all in your admittedly lovely head you'll take my advice, accept the Contessa's offer for the shares and the villa, go back to England and forget you ever knew anyone named Rossi.'

'Let go of my arm and keep your advice to yourself,' Marlene said flatly, but inside she was seething with anger and deep-down disappointment. With his words he had proved what she had thought all along. He might tease her about wanting her, about being her lover, but the bottom line was that he was really only interested in getting the Contessa what she wanted. And if he could get Marlene to agree he would have her on the next flight out of Naples without a backward glance...

CHAPTER FIVE

THE last few miles of the journey passed in a red haze for Marlene; she saw nothing of the countryside, she was so furious. Luckily Paul had dozed off in the back seat, his little head nestling on Marlene's lap. She looked down at him and gradually her anger dissipated and her usual good humour reappeared. With it, she became aware of the irony of her situation. She should be flattered, she told herself. Here she was, an intelligent, well-educated, wealthy woman in her own right, and yet apparently she had played the part of sexy but brainless mistress so well that even the astute Andretti had been fooled enough to break their journey and give her a lesson in manners!

The car stopped and Paul woke up with a start. Sliding along the seat to look out of the window, he demanded, 'Are we there?'

'It would seem so, darling,' she murmured, glancing out of the window at the huge iron gates blocking the road in front of the car.

The heavy gates swung open, obviously electrically operated, and the car moved slowly forward up a steep gradient. Marlene looked around with interest. They were moving up a long drive shrouded on each side by massive conifers, then suddenly the road swept around a bend and before them was the most unusual house Marlene had ever seen.

The sun, sinking low in the sky, bathed the brilliant white and glass structure in a rosy pink glow, and the rays reflecting back dazzled the onlooker, giving it an almost surreal appearance. Somehow she had been expecting a tra-

ditional Mediterranean-style villa. Instead, the house was
starkly modern—all angles and straight lines.

The entrance door, patterned glass set in a soaring glass
pyramid reminiscent of Pei's glass structures outside the
Louvre in Paris, was joined on one side to a stark, white-
walled flat-roofed structure that slanted to the ground at a
sharp angle with not another window in sight. The phrase
'blot on the landscape' sprang to mind. It might have been
the set for a science fiction movie set on an alien planet.
Marlene could not connect the building with what she knew
of the Contessa and her daughter—or Paolo, for that matter.

He had never talked much about his life in Italy, other
than to explain about his failed marriage, and he had certainly never mentioned a house in Amalfi. It had come as
a complete surprise to Marlene to discover after his death
that he had left the villa to his son. True, he had requested
she take young Paul to Italy, but she had simply assumed
he meant her to take the boy on holiday—stay in a hotel
or something. He had never once so much as hinted that
he was going to make the request official in his Will. In a
way she was a little hurt that Paolo had not confided in her
completely. No, that was not strictly true. She took a deep,
sighing breath. The personal letter he had left for her to
read after his death had told her more than she really
wanted to know…

The car door swung open. 'You look stunned.' Rocco's
voice broke into her disturbed thoughts. 'Not what you expected?' He smiled down into her golden eyes. 'Quite a
revelation, hmm?'

If only he knew, she thought drily. The house was nothing compared to the revelation Paolo had imparted to her
in his letter. Still, she pinned a smile on her face and said,
'Yes, quite a revelation.' And, swinging her legs to the
ground, she stood up, adding, 'It looks new.' She would
have said more, but Paul had slid out behind her and, quick

as a flash, was heading for the plain white marble steps up to the entrance. 'Wait, Paul.' She hurried after him and together they arrived on the top step just as the glass door swung open.

Bending to catch Paul, she froze and looked up into the face of Caterina. But she was not looking at Marlene. All her attention was centred on Rocco.

Marlene straightened up to her full height and it suddenly struck her that so much glass around a young child was not the safest thing in the world. So, bending again, she scooped Paul up in her arms. It was just as well she had, because for a moment it hid her scarlet face from Rocco. Scarlet because she had just heard Caterina's greeting to the man and was once again furious.

After the usual pleasantries Caterina had added, 'Pity you couldn't have got rid of the peasant and her brat on the way up, and save us all a lot of trouble and money.' And then she had laughed.

Marlene, holding Paul in front of her like a shield, straightened to her full height, this time looking down on Caterina, and she could not resist saying, '*Buena sera, Caterina*. I hope that was right—I've been reading an Italian phrase book.' She was so caught up in her own anger she did not see the sudden sharp glance Rocco shot her way, or the glint of suspicion in his dark eyes.

The next half-hour was hell! More than once Marlene had to clench her teeth to restrain herself from commenting, and if it had not been for her promise to Paolo she would have turned around and walked out.

Caterina led them all through the glass foyer and down a massive marble staircase into what was obviously a kind of formal reception room. Rocco briefly explained on the way down the stairs that they had entered by what was really the back of the house, onto the top floor. The staircase curved to one side and carried on down a further three floors. There was also a lift for those who preferred it. The middle two floors housed the bedrooms, and the ground floor contained a more informal salon, a dining room and study, plus the usual kitchen and utility rooms, and a small family room that led directly onto a wide terrace and the swimming pool.

He stopped abruptly as they entered the room, and a petite, flamboyantly dressed lady rose from a white hide armchair and simply stood in the middle of the room. The Contessa was everything Marlene had feared and more.

Rocco strolled over and kissed the woman on both cheeks before commanding Marlene and Paul to come along and be introduced. Five minutes later they were all seated like stuffed dummies around the lady of the house. The usual polite greetings were exchanged, with Rocco translating all the time. But what really made Marlene's blood boil was the way he translated.

He translated the usual social pleasantries accurately, but he omitted the most telling part of the Contessa's speech. In a scathing aside to Rocco, she said, 'The boy I can see is certainly Rossi's son—he has the same coarse features. No doubt a blood test will prove the relationship. As for the woman,' she said scathingly, 'you…' And then she hesitated, turning her gimlet black eyes on Marlene, coldly assessing. Then, as if she had thought better of insulting Marlene, she continued, 'No, it doesn't matter—not now. I need to think.'

At that point a pleasant-looking woman introduced as Eta, the chauffeur's wife, arrived with a tea-tray laden with small sandwiches, scones and cakes, plus teapot and cups, of course. According to Rocco, this was supposedly in honour of the English guests. Marlene burned from red to white with anger. She drank the tea and ate a scone, and was grateful when Paul declared he had eaten enough, he was tired and wanted to go to bed. Pinning a smile on her face, she excused them both and followed Eta down to the next floor and the rooms allocated to them.

Standing at the large window, staring out at the now dark sky, Marlene sighed dispiritedly. Paul, after very little fuss, was safely in bed in what was the dressing room of her room. His day was over. But for her, she had no doubt, worse was to come. 'Dinner at nine,' were the last words Rocco had said to her. She had not looked at him but had simply said yes as she'd led Paul away from the adults. Alone at last, the enormity of the task she had taken on was beginning to hit her.

In some respects the Contessa had come as something of a shock. In Marlene's mind she had pictured a middle-aged lady, very formal, very conservative. But the woman was nothing like that. Small and quite attractive, she couldn't be more than forty-five and might easily pass for thirty-five. Her clothes were designer label—Versace, probably—brightly coloured and quite avant-garde. But the eyes gave her away. She was very like her daughter, but whereas Caterina's dark eyes were easily readable, showing all her emotions, the mother's were the opposite, showing no emotion even when she smiled. There was a hardness, a guarded, almost cunning look about the woman that made Marlene shiver just to think about it.

Suddenly chilled, although the temperature outside must have been in the nineties, Marlene turned away from the window and walked quickly across the room to the *en suite* bathroom. She was being fanciful, she told herself. A nice long soak in the bath and she would feel much better.

Fifteen minutes later, stretched out in the luxurious tub, which was filled to the brim with warm water and a fragrant layer of bubbles, Marlene closed her eyes and let her mind drift. It had been a fraught five days since that fateful afternoon when Rocco Andretti and Caterina had appeared in the herb garden and she had decided to play the part of Paul's mother.

Looking back, she realised it had been the behaviour of the other couple that had goaded her into it, but realistically she knew she was not going to be able to keep it up for very much longer. Twice already young Paul had almost given her away; it was only a matter of time before the truth came out. She had panicked when she'd overheard Caterina and Rocco discussing getting control of the boy, when in reality they had no chance. After all, she was Paul's legal guardian and as closely related as Caterina— plus, she had the added advantage of having always looked after the boy.

Picking up a bar of soap, she raised one leg and began to wash herself. Yes, she decided, it didn't matter if the truth came out. In fact she would tell them all after dinner tonight. Her mind was made up. Briskly she completed her ablutions, not once admitting even deep down that her decision had more to do with letting Rocco know she was not the immoral woman he thought, but simply a caring young woman looking after her brother, than with a desire to tell the truth.

Dried and dusted, Marlene walked back into the bedroom. Her suitcase had been brought up earlier by Aldo and unpacked by Eta, she presumed as she slid back the wardrobe door. Oh, no! She eyed the few clothes and could have wept. The day before leaving England she had shopped at one of the high-street stores for clothes that would fit the image she was hoping to portray, and, looking at them now, she realised she was stuck with it. She could reveal the truth of her relationship with Paul all right, but until the day of the board meeting she was still going to have to appear in clothes she would never ordinarily have bought.

She withdrew a bright yellow jersey silk dress and

sighed, thinking longingly of her wardrobe at home. What wouldn't she give for her favourite Calvin Klein peach silk trouser suit? But it was her own stupid fault and she would have to make the best of it.

Five minutes later, as she surveyed her reflection in the full-length mirror, she groaned. It was a simple mini-skirted slip dress—apparently all the rage! With tiny shoestring straps and a deep, curved neckline showing a great deal of cleavage, the jersey silk skimmed her hips to end at mid-thigh. At five feet nine she should have remembered exactly how short a normal mini-length garment would appear on her. She tugged and tugged at the skirt, hoping to stretch it, and finally gave up, resigned to the fact that no amount of tugging at the thing was going to make it any longer.

Quickly she applied a minimum of make-up to her face—a moisturiser and sweep of translucent powder that allowed her naturally golden skin to show through. She paid a little more attention to her eyes, brushing the lids with a beige-brown eyeshadow and accentuating them with a fine light brown line and a few sweeps of brown-black mascara to her long lashes. She coloured her full lips with a soft rose lipstick and was almost ready. She brushed her long hair until it shone and fastened it behind her ears with two gilt combs. After slipping her feet into flat gold pumps, as a final touch she sprayed her throat and behind her knees with her favourite perfume, Dune. Then, straightening up, she headed for the door.

But just as she reached it somebody knocked. Turning the handle, she pulled it open and stared...

'Waiting for my knock, were you?' Rocco asked flippantly. 'I'm flattered.'

Marlene was speechless. She'd known he was handsome, but in a formal white dinner jacket he was devastating!

'Cat got your tongue?' he drawled huskily, his eyes appreciating every exposed inch of her with bold, sensual delight. 'Try mine instead.'

Before she could utter a word he had pulled her into his arms, and his mouth caught and clung to hers as he kissed her with a passion and intensity that made her legs buckle. His tongue plunged into her mouth and she met him with equal intensity, her body pressed against his hard frame, her breasts tingling with the contact.

Rocco finally raised his head, breaking the kiss. His breathing unsteady, he stared down into her flushed, confused face. 'My God!' he muttered. 'I can almost understand Rossi throwing away his life for you. You're incredible.' And, as he held her away from him, his smouldering dark eyes swept down over the proud jut of her breasts against the fine fabric.

'Paolo…' She was going to tell him the truth but she never got the chance.

'Stop,' he said fiercely, hauling her back against him. 'Don't dare say that name when you are in my arms. I won't have it,' he snarled, and, his eyes glittering with anger, his mouth clamped on hers once again. But this kiss was different—hard and ruthless, seeking no response, simply dominating.

Frantically Marlene pushed against his broad chest, fighting to break free. She twisted her head away from him. 'No!' she cried. 'Leave me alone!'

'I wish to God I could,' Rocco growled, suddenly setting her free. 'There is something between us—we only have to touch each other to go up in flames. You can't deny it, so why bother trying?'

Marlene looked up into his darkly flushed face, her heart racing crazily, and knew what he said was true. 'But you don't understand…' Again she tried to tell him the truth, and again he stopped her.

'What's to understand?' he rasped, his voice hoarse. 'I

want you. I've got to have you or go insane. I'm a wealthy man—I can give you anything you want. All you have to do is agree to be my mistress.'

She shook her head, still half-dazed by his kisses, and pushed out of his arms, trying to think. 'But what about the reason why I'm here?' They were fated to be enemies, however much Marlene wished it could be otherwise.

Rocco's hands closed over her naked shoulders and held her steady. 'No. Wait—listen. I'm not asking for for ever,' he said urgently. 'Only for a few weeks or months—whatever it takes until this fever between us burns itself out naturally. Forget about the rest. Business has nothing to do with pleasure.'

Her golden eyes widened in horror as the realisation of what he was saying hit her like a bucket of cold water. She stared at him as her heartbeat slowed and a cold fury took the place of her former mindless passion. He had just thoroughly insulted her.

'I don't believe you,' she drawled, shaking her head at the sheer arrogance of the man. But obviously his English was not as good as she had thought, because he took what she had said literally, missing the sarcasm completely.

'I'm telling you the truth—believe me. I'll take care of you and the boy, and to prove it we will leave here tomorrow. I have a place a few miles from here. It is yours if you want it. Simply let me have you.'

Her mouth tightened into an angry, bitter line and, stepping back, she roughly pushed his hands from her shoulders. 'Get out, before I scream,' she grated between clenched teeth. It was all clear to her now. 'We will leave here tomorrow' he had said. How very convenient for the Contessa and her daughter if Rocco succeeded in his plan to seduce her into leaving with him. Obviously Paul would go with them, and his inheritance would also go—straight down the drain. Rocco must think she was a complete idiot.

Rocco stared at her, his dark eyes narrowed in speculation. 'What is it I'm missing here? You melt in my arms, then threaten to scream after I've offered you anything you like.' He moved towards her but she sidestepped him.

'Perhaps I just don't like you, Signor Andretti,' she said bluntly. 'Now please leave. I need to repair my make-up and check on Paul before going down to dinner.'

He watched her for a long, silent moment, the tension stretching between them tight as a bowstring. 'I do not understand you at all. You are beautiful, basic, but there is something about you that doesn't add up...' He turned away from her with a frustrated shake of his dark head. 'We haven't time to talk now. I'll wait outside. I originally came to show you the way to the dining room and I still intend to.' And with that he was gone, the door closing quietly behind him.

Marlene took a few deep, steadying breaths. Her act was definitely slipping; he was suspicious. Her decision to tell him the truth of her relationship with Paolo was the right one. As soon as she could get him alone she would do it, then perhaps the relationship between them could develop honestly. The thought made her smile and, after quickly tidying her hair and replacing her vanished lipstick, she took a brief look at Paul before eagerly opening the bedroom door.

Rocco was waiting, leaning negligently against the wall. 'You surprise me. I thought it would take you at least another ten minutes—not because your beauty needs assistance but simply to keep me waiting. That is the usual women's ploy, I've found.'

'You obviously meet the wrong type of women,' Marlene snapped, her good humour vanishing at the thought of all his other women. She would have walked past him, but he caught her arm and, straightening to his full height, stared down into her mutinous face.

'*You* certainly are,' he muttered with some exasperation, before gently nudging her before him. 'Come on, the Contessa does not like to be kept waiting.'

The dining room was weird, Marlene thought as Rocco pulled out a black and glass chair for her, and she sat down, glancing around curiously. A huge plate-glass wall opened out onto a large patio lit with a row of sharply angled halogen lights that gave an eerie white glare, making the blackness beyond impenetrable. She imagined that in the daylight the view must be quite spectacular, but at the moment all she could see was some patio furniture and some potted cactus plants. Not a flower or rambling hibiscus in sight, yet it matched the rest of the place.

The dining room itself contained only a twelve-foot long black marble table and eleven more black and glass chairs like the rather uncomfortable one she was sitting on. A huge modern sculpture that must have been about nine feet high took up one wall where, in a more conventional house, one might have expected a fireplace. The few pictures on the other two walls were very Salvador Dali and quite possibly originals, but they were not really to Marlene's taste.

The lighting came from a selection of long black standard lamps with strange white globes which lit the ceiling rather than the table, and in the centre of the table was yet another sculpture—at least, Marlene supposed it was a sculpture—all stainless steel and wire but surprisingly functional as it held twelve black candles. The whole effect was theatrical, and to her mind chilling.

Even more chilling were her dinner companions. They were four in all and the other two females were already seated. The Contessa, at the head of the table, spoke first.

'We were beginning to think you had gone.'

Marlene's head jerked up. The woman spoke English. 'You speak English,' she said, surprised, and flashed a quick glance at Rocco. He did not look in the least surprised. So much for his need to be here and translate. The liar, she thought cynically. But she made no comment, turning her attention back to the Contessa as that lady continued.

'A little, but not so good. This—' she indicated the small, heavy man standing at her right-hand side '—is Signor Andretti—Rocco's *papà*.' And she smiled, a thin twist of her lips. 'And Caterina you know.' She glanced at her daughter, seated one place away, as the older man also sat down next to her.

Marlene sensed Rocco's hands tighten on the back of her chair, before he apparently casually pulled out the chair beside her and sat down.

'I did not expect you to be here so soon, Papà,' Rocco said in Italian, and Marlene picked up the tension between the two men immediately.

'Rocco, please—we try to talk English for our visitor, no?' the Contessa intervened, with a blatantly false smile for Marlene.

The dinner went from bad to worse. The food was excellent, but there were so many undercurrents it made Marlene's head spin. That, together with the knowledge that she was sitting here supposedly as a dead man's mistress, and they were all being so terribly sophisticated and civilised about it, made her feel slightly sick. Not for the first time she wondered if fulfilling Paolo's last wish was really worth the aggravation. Added to all this, the difficulty she had in pretending she did not speak their language was a terrible strain, as the conversation constantly switched from English to Italian, depending on who was talking.

It was after the dessert had been eaten—a rather luscious concoction of nuts, strawberries and cream and various flavoured ice creams—that the bomb fell.

'So, Marlene,' the Contessa said silkily as the dessert

dishes were taken away, 'who are you? You are not my husband's woman; this I know…'

Marlene's eyes widened in shock as they met the narrowed gaze of the Contessa. What did the woman mean? Did she know the truth? The questions spun in her brain. Then, remembering her decision taken earlier in the bedroom to come clean, she opened her mouth to speak. But she was too late. Rocco intervened.

'Really, Contessa, we all know the circumstances. I don't think we need to embarrass Miss Johanson.' He cast a sideways glance at Marlene, sitting next to him.

If he thought his smile was reassuring, Marlene thought bitterly, he was wrong. She was not an idiot. His lips might tilt at the corners, but his dark eyes held an unmistakably cynical gleam.

The Contessa shot him an exasperated glance and let fly in rapid Italian. 'Rocco, if you spent less time with your head in the ground and more in the real world you would not be so easily fooled by a pretty face. And as for you, Caterina, you are no better. The woman has fooled you both. My late husband's mistress was the same age as me, for God's sake!' And then, turning, she laid her hand on the other Andretti's arm. 'I warned you, Carlo. You should have gone yourself to England, not sent Rocco.'

Andretti senior let fly with a barked question. 'Surely you had the sense to check the woman out, Rocco?'

His response was lost in Caterina's cry. 'Of course she's the one!'

Marlene would have found the following slanging match quite funny if it had not been her they were talking about. Finally there was silence, and four pairs of eyes fixed on Marlene with various expressions.

Caterina sat in open-mouthed amazement, her mother in glittering triumph and the senior Andretti regarded her with shrewd dark eyes. Oddly enough, Marlene realised, the man was nothing like his son. Where Rocco was very tall, lean and muscular, this man, she judged, was not above five feet seven. His face was round, his nose large and his eyes small, and he was definitely overweight. Perhaps Rocco took after his mother, she mused, but was rudely brought back to the question at hand when she finally turned her head to Rocco, at her side.

'The Contessa asked you a question, Miss Johanson,' he grated scathingly from between clenched teeth, his dark eyes blazing with anger, his hard mouth a tight line. 'Now answer it…'

'What was the question again?' she asked blandly, playing for time. 'You all started talking at once.' She shrugged. 'Not that I understood a word.'

'Who exactly are you, Marlene?'

She pushed her chair back and slowly got to her feet, her mind working like lightning. Just how much was it safe to reveal? she wondered. But Rocco, mistaking her action as an attempt to leave, leapt to his feet and placed a firm, restraining hand on her shoulder.

'No, you are not walking out on this, lady. No one makes a fool of me and gets away with it. Just who the hell are you?' he said in a deadly voice, the other people in the room forgotten. 'You either answer to me or to the police.'

'Police!' she exclaimed in astonishment, glancing up into his angry face.

'Fraud is a serious offence.' His eyes duelled with hers, implacable, black as jet and just as cold.

'You should know.' She tried to sneer, but the pressure of his hand on her shoulder increased until it physically hurt her.

His father interrupted. 'Let the lady speak.'

As if suddenly realising there were other people present, Rocco allowed his hand to fall from her shoulder. 'Well, Marlene?'

The moment of truth had arrived. Or partial truth, she qualified silently. Taking a deep, slow breath, resting her hands lightly on the back of the chair she had just vacated, she turned all her attention on the Contessa. 'I am Marlene Johanson—the Marlene Johanson mentioned in your late husband's will as his son's guardian. You can check it and you will find it is all perfectly legal. I am Paul's legal guardian but I was never your husband's mistress. My mother was. She died two years ago.'

'The boy calls you Ma,' Rocco sneered. 'Maybe Rossi went from mother to daughter.'

Without a second thought Marlene swung her hand through the air and slapped him soundly in the face, knocking his head back with the force of the blow. She vaguely heard the gasps of outrage from the rest of the table but she was past caring. This man had insulted her once too often.

Before he could recover she was out of the door and racing up the stairs to her room. The door safely locked behind her, she leant against it and tried to recover her breath and her temper. God knew what the rest of them thought. That she was crazy, probably.

A few moments later, when she had finally calmed down enough to think straight, she realised that her show of violence might have harmed her case for keeping young Paul—if the Rossi family decided to make a case of it. But on the other hand she had something they wanted even more—the shares in the Rossi empire—so perhaps all was not lost, she mused as she slid gratefully into the wide bed.

A quick glance at the headboard was not reassuring; it was a curved black railing topped with gilded spikes. Her last thought before sleep finally overcame her was that she did not like the house or the décor, never mind the inhabitants… She didn't hear the soft tap on the door, or the deep voice whispering her name over and over again with rising masculine frustration…

CHAPTER SIX

'MAR, wake up—wake up!' Marlene groaned and gripped the little hand pounding on her chest. 'Not there, Paul, that hurts.' Forcing her eyes open, she looked up into the grinning face of her brother. His black hair was all awry and his pyjama jacket had disappeared. Clad only in Batman-printed pyjama bottoms, he sat astride her waist, his little hands pressing on her chest and his face only inches from hers.

'You're awake. You've got to see. Come on—quick.' His excitement was infectious.

'What have I got to see?' Marlene queried, hauling herself up the bed and depositing Paul on the floor at the same time.

'The sea and the cliffs, Mar. I've never seen such big cliffs. And a swimming pool and the sun.'

'OK, OK.' And, swinging her legs over the side of the bed, she stood up, and put her hands above her head, stretching and yawning at the same time. Paul was already standing with his face pressed up to the window as Marlene, with a wry smile at his early morning enthusiasm, strolled over to join him. Resting her hand on his little shoulder, she followed his gaze. He was right, she thought wonderingly. In daylight the view was spectacular.

The cloudless sky blended into the sea at the horizon, a deep clear blue, and, closer, the water changed to a vivid aquamarine, with dark rocks and vegetation clearly visible beneath the surface. The house itself appeared to be carved into the soaring cliffs. Looking immediately down, she saw the patio that ran the length of the villa, and a diamond-shaped swimming pool sparkling clear jade in the morning sun. Then several steep terraces ran down in layers for about five hundred yards, before appearing to fall into the sea.

The drop down the cliff must be astronomical, she thought, going by the distance to the next view of the rocks as the sea lapped at their base. Again it occurred to her that the house had not been planned with children in mind. Paul would need watching like a hawk for however long they stayed here. The steps were too steep for a young child, and there was not a guard rail in sight.

'Can I go in the pool, Mar?' Paul asked, tugging at the hem of her short cotton nightie.

'Yes, come on, pet. I'll get you washed.'

'But I don't need a wash—the pool will wash me.'

There was no answer to that, so Marlene simply picked him up and carried him into the bathroom.

Ten minutes later, with Paul dressed in his swimming trunks and a T-shirt, leaping up and down with impatience by the bedroom door, Marlene pulled a loose knee-length cotton jersey sweater dress over her white Lycra bathing suit, picked up a towel and glanced ruefully at her watch on the bedside table. Seven a.m. Still, she thought bracingly, a few lengths of the pool would do her the world of good, and maybe help her get her thoughts in order.

Opening the bedroom door, she ushered Paul out, with a finger to her lips to remind him to be quiet. She very much doubted if the other members of the household would be awake this early.

In that she was mistaken. Quietly she led Paul downstairs and in a false start opened a door to what was obviously a study. She shut it again. Her next attempt revealed the kitchen, where Eta and Aldo were seated at a hideous—to Marlene's eyes—stainless-steel table, enjoying a pot of coffee.

'*Scusi, signorina*—you should have rung.' Eta jumped to her feet. 'It is my duty to bring you your morning coffee and breakfast,' she said in rapid Italian, with a look of dismay clouding her pleasant features.

Marlene smiled and responded quietly in the same language. 'It's perfectly all right. We're going for a swim—coffee and juice will do fine, thank you.' The wide grin that spread over Eta's features alerted Marlene to her mistake.

'Yes, immediately, *signorina*,' Eta said.

With an inward groan Marlene realised that, still not properly awake, she had rattled off her statement in Italian. She toyed with the idea of trying to explain to Eta that she wanted to keep her linguistic ability a secret, but quickly discarded the notion. She had no idea how close the woman was to her employer, and she might just make matters worse. Instead she took the cup of coffee Eta handed her, and drank it quickly while Paul swallowed down a large glass of fresh orange juice. Then, with a simple nod of her head and a smile, she hurried Paul out through the kitchen and onto the patio.

The morning air was warm but fresh, and Marlene took great gulps into her lungs. She felt as though she had been confined for ages, what with the plane journey and the car journey yesterday, and then the disastrous evening. But outside in the clear air, with the sound of the sea splashing against the rocks the only noise, at last she felt a sense of freedom. With Paul's hand firmly clasped in her own she led him along the terrace to where the swimming pool sparkled in the sun.

Sitting on a convenient lounger, she quickly divested Paul of his T-shirt and herself of the sweater dress, then gingerly walked to the edge of the glistening pool.

'Now, wait there and don't move until I come back and lift you into the water. Promise?'

'But why, Mar?'

'Because there are no markings and I have to find out which is the safest part.'

'But I can swim.'

'Don't argue,' she said, and, dropping the towel on the ground, added firmly, 'Wait.'

It was as she had suspected, she found, after a speedy crawl around the pool. There was no part shallow enough for Paul to stand up in. Hauling herself out of the pool beside him, she led him to the point of the diamond that faced out to sea. Here the water was four feet deep; the boy would not be able to stand, but she felt he might be marginally safer.

Ten minutes later, standing up to her chest in the water, she brushed the wet hair out of her eyes and picked Paul out of the water by the armpits and swung him around. 'Tired yet, darling?' she asked, laughing. He was a great little swimmer—she had taught him herself—but there was only so much a boy of his age could do. 'Come on, sit on the side and rest for a second.' Lowering him onto the edge, so that only his feet dangled in the water, she turned and pushed herself up to sit beside him. 'Do you think you would like to stay here?' she asked quietly, and, picking up the towel, she rubbed the black curls on the top of his head.

'That is a leading question if ever I heard one,' a deep voice commented. Marlene got such a shock that she slid back into the pool, and Rocco's shout of laughter did nothing for her temper.

But Paul had no such trouble. He jumped to his feet and spun around, racing across the terrace to where Rocco stood at the top of the steps. 'Roc! I've been swimming—did you see me? Did you?'

'Yes, you were great—and so was your mother.'

'Not mother, silly. Marlene's my sister.'

The conversation was lost to Marlene. She was too busy hauling herself back out of the pool again, the dripping towel still in her hand. Trust him to be up at the crack of dawn, she thought resentfully. He must have been down at the bottom terrace before they'd come out of the house. Leaving the towel on the ground—it was useless now—she stood up. Catching her hair in a bunch, she wrung the excess moisture out of it, before straightening and looking across at her tormentor.

He had dropped to his knees to talk to Paul, and she had time to study him. Rocco was wearing brief black bathing shorts and, apart from a white towel slung around his neck, nothing much else except for a pair of black rubber flip-flops on his feet. A sudden coil of attraction twisted to life in the pit of her stomach at the sight of his tanned legs with their light dusting of black body hair. The graceful curve of his broad, tanned back made her itch to run a finger down his spine.

He turned suddenly. 'Good morning, Marlene. You're looking well.' Rocco rose to his full height and quite deliberately let his eyes roam over her from head to toe in a sensuous appraisal that made her one-piece suit suddenly seem too small and too tight.

The colour surged into her cheeks. But she said very curtly, 'Good morning and goodbye,' to some point over his left shoulder. 'Come on, Paul, time for breakfast.' And, stepping forward, she reached out her hand to Paul. But he was not so easily persuaded.

'No, Mar. Me and Roc are going to swim.'

Grasping Paul's hand firmly in her own, she tilted her head back and forced herself to look at Rocco. 'It is time for his breakfast. Perhaps later,' she said bluntly.

His black eyes narrowed on her flushed face. 'Too late, Marlene—or should I call you Mar, like your brother?' he drawled sardonically.

The anger of last night was still very evident. She might have guessed he would not let her off lightly for pretending to be Rossi's mistress and making a fool of him in front of his father and the Contessa. 'Call me what you like. I'm sure you can think of a few choice names.' She tried to joke, hoping he would put her heightened colour down to amusement, when really she was deeply embarrassed by the way she had behaved—or perhaps, more honestly, by being found out in a lie.

'You have a good reason to blush, after last night,' Rocco taunted cynically. 'I'm only amazed your nose hasn't grown a foot long, you devious little liar.'

'You believed what you wanted to believe. I can't help it if you have a mind like a sewer,' she shot back defensively.

'Why, you—' His black eyes glittered with fury and she instinctively took a step back, but before he could say anything more Paul saved her.

'Mar, are you and Roc fighting?'

'No,' she snapped, and, instantly regretting her sharp response, she gently squeezed Paul's hand and smiled down at him. 'No, darling. Sorry, it's just a slight disagreement. You can swim again later. Now come on.'

Paul recognised that she was serious by the tone of her voice and made no more attempt to argue. Instead he quite happily skipped along beside her as she turned around and strode back towards the house, calling over his shoulder, 'See you later, Roc. I'm hungry now.'

She heard a splash behind her and guessed that Rocco had dived into the pool. Probably to cool off; he had looked absolutely furious.

Marlene had to hide her own fury a few minutes later when, on walking into the kitchen, she was accosted by the Contessa.

'Breakfast is taken alfresco, at nine. Time for you and

the child to dress,' she said with a disdainful look at Marlene and Paul's scantily clad bodies. 'I preserve a certain standard always.'

'Of course,' Marlene mumbled, and dashed Paul back upstairs as quickly as she could, thinking all the while that there was no way she could stand living in this house with that woman for two weeks, never mind two months.

By the time breakfast was over, she had amended the thought from two weeks to two days, having remembered that Rocco had said she and Caterina were only staying a night or two. The Contessa and Andretti senior had sat together, whispering all the time. Caterina had not appeared, and Rocco had sat in a brooding silence, watching every movement Marlene made. In the end she'd barely eaten a thing, she was so disconcerted. Only young Paul seemed oblivious of the tension in the air, and munched his way through a bowl of cornflakes and a plate of scrambled eggs, finally declaring that he was full and asking what they were going to do next. Marlene felt like saying, Leave…

It was almost a relief when the Contessa commanded her to meet her in the study in fifteen minutes.

'Yes, but what about Paul? This is not the safest place to allow a child to run around in,' Marlene responded evenly. She had no intention of allowing the Contessa to order her about.

'I will look after Paul,' Rocco said smoothly. 'So you can concentrate on the business at hand.'

Marlene cast a time-wasting glance around the terrace, but eventually she had to look at him—something she had been studiously avoiding for the past half-hour, although she had been intensely aware of him every second. Her golden eyes, narrowed against the sun, met and clashed with his. There was a stillness, a waiting about him that she found terribly threatening even as her body acknowledged her sensual awareness of him with rapidly beating heart.

'You can trust me with him, Marlene,' he said, not taking his eyes from her face. 'I will look after him.'

'How very noble of you. Thank you,' she said sarcastically. But who was going to look after her? she pondered as she slid back her chair and got to her feet. 'Fifteen minutes, you said?' She spoke to the Contessa. 'Do you mind if I use the telephone? I have a couple of calls I need to make.'

The Contessa agreed; she hadn't much choice.

Marlene almost laughed when she saw the questioning looks that flashed between the three of them. Let them wonder. Her business was her own affair, and, with an admonishment to Paul to be good, she walked back into the house. At last the gloves were coming off, Marlene thought, and perhaps this whole mess could be sorted out painlessly and quickly for all parties.

She had already decided there was no way she was hanging around just so Paul could keep the villa. The thought of following the boy around this place every summer for the next five years, simply to make sure he did not plunge down the steps, the cliffs, or drown in the pool, sounded like the holiday from hell! She didn't even like the villa, and they didn't need the money. No, she would keep faith with his father by bringing Paul on holiday every year. She would let him get to know the country and the people, but from the comfort of a hotel in Naples. According to Paolo, he had spent most of his time living in the penthouse on top of the Rossi building in that city.

Ten minutes later Marlene replaced the telephone in its cradle, a puzzled frown creasing her smooth brow. She could hear the high-pitched laughter of Paul in the distance and the deeper tone of Rocco's laughter, and for a second she wished she could join them—a bit of light-hearted fun would go down well right now. The news she had just received from her investigative friend in London was so odd it was amazing! It made no sense at all. Still frowning, she made her way to the study.

The Contessa was sitting in a high-backed chair behind a large black desk. Whoever designed this place must have had a passion for black! The inconsequential thought fluttered in Marlene's mind, and then she noticed that Andretti senior was standing at the Contessa's side.

Two against one was hardly fair, but Marlene said nothing; she simply sat down in the black leather chair the Contessa indicated.

'Miss Johanson, you must realise this is a very delicate situation,' Signor Andretti began, in slow but good English. 'As my son told you, my firm is dealing with the late Signor Rossi's estate. As you also know, this house is bequeathed to your half-brother on certain conditions. I must declare my interest here. I did not agree with Rossi leaving the boy this property on any condition, and if you will allow me I will explain why.'

'Yes, please go on,' she responded coolly, while wondering sadly if Paolo had ever realised before he died just how disloyal his friend and lawyer really was.

'I can see you are a sensible lady,' he said ingratiatingly, before continuing, 'I dislike speaking ill of the dead, but I feel Rossi left the villa to the boy simply out of spite.'

Marlene stiffened in her chair. The Paolo Rossi she had known had not had a spiteful bone in his body. 'I don't—'

'No, please allow me to finish. The original house on this site was a small, shabby affair—nothing like the beautiful building you see now. And it is all the Contessa's doing. It was designed and built to the Contessa's specifications. It was her creation, if you like, ten years ago, and she is very reluctant to part with it, as you can imagine. Her late husband admittedly owned it, and paid for the complete rebuilding, but he never appreciated the style and only ever visited the new villa once.'

Somehow Marlene was not surprised. The house suited the Contessa; it was as sharp and sterile as the woman herself appeared to be, and in a way it was a relief to know that her beloved Paolo had never considered the place his home.

'He altered his will some three and a half years ago, bequeathing the villa to the boy simply, I am sorry to say, because the Contessa— quite rightly, as a good Catholic— refused to give him the divorce he wanted. Now we are hoping you will be reasonable. The Contessa loves this place and is prepared to pay you a considerable amount of money to retain her sole ownership of the property.'

'How very generous,' Marlene drawled, the sarcasm lost on the other two.

'Yes, we are prepared to be so.' Andretti mentioned a figure that Marlene knew was ridiculously cheap for a prime piece of real estate in a prestigious area like Amalfi. 'And of course the Contessa will not insist that the boy comply with the conditions of the will before handing over the money. It can be arranged in a couple of days, and then you and the boy have no need to stay two months this year or any other year.'

'But I did promise Paul a holiday,' Marlene objected, simply to make the man squirm. 'He will be very disappointed.'

'No, no…you misunderstand. Now you are here, obviously you must enjoy your holiday. That goes without saying,' the older Andretti shot back placatingly.

As it happened, Marlene wasn't bothered on either count—the money or the holiday. She had already made her decision, but she was not about to tell them that. Instead she spent an eventful half-hour haggling up the price, and then, with handshakes all round, it was agreed. As compensation it was a derisory amount, given the value of the property, and the avarice she could see in their eyes said as much, but Marlene pretended not to notice, nor to hear their brief exchange in Italian.

'I told you, Carlo, she is a fool—she knows nothing. I don't know why your son could not have settled this business last week—the shares, the villa, everything—and then the woman need never have come here.'

'You're right—typical of him. He is probably more interested in getting the woman into his bed than in business.'

Marlene hid her smile behind a pretend yawn. The father surely knew his son, and obviously did not think much of his legal skills. 'If you don't mind,' she interrupted, rising to her feet, 'I find all this business talk tiring. I could use a cup of coffee.'

'There is one other little matter I would like to discuss with you,' the senior Andretti said quickly. 'Your shares in the company.'

'Oh, please can we discuss that another time? Today is Sunday—a day of rest. I imagine it will take a few days for all the legal documents to be organised, and, as I said, I did promise Paul a holiday. So, if it is all right with you, Contessa, we will leave next Saturday.'

Surprise fought with triumph on the Contessa's fine features. She had obviously not hoped to be rid of her so quickly.

'But of course, Miss Johanson. Enjoy your week.' The woman agreed so speedily it was almost insulting. 'Unfortunately we have to return to Naples today, but Signor Andretti will return later in the week and conclude our business, *sì*?'

Marlene almost said no, but she saw no reason to enlighten the woman after the information she had received this morning. The board meeting was on Friday; the timing was perfect for Marlene. She could stir up a hornet's nest and walk away the next day. She might not save Paolo Rossi's name, but she fully intended to expose the people who had betrayed him. 'I will look forward to his visit,' she replied noncommittally.

'Good. Now enjoy the weather. I will send Eta out to the patio with coffee.'

As a dismissal it was classic, Marlene thought, but with a bland smile she said, 'Thank you.'

It was a relief to get back out into the fresh air. Paul and Rocco were nowhere in sight, and she did not feel like looking for them. She needed time to assimilate all she had learned from her telephone conversation, and form a plan of campaign. She sat down on an intricately wrought iron chair, one of six around the large oval matching table. Yet more glass, she mused as Eta appeared with a tray holding a coffee-pot, cup and saucer, milk and sugar.

'*Grazie, Eta,*' she said with a smile and, lifting the pot, she filled the cup with the rich aromatic brew. She stirred in a little sugar, and was just raising the cup to her lips when Paul suddenly appeared at the top of the steps from the lower terrace.

Marlene took a drink of the hot liquid and set the cup back on the table, flashing the boy a broad smile. 'Having fun?' she called.

He raced across to her side. 'Mar, Roc took me right down to the bottom of the cliff.'

'What? Wasn't that dangerous?' Marlene asked anxiously. It looked impossible from where she was sitting.

'No, it wasn't,' Rocco answered, crossing the terrace in a few lithe strides to stand towering over her.

She tilted her head back to look up at him, shading her eyes from the sun with her hand. 'So you say,' she said curtly. She had not forgotten Caterina's comment when they had first arrived, about getting rid of the pair of them.

'You are doubting my word? You seriously think I would

put the boy's life in danger?' Rocco demanded, sliding into
the chair opposite her, the brief smile curling his sensuous
lips belied by the hard gleam in his black eyes.

She eyed him dispassionately. Rocco was wearing plain
white shorts and a white sleeveless sweatshirt, and the overall effect of his midnight-black hair and deeply tanned skin
against the white was stunning. But then he would be a
striking male in any company; he had an intrinsic aura of
danger about him that even his seemingly relaxed position—one foot casually lifted across one knee—did nothing
to dispel. She shivered for no apparent reason.

'Well? Do you?' he demanded, stony-faced.

She met his eyes levelly. 'I really don't know. I don't
know you.' Marlene doubted he would harm a child, but
she refused to back down beneath his quelling gaze. 'I don't
know how far you would go to protect those you consider
your friends, like Caterina and the Contessa.'

'My God, you have some opinion of me.' Rocco sat up
in the chair and, leaning across the table, explained tautly,
'I carried Paul down the steps that are cut into the cliff to
the sea. *Carried* him! Understand? He was never in any
danger. I showed him where his father used to take me as
a young boy, where he taught me to fish, before he was
even married to the Contessa. I thought it might help Paul
to know something of his family history.

'The Rossis were the…what is the word?' He frowned.
'The blacksmiths in Amalfi for generations. Originally
Paul's grandfather built a house here in the thirties. He was
a shrewd man. He could see even then that the area was
becoming a haunt of the rich and famous. He rented it out
to supplement his income and then Paolo Rossi lived here
when he first started his engineering business. My mother
owned the next house around the cliff. Rossi and my parents were good friends until—'

'I got a piggy-back, Mar—all the way down and all the way up.' Paul chose that moment to butt in.

Until what? she wondered, fascinated by the brief glimpse of the past. But she did not ask; instead, dragging her eyes away from the furious glitter in Rocco's, she turned to Paul. 'That's lovely, darling, but don't ever try to go down the steps yourself. Promise?'

'I already promised Roc. Not ever.' He shook his little head to emphasise the point.

'Satisfied?' Rocco drawled sardonically.

'I suppose I will have to be,' she said with bad grace, and was saved from having to say anything further when Eta appeared.

She pretended not to listen as Rocco asked for another cup and an orange juice for the boy. Instead she picked up her own cup and sipped the coffee. But when he turned his attention to Paul she stiffened defensively.

'Go along with Eta, Paul. You can bring my cup back after you have had your orange juice.'

The last thing she needed was to be left alone with Rocco, even for a minute. 'He doesn't—' she began, but Rocco cut her off.

'Run along, Paul. I will keep Mar company until you get back.' And, with a gentle pat on the little boy's bottom, he sent him on his way.

Marlene watched the departing duo with dismay. She wasn't fooled for a second. Rocco's use of 'Mar' had been quite deliberate. He had not forgotten last night—nor forgiven, by the sound of it.

'So, Marlene…' His dark brows lifted ironically. 'Alone at last! Afraid?'

'Why on earth should I be?' she said, with a careless shrug of her shoulders. 'Paul will be back in a minute.' Marlene made herself look into his dark eyes. 'I can't see you seducing me in front of a little boy, Rocco.' She smiled—a slow curl of her full lips. 'However much you may want to.' She knew damn fine that seduction was not what he had in mind, but she wasn't going to give him the chance to vent his anger on her. Not if she could help it.

'You don't fool me for a moment, Marlene.' He reached across the table and caught her hand in his. 'If I wanted to, I could seduce you in thirty seconds flat, and you know it.' And, rubbing his thumb across her palm, he moved his fingers to her wrist.

'Let go of me.' She tried to pull her hand free. The warmth of his touch brought an immediate response to her body that she could not control, and she knew he was well aware of the fact.

'No, I like to feel your pulse flutter beneath my fingers.' Rocco laughed under his breath at her gasp of outrage. 'You shouldn't dish it out if you can't take it, Marlene.'

She threw him an angry glance. 'I won't argue with you. There's no point.'

His slow smile was chilling as his fingers tightened around her wrist. 'I'm glad you realise that, Marlene, because I want some straight answers from you and I intend to have them. This afternoon after lunch Paul will take a nap, and then you and I will talk.' His voice was as cold as his smile.

He watched her intently, the silence stretching as she sought for some response. Then Paul's little voice could be heard, yelling that he was on his way, and Marlene heaved a sigh of relief.

Rocco let go of her hand. 'Don't make me come looking for you, lady, or you will regret it,' he grated softly just as Paul arrived at his side with a cup in his hand.

Once more in her bedroom, Marlene divested Paul of his clothes and watched as he pulled on his still damp swimming trunks. Then she went into the bathroom and quickly slipped out of her clothes and back into her swimsuit. It was barely eleven o'clock, she realised, walking back into the room, and this was the third time they had dressed and undressed. A deep sigh escaped her. It was turning into a hell of a morning!

'Right, pet, back to the pool—but first some sun cream.' When she was satisfied that they were both adequately protected against the fierce rays of the summer sun, she slung a towel around her shoulders, caught Paul's hand in hers and set off for the swimming pool yet again.

Marlene hesitated before stepping outside. Rocco, his father, the Contessa and Caterina were all standing in a group, apparently arguing. Suddenly she saw Rocco gesticulate wildly, and heard his deep voice declaring angrily in Italian, 'I can understand the Contessa's point of view, though I don't agree with it—she was a deserted wife. But *you*, Papà, for God's sake! Whatever the woman was or was not the boy is innocent, and you are deliberately robbing Rossi's son of his inheritance. This place is worth ten times that and you know it.'

'It doesn't concern you any more. I ask you once in your life to make a simple deal, and you can't do it. You would never make a lawyer in a hundred years. You always were far too much like your mother—taking the moral high ground. Well, forget it. It is settled, and we are leaving now.'

What might have followed Marlene would never know, because at that moment Paul decided he had hung around long enough, and said in a high-pitched treble, 'Come on, Mar, hurry up.'

As she walked out onto the terrace all eyes turned to her, the sudden silence making it embarrassingly obvious that they had been talking about her.

'Miss Johanson.' The Contessa was the first to recover. 'I was just asking Rocco where you were. I am sorry, we must leave now.'

Marlene watched as the little woman walked towards her. Today the Contessa was dressed in a red, white and black tunic in a dramatic design, and white silk trousers, and her face was half-hidden by a large floppy-brimmed red hat. She held out a bejewelled hand to Marlene. '*Arrivederci*. I doubt we will meet again. But as we agreed Signor Andretti will finish the business, no?'

'Of course,' Marlene agreed. But not in the way this woman imagined, she thought secretly. She shook hands with the Contessa, and then, after perfunctory farewells from Caterina and Carlo Andretti, two minutes later there was only Rocco, Paul and a very puzzled Marlene left.

Through her bewilderment she managed to retain enough control to be wryly amused at the mass exodus. The bimbo had been conned and they were gone. But that did not explain Rocco's attitude. He had actually been defending Paul, and indirectly her... Nor did it explain why he was still here. Unless he still meant to have the conversation with her which he had threatened earlier...

'We're going for a swim.' She stated the obvious, unsettled by this different view of Rocco, and also filled with sympathy for the man. His father's slating of his legal abilities had been cruel, and somehow hadn't rung true. He had an aura of power, a confidence about him that was undeniable. Or was that just her reaction to him? she asked herself, and shivered. 'When are you leaving?' she asked suddenly, as it hit her that in a few short days she would be going back to England and would never see this man again.

He simply stared at her, and there was such open desire in the unsmiling look he gave her that her nipples hardened beneath the damp fabric of her bathing suit. She shivered again, suddenly overwhelmed by the intensity of her reactions. She gripped Paul's hand tighter, the silence getting to her. 'Would you like to come swimming with us?' she blurted—anything to break the tension.

'Yes,' Rocco said, his eyes never leaving her. 'I'll go and change.' But he didn't move. She had no idea how stunning she looked. Her lovely face was devoid of make-up, her long blonde hair was tied back in a ponytail, and her skin, tanned a light gold, contrasted with the plain white bathing suit. The damp suit was high-cut, exaggerating her long legs and outlining her feminine curves in intimate detail.

'Well…' she murmured, her colour high. 'See you.' And, with Paul tugging at her hand, she sidestepped around Rocco. She felt his eyes burning into her back as she walked across to the pool.

Marlene jumped into the welcoming water and, turning, held out her arms for Paul. In her peripheral vision she saw Rocco turn and enter the house. What on earth had possessed her to ask him to join them? She knew he was furious with her. She must be mad.

And five minutes later she knew she was, when Rocco appeared at the edge of the pool. For a heart-stopping moment she thought he was naked…

CHAPTER SEVEN

ROCCO was standing balancing on the balls of his feet, just about to dive in. His body was deeply tanned and supple, his muscular chest covered with a light brushing of black hair, arrowing down his belly. He was wearing a very brief pair of tan swimming trunks that cupped his manhood and nothing much else. The colour blended so closely with his skin tone that at first she really had thought he was naked.

He grinned as he saw her glancing at them. 'For Paul's sake. Normally I don't bother when I'm alone, or with a beautiful woman. Disappointed?'

Disappointed! Marlene seriously doubted there was a woman in the world who would find Rocco disappointing, even if he was dressed in rags. He was a superb specimen of the male sex, and he knew it. To hide her embarrassment at being caught staring at him, she swam across the pool to where Paul was gamely swimming along—but within reach of the side, as she had told him.

'Coward!' Rocco cried, before executing a perfect dive and entering the water with hardly a splash.

Surprisingly, the next half-hour was pure fun. Rocco surfaced right beside Paul and proceeded to play with the boy in the water. A ball was found and Marlene was roped into a hilarious game of piggy-in-the-middle—and of course the two males made her the piggy first. She didn't mind; she was simply relieved that Rocco appeared to have forgotten his anger and dire threats of earlier.

Paul was too small to play in the water, so he took up position on the side of the pool, with Marlene swimming around a few feet away and Rocco behind her. It was exhausting but exhilarating. Rocco seemed to take a perverse delight in jumping almost on top of her, never mind where the ball was. Paul roared with laughter in between yelling, 'Get Mar—get her!'

So much for family loyalty, Marlene thought, swimming rapidly to where the ball had landed in the deepest part of the pool. She closed her arms around it, and in her excitement at finally winning shouted, '*Vincita*—I win!' Only to have two strong hands close around her slender waist and drag her down beneath the water. She lost the ball, but that was the least of her worries.

In a tangle of arms and legs they sank to the bottom of the pool. Rocco's strongly muscled thigh slid between her wildly kicking legs and pressed against the most intimate part of her body. Holding her down with one arm anchored around her waist, he slid his hand up over her breast, lingering until he felt her nipple peak in stark arousal, before curving it up and around her throat.

His hard mouth covered hers. She grasped his shoulders, his neck—anywhere—and hung on, the feel of his near-naked body hard against her sending shock waves of sensual awareness surging through her. Eyes tightly closed, she opened her mouth to the pressure of his, and their tongues met and stroked and sucked. Her hand slid over his shoulder and traced his spine as she had imagined doing earlier. She was drowning in a sea of sensations she had never suspected existed before.

They almost did drown, as neither could bear to break the passionate embrace. Finally they rose to the surface, both breathless. Their eyes locked, Rocco's black with passion and Marlene's wide, golden and dazzled by the man whose strong arm was still curved around her waist. She needed the support. Her insides had turned to jelly and her flesh burned with a fire the cool water could not assuage.

For a long piquant moment they simply stared at each

other, both of one mind. The mutual need, want, had been recognised and finally accepted between them.

'You kissed my Mar,' was the first thing Marlene registered over the pounding of her heart.

She tore her gaze away from Rocco at the same time as she pushed out of his arms, and, not daring to look at him, she swam to the side and dragged herself out of the water.

Rocco was right behind her, but he did not get out of the pool. Instead, he clung to the side and, grinning up at Paul's serious face, said, 'Yes, I kissed Marlene—and very nice it was too.'

Marlene was flushed from head to toe with embarrassment and the lingering effects of her passionate encounter with Rocco. 'Really, Rocco,' she remonstrated. 'Paul is too young for that kind of talk.'

'Don't be such a prude. He is half-Italian, after all, and Italian boys understand the delightful difference between the male and the female much sooner than most.'

If it was possible, Marlene's face turned even redder. He was deliberately teasing her, she knew, but she wasn't going to let him get away with it. 'Come out of the pool and say that,' she charged, and, arching one delicately shaped brow, added slyly, 'If you dare.' She had a good idea why he was hiding in the water. Her flesh was still tingling from the pressure of his rock-hard arousal and, remembering the brevity of his swimming trunks, she doubted he was in a fit state to reveal himself.

'Dare? I dare anything. But are you sure you're ready for this, Marlene?' And, laughing at her shocked expression, he leant his arms on the side of the pool and was halfway out of the water in a second.

'No!' she cried, and, catching him off guard, she lashed out with one slender foot at his broad shoulder and pushed. He fell backwards into the water with a great splash, his arms splaying in the air as his head sank below the surface. Strike one for me, she thought smugly.

'Come on, Paul.' Taking her brother's hand, she pulled him away from the poolside and headed towards the house. 'We've both had enough of the sun for one day—we don't want to burn.' The trouble was, she thought with fatalistic conviction, it was too late for her. She would burn for Rocco for the rest of her life.

'But what about Roc?' Paul demanded.

'He's big enough to look after himself,' she muttered, and then, glancing back over her shoulder, she stopped, her temperature soaring again as Rocco hauled himself out of the pool in one lithe movement. With the water running off his splendid torso, his black hair plastered to his head and chest, he took her breath away. He looked like some mythical Greek god rising from the deep. He straightened up and his eyes caught her glance. She expected him to be furious but he confounded her. Shaking his head in a shower of waterdrops glistening in the noon sun like a halo, he strode towards her.

'Marlene, you're a constant source of surprise, with the depths of hidden secrets in your golden eyes which a man could spend a lifetime trying to unravel,' Rocco told her with a wry grin.

'I don't know what you mean,' she said haughtily.

Rocco chuckled, and, throwing an arm around her shoulders, he commanded, 'Come on, let's go inside and cool off.' Catching Paul with his free hand, he swung him up in his other arm. 'Your sister is feeling the heat, Paul, and we men have to look after the ladies,' he opined, with a wickedly sexual slanting glance at Marlene's scarlet face.

She would never understand Rocco in a million years, Marlene thought a little while later. The three of them were sitting around the stainless-steel table in the kitchen, still in their swimwear, and tucking into a lunch of various cold meats along with several types of salad and an assortment of fresh fruit. When Marlene had suggested they should get changed before lunch, Rocco had quickly declared that it was not necessary and had gone on to explain that Eta and Aldo usually had Sunday off. They had only stayed this morning because of Marlene's visit. Now they had left and would not be back until tomorrow morning. They had the place to themselves and casual was the order of the day.

She wasn't sure she liked the idea of being in the house with only Rocco and Paul for company. But as they hungrily devoured the food Rocco, with his easy humour and casual conversation and almost brotherly behaviour towards herself and Paul, lulled her into a sense of security. He really was a very nice man…

Marlene drained her glass of mineral water and after replacing it on the table sat back with a sigh of contentment. She didn't know why Rocco's attitude had changed so drastically from the brooding, angry man of this morning, but she was too happy to query it. For a while at least she was determined to forget why she was here and simply enjoy the moment.

'Had enough to eat, Paul?' she asked, smiling as he tried to stuff one more juicy strawberry in his mouth, almost missing and smearing his nose with red juice.

'Yes,' he said, and, yawning widely, added, 'I'm full.'

'You're also tired,' Rocco said softly, and, getting to his feet, he picked Paul out of his chair and swung him up in his arms. 'Time for a nap, little man.'

Marlene expected her brother to protest, but to her amazement he laid his head on Rocco's broad shoulder and mumbled, 'Yes.'

They made a lovely picture—the boy's dark head cradled close to the man's equally dark one by a strong, protective hand. They could almost be father and son, she thought, and the idea brought a dreamy glow to Marlene's eyes. To have Rocco's baby, to have him hold her in the same protective way as he held Paul would be heaven…

'I hope you're not falling asleep on me as well.' Rocco's husky drawl snapped her out of her daydream and, flushing scarlet, she jumped out of her seat.

'No, no, of course not. Give him to me.' She faced him with her head high and her back straight. Her dishevelled blonde hair was almost dry now, and beginning to curl haphazardly around her shoulders. 'I'll put him to bed.' And she held out her arms expectantly.

His eyes held hers for a moment, and then they dropped, travelling over her, insolently lingering where her swimsuit moulded to her breasts and hips. A mocking smile curved his lips. 'No, I will. I think you'd better get some clothes on—unless you want me to put you to bed as well.'

Marlene bristled like an angry cat. 'In your dreams,' she snapped.

'You're already in my dreams,' he said throatily. 'And if I wasn't carrying Paul I'd give you a taste of the reality.' A gleam of sensual amusement made his dark eyes sparkle, and ignited an answering sparkle in Marlene's.

'You're impossible,' she opined, with a slight smile and a rueful shake of her fair head. She glanced at Paul; he was fast asleep in Rocco's arms. Now was no time to argue, and, turning, she said, 'Follow me.'

She walked straight through her bedroom and into the dressing room. She picked up the coverlet from the narrow bed and murmured softly, 'Be careful—lower him down gently and I'll tuck him in.'

'I'm not about to drop him from a great height,' Rocco drawled sarcastically, while placing Paul carefully on the bed.

'I know.' Marlene felt ashamed of herself. 'I didn't mean to imply you would,' she said, keeping her voice low.

'Good.' Rocco straightened up and inadvertently brushed

against her shoulder. He put out a hand to steady her, and the light touch was enough to make her tense.

She glanced up at him. Their eyes met and held and Marlene felt her heart begin to beat faster. She dropped her head and bent over the bed. Fussily she set about arranging the cover over the sleeping child—anything to avoid looking at the man beside her.

'Relax, Marlene, I'm going for a shower and to change. I suggest you do the same.' And with a last look at the sleeping boy Rocco walked out of the room.

Marlene tossed her head back and let the powerful spray wash the last of the shampoo out of her long hair, then, turning off the shower, she stepped out of the cubicle and picked a fluffy white towel off the black towel rail. She wrapped it around her naked body, tying it in a knot between her breasts. Taking another, smaller towel, she briskly rubbed the excess water from her hair and crossed the vanity basin. A hairdryer was conveniently attached to the wall, and with little effort she turned it on and began the tedious process of drying her hair.

Gradually her mind went back over the events of the past two days as mechanically she brushed and blow-dried her hair. Rocco's meeting her at the airport had been a shock, but she could not deny that her heart had skipped a beat, and the instant attraction she had felt for him the first time she had seen him had been as strong as ever, if not more so... But the fact that he worked for the Contessa—even if he had appeared to defend Paul over the sale of the house this morning—meant that though she might love him she could never trust him. Her hand stopped in mid-sweep, and she stared at her reflection in the vanity mirror. The dreamy-eyed image that stared back at her horrified her.

Love! Oh, no! She couldn't! She must not love the man. Physical attraction, lust—anything but love. She brushed her hair with renewed vigour, trying to blot out her way-ward thoughts with the sound of the dryer. Think of the information from the telephone call this morning, she told herself firmly, which virtually confirms Andretti's deceit. But somehow all she could think about was being in Rocco's arms.

She remembered the first evening he had taken her out to dinner, how she had returned to her own home and melted into his arms in her own hallway. She had almost let him make love to her! It was no wonder he had believed she had been an old man's mistress—a woman who made love easily and freely. She had behaved no better today, entwined in his embrace in the swimming pool. It was an intolerable situation. She had to keep him at arm's length for the next few days—at least until the board meeting was over.

A small voice whispered derisively in her head, Who are you kidding? He touches you and you melt. Marlene wanted to deny it, but her own innate honesty would not let her. She sighed and, tilting her head to the side, flicked the hairdryer under her hair one last time. Then, straight-ening up, she reached to switch it off. But another hand was there before her.

'What…' The word echoed in the sudden silence. She half turned, and Rocco was standing right beside her. The sound of the hairdryer had masked his entry.

His hand slid into her hair and he stroked its length. 'It's beautiful, like spun gold,' he said huskily, his dark eyes fixed on her shining hair.

Marlene trembled. She was standing naked but for a towel, and Rocco was far too close and far too tempting. He had changed into shorts and a short-sleeved shirt he had not bothered to fasten. 'Wh-what are you doing?' she stam-mered inanely.

His hand tangled in her hair and he tugged, pulling back

her head. 'I'm kissing you,' he said, and his mouth slowly lowered to her lips, as if he was giving her time to object.

She knew she should reject him, escape, but her foolish heart would not let her. She felt his muscular arm enfold her and draw her close even as his mouth touched hers, warm and strangely tender, as if he was reassuring her, dispelling all her fears. All thought of resistance vanished. She met his kiss with her own, mouth soft and lips gently parted, and when his tongue probed the warm, moist depths a shudder of desire arched through her body.

His hand tightened in her hair and then loosened, his fingers drifting to where the towel was secured between her breasts. His thumb brushed enticingly across a hard peak, and then with one swift movement the towel fell apart.

Marlene made a little cry of protest which died when his other hand stroked down over her bottom and the towel fell to the floor. His mouth lifted from hers and he looked down into her golden eyes, then lower, to where the fullness of her breasts was exposed to his hungry gaze, and lower still, to where golden curls marked the centre of her femininity. Cool air touched her and with it doubt. But even as she thought of resistance he groaned—a harsh, guttural sound.

'God, but you're magnificent,' he grated as he bent her over one arm. His dark head lowered and his tongue rasped across one aching breast; with his other hand he cupped its partner and teased the sensitive peak between his fingers. As his mouth suckled her she knew she was powerless to deny him, or herself…

Her hand came up and clasped his head, holding him to her breast, inviting him, urging him to continue. His fingers teased and tortured, and heat and hunger for him welled up inside her like a tidal wave. She gasped and clung to him when he lifted his head and drew away slightly. She stared up at him and saw the stark, glittering desire glowing in his eyes. He wanted her as desperately as she wanted him.

'Rocco.' She whispered his name and then his mouth covered hers again, and she was lost in a sensual world of feeling where only his touch existed. She slid her hands down over his hair-roughened chest and up and under his shirt, her hands stroking up his bare back.

'Yes, yes,' Rocco growled, and, swinging her into his arms, one arm beneath her knees and the other around her back, he carried her into the bedroom.

'Paul—we can't—' She tried to object but he simply lifted her higher, his hair brushing her burning skin as he buried his head between her naked breasts, kissing the silken hollow before letting his tongue flick each taut nipple in turn. And she was lost once more—lost in realms of sensual pleasure she had never dreamed possible.

'We can.' He spoke against her flesh. 'Trust me.'

He lowered her onto the bed, and her eyes flew open when he left her. She had just begun to focus enough to realise that she was stark naked in a room she had never seen before, and to wonder how on earth she had let it go so far, when her gaze fell on Rocco and she had her answer. He had thrown off his shirt and was un-fastening the snap of his shorts. Mesmerised, she watched as he removed a packet from his pocket, dropped it on the bedside table, then stripped off his shorts and briefs in one fluid movement before turning to her.

Her gasp of awe was tinged with a feminine fear. He was unashamedly, magnificently male, his bronzed body gleaming in a ray of sunlight streaming through the window.

Then he was beside her, and he breathed her name in a low, throaty growl. 'Marlene—at last. Let me look at you.' And, propping his head on his arm, he stared down at her softly shaped feminine form with rapt attention. He trailed one finger from her mouth to her chin, down her throat, over the valley of her breast, across her navel and to the tangle of curls at the juncture of her thighs.

'Rocco, it's daylight,' she groaned suddenly, overcome with embarrassment even as her flesh quivered in ecstasy at his touch. 'We should talk…' She was babbling, but the enormity of what she was about to do had finally sunk into her bemused brain. She had only ever had one lover—Julian—and it had not been much fun. She had not really enjoyed it.

Rocco, his black eyes burning into hers, rasped, 'Later, my lovely little liar. I have to have you now.' And he blocked any response by kissing her, his mouth hard and demanding, branding her his.

A brief warning flashed in her mind. 'Lovely little liar'— he had not forgotten. Fighting her arousal, she tried to say no. But as his long fingers delved into the soft curls to the hot, moist warmth beneath she betrayed herself and moaned, 'Yes,' her legs parting involuntarily as he stoked the fire of her sexuality with teasing touches and silken caresses. Marlene let her love and her need for him sweep away all her reservations and inhibitions, glorying in his masculinity.

Her small hands curved up over his broad chest. She scratched a small male nipple and felt him tremble. Then her hands curved round his back, her nails digging into his flesh as the tension inside her built to fever-pitch. She stroked one hand down over his hard buttock and round to his flat stomach, loving the feel of his satin-smooth flesh beneath her fingers, the pulsating power of his manhood.

It was Rocco's turn to groan. 'Yes. God, yes!' And, reaching to the bedside table, he quickly found the protection.

Before Marlene had time to realise what he was doing he was kneeling between her thighs, his hands curved under her bottom. He lifted her up to him and then he kissed her. Her head fell back and her heart seemed to stop. Never had she been kissed so intimately. She tried again to say no, but it was lost; she could not deny her innermost desire as he moved swiftly over and into her. She winced once, and he stopped.

'You're not a virgin?' he groaned, his muscles bunching as he fought for control, his tormented black eyes burning down into hers.

But her body was adapting to his size and power and she clenched around him. 'No—no!' she cried, desperate for him to continue. 'It's been a long—' She didn't finish. Rocco thrust again and their bodies fused in a fierce, primitive rhythm.

The passion that exploded between them was ferocious and total. The climax, when it came, was so savage and so exquisitely prolonged that Marlene realised in a moment of blinding clarity that this was the man she had been born for. Her past experience was as nothing to the wonder of Rocco. She lay entangled with him as passion gave way to languor, relishing their closeness as she held his hot, sweat-soaked body against her, and as he moved her arms tightened around his back, reluctant to let him go.

'I'm too heavy,' he gasped raggedly, fighting to steady his breathing.

'No,' she murmured, looking up into his dark face, 'you're perfect.'

He smiled and gently brushed her swollen lips with his. 'No, darling,' he said, and, easing onto his side, he leant over her, carefully sweeping a few strands of blonde hair from her damp brow. '*You're* perfect.'

Her golden eyes gleamed up into his. 'Are we going to argue again?' she teased, lifting her hands to rest on his broad chest, loving this tender side of him.

He caught her hands in one of his, and slid his other arm under her shoulders, holding her close to him. 'We are never going to argue again,' Rocco declared emphatically. 'What we have together is too magnificent…too…' He squeezed her hands against his chest, his dark eyes searching her lovely face. 'I can't find the words in English to tell you how you make me feel.'

She gazed up at him, her golden eyes still glowing with the embers of passion. 'I know,' she said simply. An arrested expression flitted across his handsome face, and she wondered if he had realised she loved him. But she could not have been more wrong.

His shrewd dark eyes narrowed on her upturned face. 'You and I have to talk.'

'Must we?' Marlene murmured, running her foot lightly up his muscular leg, trying to divert him. For some reason he sounded grim, and it frightened her. She did not want to lose the elation, the intimate bonding their lovemaking had created—not yet! Not ever!

'Stop that.' His legs moved to trap hers and, freeing her hands, he lifted his hand to cup her chin. 'You cried out in the pool today in Italian, and I haven't forgotten how you pretended to be Rossi's mistress and Paul's mother.'

'Rocco, I… Paul will be awake…' She was searching for an excuse to delay the inevitable.

He stopped her words with a hard command. 'Whatever you are going to say, try making it the truth this time, Marlene.' His voice was flat, devoid of any emotion, and a chill shivered over her naked flesh.

She looked into his taut face and cold black eyes returned her gaze. Her teeth worried at her lip; she wasn't sure what to say, what to do. Surely he could not make love to her so desperately one minute and then reject her the next? Yet that was what it felt like. Maybe to him it was just sex… Shame and humiliation swept over her. She had given her heart and he had given nothing.

She closed her eyes, fighting back the tears, battling to regain her self-control. She refused to give him the satisfaction of knowing he had hurt her, and, adopting a mantle of cool reserve, she said simply, 'Let me up and I'll explain.'

'All right.' His voice was clipped. His hands and legs left her and he stood up.

She opened her eyes and, very aware of her naked state, sat up and pulled the coverlet up to her chin.

Rocco pulled on his shorts, sat down on the edge of the bed and said curtly, 'Begin.'

She searched his starkly austere face for some sign of the lover of moments ago, but it was a futile task. He had hooked one leg over his knee, his body angled towards her, and the light gleamed on his broad, tanned shoulders, outlining his handsome features. But she could see no expression in his partially hooded eyes. 'I don't know where to start,' she began, all her earlier reservations about Rocco suddenly returning to torment her.

'At the beginning is usually a good idea,' he said sardonically.

'Thank you,' she replied sarcastically, and, remembering the beginning, she went white to the lips. How could she have been so dumb? His plan had been to seduce her and he had certainly succeeded. With the realisation something snapped inside her. She sat up straighter, tucked the coverlet under her arms and let him have it...

'Paolo and my mother loved each other deeply—something you would not understand.' She fired the words at him, thinking bitterly of how very recently she had deluded herself in his arms. But she would not let herself think of her humiliation; she was too angry. 'You and Caterina appeared at my home, decided I was Rossi's mistress and roundly insulted me, my mother and Paul. And, yes, I *do* speak Italian—very well. As I recall, ''low-life'' was mentioned, ''peasant'' and ''bastard'', to name but a few.

'Then, of course, there was the plan to seduce me—the unfit mother scam to gain control of the boy.' Her eyes spitting fury as she warmed to her theme, she continued, 'Oh, and let's not forget Caterina's latest idea. You should have dropped us over a cliff on the way here. You make me sick. You have the audacity to question *me* about the truth? Don't make me laugh... Just get out!'

His face went grey beneath his tan. 'Oh, my God!' he breathed, and for a moment she thought she saw anguish in his dark eyes. But she was wrong. It was anger. With a terrific effort of will he suppressed the violent emotions her tirade had aroused and said coldly, 'But you know the old saying—eavesdroppers never hear good of themselves. I did ask if you spoke my language.'

'I see, so it's all my fault?' she spat.

'No, I am as much to blame. And I apologise if anything I said offended you. But I had seen you in a restaurant years earlier with Rossi—we were introduced. It was a natural mistake to make. A mistake, moreover, you could have corrected immediately with one word,' he drawled harshly.

'On that particular day Paolo and I had just come from the mortuary after identifying the mangled body of my mother. We couldn't have cared less what opinion you formed in your dirty mind. We had lost a woman we loved and had a one-year-old child to worry about. Whereas, if I recall correctly, your only problem was the red-haired woman hanging on your arm and a contemptuous holier-than-thou attitude. An attitude you still had when you appeared last week at The Johanson Herb Garden. Why the hell should I tell you anything?'

Rocco sucked in a deep breath, closed his eyes for a second and shivered. 'I did not know. I could not have known about your mother, and I'm sorry from the bottom of my heart.' And he looked at her with such compassion that Marlene almost believed him. Until he qualified his behaviour. 'I freely admit I should not have spoken to Caterina about you the way I did, but she is a friend of long standing and you I had only met once before. I was only trying to help her and her mother.'

'Help the Contessa to rob a young boy?' Marlene interjected.

'No, never that.'

'You're a lawyer—I thought they were supposed to have ethics? Though according to your father you're not a very good one,' she sneered.

A grim smile curved his hard mouth and, leaning forward on the bed, he grabbed her by the shoulders. His dark face was only inches from her own. 'I am not a lawyer. I was simply doing a favour for my father by accompanying Caterina to England and repeating what he had told me to say.'

'But you said—' she began angrily, then she stopped, confusion clearly visible in the golden eyes that met his gaze. Had he actually told her he was a lawyer? Or had he just said he was representing his father's firm?

His long fingers dug into her shoulders. 'Marlene, I think it is time for me to explain, before the confusion gets any worse. I am a consultant geologist for a host of large companies worldwide. I spend most of my time abroad—South America, Australia, Africa, wherever I am needed. I have a house not far from here, as I told you—my mother left it to me. It is my home, and I also have an office in Rome. My father has his law practice in Naples and an apartment there. We rarely see each other. As you have probably noticed, we do not get on very well together.'

'Why not?' The question slipped out. Her anger was fading in the face of his revelation. She was intrigued. She could see him as a geologist much more easily than as a lawyer. Now she understood the Contessa's comment about Rocco with his head in the ground and her lips twitched in amusement.

His hands loosened on her shoulders, stroking gently. 'It

isn't funny. I was ten when I first discovered my father had a mistress and I saw my mother in tears. My mother should have left him then; she was a wealthy woman in her own right, half-Italian and half-Irish. Her father owned a large brewing company and a vineyard, and she was his sole heir. But it would not have suited my father; he liked having a string of mistresses,' Rocco said with a tinge of contempt.

'As a young man I had very little respect for my father, and the fact that I would not follow him into the law put a bigger strain on our relationship. A week after the death of my mother I went to South Africa, and when I returned to Italy, a couple of weeks ago, I suppose I thought I should try one last time to get on with my father. He is the only relative I have left. When he asked me to go to England and sort out the money-grubbing mistress Paolo Rossi had left behind, for the sake of the Contessa and Caterina I agreed.

'Our families have been friends for years, both spending the holidays here in Amalfi. I've got to know Caterina well—I think of her almost as a sister—and I learnt long ago the only way to handle her is to humour her. As a small child she would fly into a tantrum to get her own way, and though I have not seen as much of her over the past fifteen years it seems old habits die hard. An argument with Caterina is a futile exercise; it is much easier to agree with her even if one does not. But believe me,' he added darkly, 'no one regrets what was said more than me.

'I can't entirely blame Caterina; I was quite happy to go along with her. I have no excuse. I listened to my father's side of the story, damning the English mistress, and believed him. Perhaps I wanted to believe him because I had never quite been able to put your face out of my mind from that very first time I saw you in the restaurant with Paolo. I spoke to you and you barely registered I was there. I suppose my male ego took a blow... I thought, How could such a beautiful young girl possibly prefer an old man? Then, when I saw you again, the same thought taunted me and I wanted to believe the worst.

'I should have remembered there are always two sides in any broken relationship. I had no right to judge why Rossi parted from his wife or his choice of mistress. I wish I could take back the hard words I said about you and yours, but I can't. I formed a judgement on prejudice and my own wounded pride. I had no right. I can only say I am sorry. I hope you will forgive me.'

His apology sounded as sincere as it had been revealing, and Marlene would have liked to be able to accept it whole-heartedly and apologise honestly in return. But unfortunately she could not...

Picking her words carefully, she said in a voice tinged with regret for what might have been, 'We have both been playing games.' But a relationship without trust was a non-starter—even with her limited experience she knew that much—and even now she could not tell him the complete truth. 'I'm sorry for pretending to be Paolo's mistress and Paul's mother, and for not admitting I speak Italian. But my business will be settled and I will be out of here by next weekend. Perhaps we should just leave it at that.'

'I can't.' Rocco gave a small, ironic smile. 'Nor, I think, can you.'

'What do you mean?' A glimmer of hope leapt in her breast. Did he mean he cared enough to forget all the past mistakes?

'I behaved like a swine in England, and I'm sorry. But this thing between us is too good to let go. After all, ge-ologist and gardener is a much more compatible relation-ship than that of lawyer and gardener. I think we should investigate the possibilities, don't you?' And, bending slowly, he planted a soft kiss on her swollen lips. Then, raising his head, he smiled into her wide, astonished eyes.

'No more games. Complete honesty between us from this moment forth.'

She was tempted to tell all but, lowering her lashes to disguise the guilt that shaded her golden eyes, she only murmured, 'I hope so.' Rocco was being so open, but she still had doubts.

'And, Marlene,' Rocco continued, 'Caterina did not have to tell me to seduce you. I decided to do it the moment I set eyes on you—for my own sake and nobody else's—and I hope to do it over and over and over again,' he opined in a husky drawl, and, sliding his hands from her shoulders down her back, he pulled her against him. Her breasts nestled against his chest and her gasp of surprise was swallowed by his mouth capturing hers in a long, hot kiss. Her doubts were going up in smoke as her temperature rose…

CHAPTER EIGHT

RELUCTANTLY Marlene raised her hands to his bare chest and pushed out of his embrace. 'Wait, Rocco,' she demanded breathlessly. She loved him too much to deceive him. He had to know about her real career, her primary reason for coming to Italy, the suspicions she had about Andretti. Obviously her informant had meant *Carlo* Andretti, and not the wonderful man in whose arms she lay. She was convinced of that…

'I know, I know,' he said, giving her a quick squeeze and then standing up. 'Paul will be awake any minute. I'll go and check on him.'

With a little space between them, Marlene's common sense returned and—coward that she was!—she leapt at the excuse he had given her to avoid the confession. 'Yes,' she agreed, with a wide smile that was part relief as well as pleasure. It could not hurt to delay a little longer, she told herself. Why upset their new relationship so soon? And telling the truth might well do that. Tucking the sheet firmly around her body, she began to get up, adding, 'And I'd better get dressed.'

'Stay where you are for an hour or so. I will amuse Paul,' Rocco drawled, his lips curling in a sensuous smile. 'I want you wide awake later; I fully intend to take up where we left off.'

'You're incorrigible,' she chuckled. 'But a siesta is out. I don't want Paul to find me in your bedroom,' she said, with a quick glance around the room, surprised to notice that it was almost the same as hers, but smaller.

'This isn't my room.' The sensual gleam in his eyes

deepened as his large hand curved over her naked shoulder and pushed her back. 'If you recall, we were in rather a hurry to get into bed.' Marlene blushed bright red at the reminder, and Rocco's grin widened. 'Your bed was out, in case Paul walked in, so I simply carried you to the room next door.' His gaze dropped from her lovely face to her full breasts, sending a delicious shiver of awareness through her body. He noticed, and added wryly, 'And if I don't get out of here in the next second I'll be back in the bed with you.'

'Promises, promises,' Marlene teased.

'Witch,' he shot back, and, placing a swift kiss on the top of her head, he straightened up. 'Do as you're told and have a rest.'

'As you command, O Master.' Marlene lay back, a slumberous smile tilting her lips. Her eyes travelled over his wide shoulders, down to his flat stomach and on to where his shorts, open at the waist, clung perilously to his lean hips. The promise of the night to come was enough to make her stomach curl. A rest was a good idea…

Rocco grinned down at her. 'Cheeky,' he said, and, turning with a last glance around at the stark black and white décor of the room, he added as he crossed to the door, 'Mind you, all the rooms in this house look the same. Awful. I can't imagine why anyone would want the place.'

At the door he blew her a kiss, but Marlene had already closed her eyes. She didn't see him leave. She opened them when she heard the door close, and sighed. What was the matter with her? Her emotions were all over the place. One minute she was ready to reveal everything to Rocco, then he made a simple comment about the villa and she was immediately suspicious again.

Had he said the house was awful simply to make her feel better about getting rid of it? He knew the deal she had made with the Contessa was all in that lady's favour. She had heard him arguing about it. Yet he had never mentioned it to Marlene. Perhaps her secrets were best kept to herself for a little while longer… One afternoon of love-making did not necessarily mean that Rocco loved her.

Much later in the afternoon, with Paul quite happily playing in the pool with Rocco, Marlene, wearing her favourite denim shorts and a blue vest-top, sunned herself on a lounger, her eyes following the antics of the two males in her life with fond indulgence. Rocco certainly had a way with the boy, she mused, and it had been kind of him this morning to show Paul where he and his father used to go fishing. Talking about the other man as his friend had probably helped the little boy accept his father's death more than any grief counsellor ever could. It was funny to think of Paolo Rossi befriending Rocco; he must have been years older.

'Why the frown? Feeling neglected?' Rocco's deep, husky voice broke into her thoughts.

She looked up. He was standing at the foot of the lounger, beads of water glistening on his bronzed skin, all vibrant male, and without thinking she asked, 'How old are you?'

He gazed back at her, a warm, quizzical look in his eyes. 'Thirty-seven—but what brought that on?'

'Watching you with Paul.' She glanced around. 'Where is he?'

'Gone into the kitchen. But you haven't answered my question.' Pulling up a lounger, he sat on the side of it.

'I was thinking of your friendship with his father. Paolo must have been a lot older than you.' Marlene turned her head to look at him. A pensive, reminiscent glow lightened his dark eyes.

'Yes, he was, but he always had time for me—even when he was still single and sowing his wild oats. And by all accounts he was quite wild…' He chuckled, and with a shake of his dark head continued, 'But I remember that shortly after I had learnt about my father's infidelities Paolo came to stay with us. I had not seen him for a long time. He had been in England, I think, on business. He must have been around thirty then, and was already very successful.

'My father was his friend and lawyer, yet when I broke down and told Paolo what I had discovered, how I hated my father for hurting my mother and how it wasn't fair, he was marvellous. He had just got engaged to the Contessa at the time, but he took time to comfort me and explained that once I was grown up I would discover life wasn't fair. That a man could only try and do the best he could, and try not to hurt anyone in the process.'

'That's beautiful,' she said softly.

Rocco shrugged. 'Yes, maybe.' His mouth hardened. 'But it didn't stop Rossi doing exactly the same to his wife a few years later.' When Marlene stared at him he added deliberately, 'Never confuse great sex with love, that is my motto.'

As a warning it was very effective. She looked at him for a long, tense moment, before returning with a sarcasm she did not try to hide, 'And I suppose you have known both and never recognised either?' And, swinging her legs off the other side of the lounger, she made to stand up.

Rocco leaned forward and caught her arm, forcing her to remain seated.

'Let me go,' she said tonelessly.

He turned her to face him, his grip gentle but firm. 'I recognise I want you,' he said smoothly, his dark brown eyes searching her face. 'Marlene, look at me.'

She lifted her lashes, giving him a hard stare. A large hand touched her hair and brushed it from her brow almost tenderly, and she trembled. He smiled, and she thought how humiliatingly easy it was for him to bend her to his will. A simple touch…

'We want each other. Let's not spoil what we have by analysing every word we say, hmm?'

'I—yes, all right,' she heard herself agree meekly, and even more meekly lifted her head for his kiss.

'That's the second time you've kissed Mar. Does that mean you're getting married?' a little voice asked from behind the loungers.

'Good God, no!' Rocco exclaimed, standing up abruptly. 'I've kissed dozens of girls in my time. It didn't mean I was going to marry them.'

Marlene laughed out loud at the look of astonishment on Rocco's face, but inside her heart shrivelled a little. He had set the parameters of their relationship in no uncertain terms. A passionate affair…

She was suddenly very glad she had not told Rocco the whole truth. Her judgement was seriously affected by the man. After next Friday, and the board meeting, if he still wanted to see her, fine. But until then she would keep her own counsel. It was by far the safest way…

'Come on, Paul.' Rocco picked the little boy up in his arms. 'I can see you and I need to have a man-to-man talk, and at the same time we'll set up the barbecue.' Smiling down at Marlene, his expression bland, he added, 'And you, lady, get to the kitchen and make a salad. You have two hungry men on your hands.' Bending down, he kissed her—a fleeting, impersonal brush of his lips over hers. And yet it sent her emotions haywire.

How did he do that? she wondered, marching off towards the kitchen, masculine laughter following her every step of the way. And why did she let him? was her next furious thought as she strode inside.

A few minutes later, pulling lettuce leaves apart like a demented shrew, she had her answer when she looked out of the window. Rocco and Paul were placing pieces of char-coal on the barbecue in between throwing them at each other, and they were both getting filthy in the process. God help her! Because she loved him...

She stared sightlessly through the window, refusing to allow herself to feel sad... That way lay an anguish too deep to be borne. Instead she concentrated on the positive. For a few glorious days she could have Rocco, the man she loved, as her lover. It would have to be enough... Enough to last her through a lifetime of loneliness. Because she knew she would never love another man. Her mother had been a one-man woman and she knew she was the same...

Afterwards, back home in England, it might not be so bad. She had a brilliant career, and the family business had provided a very respectable income for almost half a century and would continue to do so. She would never know the wonder of giving birth to her own child, but she was luckier than most in that she had Paul. She had mothered him from a very young age, and all the pleasure of watching him grow and learn would be hers. Yes, she could do it...

Her gaze dropped down to the bench and the pile of mangled lettuce. Her mind was made up. She would take whatever Rocco had to offer. She was twenty-six, more than old enough to handle a sophisticated affair, and when they parted—as they surely must—she would walk away with her head held high, no regrets, no recriminations.

Swinging round with a new determination in her step, she opened the refrigerator and took out a bowl of tomatoes and a plate of juicy-looking steaks. When Rocco and Paul entered the kitchen five minutes later she was busily slicing tomatoes and looking as if she had not a care in the world. Only a very close observer would have noticed the shadow of restraint in her golden-brown eyes as she smiled brightly and said, 'Well, that's my part done. I'll leave the burning of the meat to you two.'

Dinner was a hilarious affair. Marlene insisted on her steak being so well done that Rocco grimaced in disgust when he finally plopped it on her plate.

'You weren't kidding when you talked about burning the meat. Do you honestly like burnt steak?'

She was seated at the glass-topped table on the terrace, with Paul beside her. The salad, bread, wine and condiments had all been lined up like a row of soldiers by Paul. She looked up at Rocco with a tilted head and a wicked smile. 'I'm a lady who likes everything well done,' she drawled, with conscious provocation.

He gazed back at her, a hot, predatory look in his eyes. 'I will remind you of that later,' he growled. And he did…

Marlene lay entangled with him, her limbs heavy, her eyelids drooping, stated in the aftermath of their loving. Rocco eased his weight away but held her to his hard body. Gradually the sensual haze drained away and Marlene attempted to move.

'What do you think you are doing?' Rocco murmured, his breath against her ear.

'I have to get back to my room. Paul wakes early—and don't forget Aldo and Eta will be back in the morning. I'm not sleeping with you when they're here.'

'Damn.' Rocco rolled over on his back and laced his fingers behind his head. 'I suppose you're right.'

Marlene leaned over him and pressed a last, lingering kiss to his lips. 'You know I am.' Her breasts pressing against his chest sent a renewed tremor of awareness shuddering through her, and she sighed. The pale light of dawn was already filtering through the window. She had to go.

He swooped with the speed of an eagle. His hand clasped her nape and he brought her mouth back down to meet his in a fierce, passionate kiss. 'Not yet,' he growled, and, grasping her around the waist, he lifted her over him.

Straddled across his muscular thighs, she moaned, her head falling back as his mouth found the rigid peak of her full breast and suckled fiercely while his hand rolled its partner between his fingers. 'We can't...' she tried to say.

But his hands curved round her buttocks and suddenly she was impaled by the hard, thrusting length of him. 'Your turn, Marlene. Ride me.' His black eyes burned up into hers and she slowly rotated her hips. Her golden eyes shooting flames, she bent forward and circled his mouth with her tongue in the same rhythm.

Time didn't matter. Nothing mattered, Marlene thought as once again she lost herself in the magic of the man. She did not recognise the woman she had become in Rocco's arms, but she gloried in the freedom to discover the wanton, demanding side of her nature. She was the one in control...

Pushing her hands against his chest, she arched back and held him still, allowing her slender fingers to scrape the small male nipples and then tease them as he had done to her while her long hair streamed down her back, brushing his thighs. But she wasn't in control for long...

'You want to play?' Rocco growled throatily, and suddenly his large hands linked around her slender waist. He held her in a grip of steel and bucked beneath her until he had taken her to the heights yet again.

Collapsed on top of him, touching him from shoulder to toes, her heart pounding, she breathed reluctantly, 'I must go.'

'Yes.' And a moment later he was carrying her naked in his arms back to her own room.

'I'm amazed you have the strength,' she whispered against his now rough jaw.

Rocco lowered her down on the bed and, pressing a last, light kiss to her brow, murmured softly, 'You give me the strength of ten men. Now go to sleep.' And silently he left the room.

Later that morning Marlene, glowing from her night of passion, supervised Paul's breakfast with one eye on him and the other on the door, anticipating Rocco's appearance. She had just filled Paul's glass with orange juice for the third time when Rocco walked into the kitchen.

She glanced up. His bronzed, perfectly carved features were relaxed in a wide smile. His tall, muscular body was clad in a black shirt that emphasised the natural width of his shoulders and well-washed denim jeans that clung to his lean hips and thighs. Suddenly she could see him as a geologist, prospecting in out-of-the-way places. He looked like a modern-day cowboy—quite the reverse of the sartorial elegance he displayed when Caterina and the Contessa were around. She could not control the leaping of her pulse as her eyes met his. He looked good enough to eat…

'Rocco, did you sleep well?' Nervously she burst into speech. Even after the intimacy they had shared she was still not sure how to behave; she had very little experience in morning-after protocol. Did she pretend it hadn't happened? Or throw herself in his arms and demand more? But Rocco solved her problem…

He threw his head back and laughed out loud. 'Like a log, sweetheart.' And in two lithe strides he was beside her, bending to press a kiss to her parted lips. 'How could you doubt it after last night?' he queried, his dark eyes looking tenderly down into hers, dispelling all her doubts.

'You look different this morning. I think it's the jeans,' she opined. 'Not your usual mode of dress…' she babbled on, and he stopped her with another kiss.

'Shows how little you know me. The Contessa, as you have learnt, demands a certain standard. I did try to explain that day in Amalfi, but you took it the wrong way.' Marlene remembered their argument about manners. 'When she's around it is easier to comply than argue. She turns puce at the sight of a man or woman in jeans.' And, mimicking the Contessa's voice remarkably well, he added, 'Jeans are for workmen, and not to be worn in the house.'

Marlene laughed, thrilled to learn yet another facet of Rocco's intriguing character. 'So really you're just as much of a slob as I am?' She grinned, and was rewarded with yet another kiss.

'You kissed Mar again!' Paul exclaimed, and, screwing up his little face, added, 'Ugh—sloppy.'

'Boy, have you got a lot to learn.' Rocco turned his attention to Paul. 'Hurry up and finish your breakfast. I'm taking you and Marlene to my home today.'

'Are you, now? And do I have any say in the matter?' Marlene demanded easily.

'Not if you want me again,' he breathed in her ear, sending a delicious shiver down her spine, as he brushed past her around the table to where the coffee-percolator stood on the bench.

'Devil,' Marlene murmured under her breath at his broad back—but not quietly enough, apparently.

Turning, Rocco winked—he knew very well what he did to her—then took a cup from the rack and poured himself a cup of coffee. 'Aldo and Eta have just arrived. I heard their car pull up as I dressed. We'll wait and say hello and then take off.' And, draining his coffee-cup, he replaced it on the bench. Grinning at her scarlet complexion, he walked around the table to where she still stood. 'I seem to remember you saying last night you wouldn't sleep with me with Aldo and Eta in the house,' he drawled huskily. 'I'm giving you an alternative.'

Trapped by the sensual gleam in his dark eyes, Marlene had great difficulty recalling anything. Even so, half an hour later she found herself seated next to Rocco in his low-slung sports car with Paul strapped into the back seat. Beside him was a bag containing their swimwear, a few toys and Rocco's weekend case.

'You could have moved in with me,' Rocco said, slanting her a glance as he manoeuvred the car down the twisting road. 'It would have been much easier. My housekeeper and her husband are on holiday for the summer. We'd have had absolute privacy.'

'I told you—no. Think how it would look to Paul—and don't forget your father. He's coming out to the villa one day this week with some papers for me to sign.' They had already had this argument earlier, when, after greeting Aldo and Eta, Rocco had followed her up to her room and suggested she pack everything and stay at his place. Marlene had been tempted, but common sense had prevailed and she had refused.

'Have it your own way,' Rocco muttered, and then, his mood brightening, he shot her a wicked grin. 'Love in the afternoon it is.'

Marlene's eyes widened in wonder as the car slipped through a stone arch set in a high wall completely covered in vividly coloured creepers and a profusion of brightly coloured flowers. They stopped in a paved courtyard before a long, low stucco-washed house with a mellow terracotta roof. The white and pink of oleanders and geraniums tumbled from windowsills and dozens of hanging baskets…even the chimney was covered with purple clematis.

'Welcome to my home,' Rocco said formally as he opened the car door for her to alight, then scooped Paul, bag and all, out of the back seat.

She stood up and simply stared. It was exactly as she imagined a Mediterranean villa should look. The contrast with the stark, barrack-like lines of the Rossi villa was incredible.

'Do you like it?' The question was almost hesitant.

She lifted glowing eyes up to his. 'It is beautiful—the most beautiful house I have ever seen,' she said. And it was.

Steps led up to a covered terrace supported by a row of Moorish arches covered in vines of every description. They walked up the steps and across the terrace to where a heavy arched door opened into the house. The hall stretched from front to back, with a corridor leading off either side. The floor was a brilliant blue and white marble mosaic, with a circle in the middle enclosing a marvellously mosaic picture of the god Bacchus. At the rear large French windows opened onto the garden beyond.

'Bacchus?' she queried, arching one delicate brow. 'A bit naughty.'

'Not at all. I told you—the house belonged to my mother's family; they were brewers and also kept a vineyard not far from here. I'll let you sample a bottle later, if you're good.'

'I always am,' she joked, looking up at him, and was stunned by the glitter of naked desire she saw in the depths of his eyes. A flash of awareness shot through her, frightening in its intensity.

'God! Don't I know it,' he husked; then, as if remembering they were not alone, he swallowed hard and continued calmly, 'To the right are the reception rooms, kitchen and utilities, and to the left the bedroom suites.'

With Paul in one arm, he took her hand in his and led her along the corridor to the left. He stopped outside the first door, and with a quick squeeze of her hand let her go. Opening the door, he indicated the room with a tilt of his dark head. 'You can change in here, but feel free to explore the place. Unfortunately I have a few calls to make, but I'll catch up with you later in the garden.'

Marlene looked around the room and smiled. It was charming. It had obviously been a young boy's room at some time. A single bed with a carved polished oak head-board stood at one side of the window, on the other side a matching wardrobe and desk. The furniture was old but classical. What really gave the game away was a long-forgotten poster of some footballer over the bed and a col-lection of pennants strung along the whitewashed wall. Somehow she could see Rocco as a young boy, spending his summers here.

With a delighted sigh, she swiftly divested Paul of his clothes and got him into his bathing trunks. Equally quickly she shed her shorts and shirt and slipped into her swimsuit. 'Come on.' She took Paul's hand. 'Let's explore.' And they did.

They headed straight for the French doors and the gar-den. A paved area led to a few steps down to a green lawn. It must take gallons of water to keep it so fresh in this heat, Marlene thought as they walked down the gentle slope to where another few steps led to the next level.

Here the mosaic of the hall was repeated in a huge square. In the centre of the square a shallow pool fed a waterfall that tumbled about two feet over rocks into a large circular swimming pool, the bottom of which sported an-other mosaic, this time of the god Neptune. It was obvi-ously quite old, but in tip-top condition. It reminded Marlene of pictures she had seen of Roman baths, even down to the steps in the side that led gently into the spar-kling water. There was no danger to a child here. Paul could quite happily play in the shallow pool when he got tired of swimming.

At one side there was a row of three changing cabins, and at the other a few loungers set around a low stone table. Beyond the pool the garden dropped again, in row upon row of shallow terraces which were covered in a mass of shrubs and flowers of every scent and hue. Dotted about were ancient stone sculptures, weathered by time, that looked like the gods of legend. The garden ended on a small sandy beach with the turquoise water of the Mediterranean flowing away to the distant horizon. Enclosed on both sides by rocky headlands, it was completely private and perfect.

Marlene stood for a moment, savouring the peace and perfection, and had a moment's regret that she had not agreed to move in here with Rocco. But she did not have time to dwell on it as Paul demanded her attention.

Later, as she lay on a lounger keeping one eye on Paul playing happily in the pool, she heard Rocco call her name.

She watched him approach, unaware of the hungry gleam in her golden eyes. He moved with an easy grace that was unusual in such a large man. His tanned, muscular physique was a picture of perfect symmetry—a joy to behold. She sat up on the lounger, unconsciously licking her bottom lip as her eyes roamed over him. Today he was wearing slightly more conservative swimming shorts in plain black, but nothing could disguise his masculine perfection.

'Shut your mouth—you're drooling, sweetheart,' he declared outrageously, and dropped down to sit on the ground at her feet.

Marlene blushed from head to toe. 'Think of Paul…' she spluttered.

'No, thanks, I don't fancy him,' he quipped, and, wrapping his hand around her ankle, he slowly stroked up her leg. 'But you! You I *do* fancy. I am at your feet—what more could a woman want?' he asked mockingly.

'Fool! Get up!' she exclaimed. His hand had reached the back of her knee and it was doing impossible things to her breathing.

'Oh, that I could,' he said, and, jumping to his feet, leant over her, so only she could hear, and told her exactly what he would like to get up to.

'Rocco…' She murmured his name, her slender hands reaching up to clasp his biceps, the blood hot in her veins.

'Soon, very soon,' he told her, and, devilment lurking in his eyes, he swept her up in his arms. 'But first I need to cool you down and then make sure Paul will be tired enough to take a nap.'

Flinging her arms around his neck, she cried, 'No, don't you dare!' But he did. He dropped her in the big pool, and she hit the water with an almighty splash. She surfaced, spluttering and choking, to see Paul and Rocco standing on the waterfall, laughing their heads off…

Later, when they were all dried and dressed again, Rocco provided a light meal of salad and grilled fish in the small breakfast room that led off a typical country kitchen. He introduced Marlene to a local wine—not the best-known wine of the area, Lacryma Christi, but a delicious sparkling Liquoroso that was made in his own vineyard. Later still he carried a sleepy Paul back to the little bedroom and watched as Marlene tucked a fine sheet over the little boy.

'Do you want another drink? A coffee?' Rocco asked rather formally.

She looked up at him as she closed the door on the sleeping child. He was watching her, his dark eyes intent, and was that a flash of vulnerability she saw in his gaze? 'A siesta would be nice,' she said boldly, her heart in her eyes.

Pulling her into his arms, Rocco murmured, 'You give so generously, how could I ever have thought you were mercenary?' He groaned throatily and covered her mouth with his.

She might have been annoyed at his remark, but with his whole length pressed against her and his mouth doing wonderful things to her lips, her eyes, her throat all conscious thought left her as she became a slave to her passionate emotions. He swung her off her feet, his mouth once more on hers, and she closed her eyes, her arms around his neck.

She didn't see the bed, she only felt it at her back, and his large body over her...

That day set the pattern for the next two days. Rocco took Marlene and Paul back to the Rossi villa at night, shared dinner with them and then left, to return early the next morning and whisk them back to his home.

They spent the mornings playing in the pool, and in the afternoons, when Paul was asleep, Rocco carried Marlene off to the wide bed in the master bedroom, where they indulged themselves in an orgy of lovemaking. When they talked the conversation was light-hearted—the kind of stupid things lovers say. They consciously avoided the real reason for Marlene's being in Italy. Neither one of them was prepared to upset their idyllic existence...

On Wednesday night the idyll was broken...

'Come back and eat your ice cream,' Marlene remonstrated with Paul. They were eating out on the patio and Paul had slid off his chair and was trying to catch the fireflies dancing around in the soft, scented night air.

'Let him be,' Rocco murmured, reaching across the table to take her hand gently in his. 'I used to try and catch them as a child, but I rarely did. He will soon tire.'

'Yes, when the ice cream is a pool of cream,' Marlene opined with a wry smile. 'You spoil the boy.'

'But of course.' He chuckled. 'I want to keep in with his sister.' And, lifting her hand to his lips, he pressed a tender kiss to her soft palm. Marlene marvelled anew at the flush of pleasure his lightest caress gave her, and was about to tell him so when Eta appeared.

'Signorina Marlene, telephone for you—it is Signor Andretti.'

Rocco dropped her hand, his expression suddenly remote. 'You'd better answer it.'

Returning to the terrace five minutes later, Marlene saw that Paul was back at the table and eating his ice cream.

She resumed her seat beside him and studied her plate, not sure what to tell Rocco.

'So what did the old man want?' Rocco asked lightly, breaking the awkward silence. 'Obviously not to speak to me.'

Marlene shot him a surprised glance. He seemed remarkably unconcerned. 'No, you weren't mentioned,' she said quietly. 'He has the agreement drawn up for the Contessa to buy out Paul's interest in the villa. He's calling here tomorrow at noon for my signature.'

'No doubt you'll be pleased to get it all settled at last.'

'Yes.' She waited, wondering if at last they would have a frank discussion about the business that had brought her here. But to her astonishment he simply looked at her and smiled.

'Good, but not so good,' Rocco drawled ruefully. 'No more love in the afternoon!'

Marlene's heart leapt with hope. Now he was going to tell her she was being ripped off—prove his loyalty to her, and maybe his love. But with his next words the spark of hope withered in her breast.

'But as it happens I have to go to Rome tomorrow anyway. I've been offered the opportunity to lecture in geology at a top university—a sabbatical from fieldwork—and I am seriously considering accepting. I'll be staying overnight, so you and my father will have plenty of time to sort out your business without me getting in the way.'

'He also wants to discuss the company shares I hold,' she couldn't help adding. The news that Rocco was leaving for two days was bad. She might never see him again, and she prayed that now he would show in some small way that he was interested in her business and not just leave her at his father's mercy. Surely if Rocco cared anything at all for her as a person, and not just a body in his bed, he would want to protect her and Paul's interests? The past four days they had spent together must mean something to him, she thought desperately… But she was instantly disillusioned.

'Marlene, you're an intelligent woman. You run your family business successfully; you speak Italian well. Get rid of the shares or attend the board meeting first, if you must. Either way, I'm sure you'll make the right decision.'

'You think so?' she asked, mollified slightly by his faith in her even if she was furious at his lack of support.

'Of course. But get it settled. I want nothing to upset our meeting again on Friday night. We can make it a celebration.' His intimate gaze slid over her blonde head, down to where the soft curves of her breasts were displayed by the ubiquitous yellow mini-dress and then back to her face.

'I don't know exactly what time I'll be back—early evening, probably. But I'll leave you the key to my house and arrange for Aldo to drive you over.' Putting his hand in his trouser pocket, he withdrew a key and put it on the table in front of her. 'You and Paul can spend your last night there, and I'll join you.' He curved his hard mouth into a confident smile, sure she would agree.

He had it all planned. He couldn't care less if she lost a fortune so long as she was there to share his bed one last time. The smug swine, she thought bitterly, and if she could have reached him she would have punched him. It was only by a terrific effort of will that she refrained from throwing her coffee in his face.

But she had her answer, she thought grimly. Rocco had no real feeling for her. He was a virile man and she was a convenient body to while away a few hours with—nothing more. He might say he didn't get on with his father, but his loyalty was to his family and friends, not to her. Yet he still had the arrogance, the audacity to say there would be no more love in the afternoon, so how about spending her last night in Italy in his home and in his bed?

'And I suppose you'll give my brother and me a lift to

the airport Saturday morning?' she prompted sarcastically. She was longing to say more, but with Paul at the table she had to restrain her temper.

'We'll see about that when the time comes.' Rocco grinned.

No doubt he would quite happily shove them in a taxi with a quick goodbye and good riddance, she imagined. But she never knew what she might have said next in her anger, for at that moment Eta arrived to clear the table, and she was left speechless with amazement as Rocco casually proceeded to arrange with the woman for Aldo to take Marlene and Paul to his home on Friday afternoon.

She watched, silently fuming, as Eta walked away with a loaded tray of dishes, and wondered why she had taken the key Eta had picked up off the table and handed to her.

'There you are, Marlene, all arranged.'

'I never said yes,' she got out between clenched teeth.

'But you were going to.' Rocco stood up and walked around to place his large hands on her shoulders. She tried to shake him off but he began massaging the knot of tension between her shoulderblades. 'Relax, sweetheart. Let me work it out,' and bending low, he brushed the top of her head with his lips.

'Ugh! You're getting sloppy again. I want to go to bed,' Paul piped up, and Marlene jumped at the chance to get away from Rocco. Shrugging off his hands, she got to her feet. She picked Paul up out of his chair and swung him into her arms. Holding him in front of her, she turned and raised her head, and was caught and held by the intensity of Rocco's glittering gaze.

'I'm taking Paul to bed.' She said the first thing that came into her head, stating the obvious.

'I can see that.' His lips quirked in a gentle smile, and to her surprise he added, 'You look wonderful with a child in your arms.'

'Oh,' Marlene said, totally ineptly. 'Yes, well... goodnight.'

'Is something wrong?' he demanded, and, raising one hand, he lightly tapped her cheek. 'You seem rather flustered.'

He had finally realised she was not the willing woman who had spent the afternoon in his arms, in his bed. He had to be the most insensitive jerk in the universe, she told herself, and opened her mouth to tell him so. But she was stopped by his lips pressing briefly against hers.

'You're tired. The pair of you go to bed. I'll see you the day after tomorrow.' And then, brushing a few stray strands of hair from her brow, he added, 'I won't come in with you. I may get distracted by the bedrooms.' With a grin, he spun on his heel and strolled towards the side of the house, where a flight of stone steps cut into the rock led to the top and the road.

CHAPTER NINE

MARLENE stood on the terrace and watched his departing back. Suddenly he halted and slowly turned. The white light of the halogen lamps starkly revealed his handsome features, highlighting the intensity of his dark gaze as it clashed with hers.

For a long, tense moment he simply stared at her with the boy in her arms. Then he shook his head, as if to clear it, and said, 'Friday night is important. Be waiting for me, Marlene.' And to her astonishment he added, 'I will take care of everything—trust me.' Then, turning, he disappeared around the side of the house with the speed of light.

Marlene spent a restless night, her emotions fluctuating wildly between anger at Rocco's high-handed attitude, being convinced it was all over between them, and a desperate yearning to be back in his arms. The next morning she awoke with a splitting headache. It was not improved when she cast a quick glance out of the window to discover that the brilliant sunshine of the past few days had been replaced by a ferocious summer storm. Black clouds rolled over the sky, lightning flashed and torrential rain splattered down the window. A portent for the day ahead, she thought drily.

An hour later, with Paul safely ensconced in the kitchen with a colouring book and Eta's watchful eye on him, Marlene was seated in the study, the telephone pressed to her ear. What she heard was music to her ears. Her contact in England confirmed that it was a Mr *Carlo* Andretti who had been buying shares in Rossi International at a knock-down price. But she had nothing to worry about. A broker colleague had followed her instructions to the letter, and with the help of a handful of her clients a further seven per cent of Rossi stock had been bought. The voting proxies in her name would arrive by the evening, giving her thirty-one per cent of the overall vote at tomorrow's board meeting.

The icing on the cake was the name and address of a Signor Toni in Amalfi, who might be able to help her further. The man held twenty per cent of the stock. Apparently years ago, when Paolo Rossi had started the company, Signor Toni had lent him some money and had been made a silent partner in the business. According to Marlene's informant, Signor Toni was loyal to his late friend and had refused all offers to sell.

Another telephone call, and then ten minutes later Marlene and Paul were in the back of the Mercedes, being driven into Amalfi by the demon driver Aldo! Marlene was not sure how far she could trust Aldo. He seemed pleasant enough, but she didn't dare make a mistake at this late stage. So she instructed him to drop them off at the port and call back in two hours. He looked at her rather oddly, but obeyed.

Finding the house of Signor Toni was simple—the first person she asked took her to the door. She had to smile when she met him. He was the local undertaker, and looked the exact opposite: small and round, with a cherub-like face and rosy red complexion, and his beaming smile was irresistible. He took one look at Marlene and Paul, and tears of emotion slid down his cheeks.

'Come in, come in out of the rain,' he urged, and, ushering them into his house, turned and said, 'He is so like his father. It does my heart good to see him at last.'

'You knew!' Marlene exclaimed.

'Of course… Paolo was my oldest friend and confided

in me. I also know he was your father as well. You have his eyes.'

'Yes,' Marlene said simply, taking the chair that was offered her. 'I only found out myself a few months ago. My mother had always taught me what a good man my "father" was—the man she married—and apparently did not have the courage to disillusion me later. Paolo didn't agree, but he loved my mother so much he promised her he wouldn't tell me. But he left a letter for me to read after his death, explaining everything and telling me how much he loved me.'

It was a relief to Marlene to be able to talk honestly at last, and over a cup of coffee Signor Toni gave her an insight into her natural father's life as a young boy, with several hilarious anecdotes and some not so funny. Then they got down to business…

Almost two hours later the old man kissed her on both cheeks when she left, and promised to be waiting for her in the morning. Marlene was ecstatic. Success was assured. Even the weather had cleared up and the sun shone bright and clear once more. She had done it! Well, just about, she qualified as Aldo stopped the car outside the villa again and she saw that Signor Andretti had already arrived.

It was not a pleasant interview. Seated in the study behind the large desk, Signor Andretti was in charge—or thought he was. Marlene, on the other hand, knew differently, but she forced herself not to show her true feelings. Instead, with a smile, she signed away Paul's right to the villa. She felt a slight stab of regret—according to Rocco, this piece of land had been in the Rossi family for decades—but looking around, she recognised that the Contessa had destroyed any trace of Rossi influence with the stark ugliness of the building.

But the woman was not going to get the chance to do the same to the Rossi name, Marlene vowed, and, playing her part of a simple country woman, she resisted all Signor Andretti's demands to sell her shares in the company.

Oddly enough, she realised that the man still did not know she spoke Italian. As she had given up pretending since Rocco had found out on Sunday, Aldo and Eta also knew now. Obviously Signor Carlo Andretti was no closer to his son than he was to servants. Unless Rocco had been deliberately quiet on her account. If so, she silently thanked him for it. It made her task so much easier. His father took her for a stupid woman and that was his mistake, and the more she refused to sell, the more aggressive he got. He even had the gall to wave another cheque in her face. But she could not help noticing he had not upped the price from the original two pounds a share that Rocco had offered her in England.

Finally, after she had listened to the man go on and on about the advisability of selling her shares, she got to her feet. 'No, Signor Andretti, I'm sorry. I'm hanging onto them. Who knows? They might go up in price after to-morrow's board meeting.' She could not resist the sly dig. She knew perfectly well that the price was already rising after her intervention in the market.

For one awful moment she thought he was going to have a fit. His eyes bulged and his fat face turned scarlet. He really was nothing at all like his son. The inconsequential thought fluttered in her mind, but quickly vanished under the barrage of abuse he heaped upon her before storming out. In a fierce, low voice he grated in Italian, not expecting her to understand, 'You're a mercenary, gold-digging little bitch. I hope you and your bastard brother rot in hell.'

Marlene collapsed back on the chair she had just vacated, shaking with shock. Never had she suffered such abuse and, taking slow, deep breaths, she struggled to regain some semblance of control. With control came an icy, bone-deep anger…

Never mind being Paolo's lawyer, Signor Carlo Andretti was supposed to have been a lifelong friend of the man, and yet she knew without a shadow of a doubt that it was he and the Contessa who, over the past few months, had deliberately started the rumours which had made the share price drop. And it was Carlo Andretti who had bought at rock-bottom prices. The only part she could not make any sense of was why the Contessa would deliberately try to ruin her own husband's business and so decrease her own income. Unless the woman was simple or crazy, Marlene thought, and, getting to her feet, glanced around. Or both! Anyone who could design a house like this had to be…

And, come tomorrow, she was not going to be welcome here, so she might as well spend the afternoon packing. With Paul in bed for his nap, she opened the wardrobe door, and pulled the two suitcases out of the bottom. She carried them to the bed and stopped, suddenly remembering how she had spent the last few afternoons in Rocco's bed. She shuddered, her body flushing with heat at the memories. Then she noticed his key on the bedside table, where she had dropped it last night. She picked it up and turned it slowly in her hand. He had given her the key to his house, but it was the key to his heart she really wanted. Or just his loyalty would have done, she thought resentfully, and, swinging around, she headed for the door.

She didn't want to think about Rocco or his lovemaking; she didn't want to think at all. A walk in the fresh air was what she needed.

But it didn't help. She passed the swimming pool and it brought back another memory, of a passionate underwater embrace. Shaking her head, Marlene strolled down to the lower terrace. She looked out to sea. The usually calm waters were dark and turbulent, white horses riding the waves. Her own emotions were equally turbulent.

She loved Rocco, and she knew he was not directly involved with the troubles at Rossi International. By his own admission he had only returned from South Africa a fortnight ago. She should have told him the whole truth about herself, trusted him. Last night he had said 'trust me' but she had been too angry at what she saw as his betrayal. Perhaps if she had told him everything he might have appreciated her point of view. But she hadn't given him the chance. After all, Rocco had his own life, his own career, she rationalised.

An image of them naked in bed, sated in the aftermath of loving, sipping wine and lazily talking filled her mind. He had spilt some on her breast and lapped it off. She had laughed and told him to behave and his response had been that he couldn't help it. He was a basic, earthy type of man. He owned the vineyard and a lot more, but, though he enjoyed the physical labour involved on occasion, and the profit, he was a firm believer in employing the best accountants and business managers, leaving him free to follow his first love—geology. He was in Rome now, doing just that, Marlene acknowledged.

She was clutching at straws, she knew. But was it really so terrible of him to leave her to sort out her own business? Rocco had approached her in the first place at the request of his father. By his own admission it had simply been because he had felt he should try and mend the breach between them, not because he had any vital interest in the affair himself. Last night it had seemed as if he had faith in her. So why had she been so angry? Wryly she finally admitted to herself that her anger and resentment had more to do with the shock of hearing that Rocco was leaving for two days than anything else.

Perhaps there was still a chance for them—and the only way to find out was to use his key tomorrow. She opened her hand and turned the big old key over in her palm, studying it, as if it could somehow give her an answer.

Suddenly the sun burst through a break in the clouds, covering Marlene with its warm embrace. Her hand tightened into a fist and she tilted her head back to look up at the sky. It was an omen, she thought. She was a fighter—always had been. She had spent her childhood without a father, but with lots of happy memories of him which her mother had instilled in her. All false, as it turned out...

She had overcome the hurtful gossip when her mother had taken a lover. She had pulled herself around after her mother's death and had happily taken charge of her brother. In business, with no false modesty, she knew that she was dynamite. And in the past few months she had reconciled herself to the biggest shock of all. That Paolo Rossi was her natural father. His death had been a double blow. Now she was fighting for his good name. By the same token she was going to fight for the man she loved. Rocco had left the key to his home, and tomorrow, after the board meeting, she was going to use it.

Turning, she headed back up the steps, her mind made up. Anyway, she thought with a wry smile, by tomorrow afternoon she would certainly be *persona non grata* in this place. Spending the last night at Rocco's made sense. When he discovered what she had done he would either kill her or kiss her. Either way she was going to take the chance...

The next morning her heart briefly picked up speed as she thought of the battle ahead. Very soon she would be in her natural element again—in the world of business—fighting for her father's name and almost certainly winning. The proxies she needed had arrived by special delivery last night; she had nothing to worry about.

Standing under the shower spray, she smoothed soap over her arms and around her full breasts. Unexpectedly her stomach curled as she recalled Rocco's hands doing the exact same thing. God, how she wanted him! With a shake of her head she dispelled the erotic images invading her mind, finished her shower and washed and dried her hair. Walking back into the bedroom with a large fluffy towel wrapped around her body, she skirted the packed suitcases standing in the middle of the floor and crossed to the wardrobe. A holdall with enough clothes for an overnight stay and a suit hanging on the rail were all it contained.

Paul was downstairs with Eta. Marlene had explained to him that she had to leave him for the morning but would be back for lunch, and that afterwards they were going to stay at Rocco's before returning to England. Paul had accepted the idea quite happily, saying that he liked Roc's house better, that the swimming pool was the best…

Marlene heartily agreed, only wishing she had Paul's same sunny disposition. She had hardly slept a wink all night, tossing and turning in the wide bed. Images of Rocco and the time they had spent together had filled her mind, and filled her body with the ache of frustration.

Taking a deep breath, she surveyed herself in the full-length mirror and a tiny smile curled her full lips. Gone was the casual blonde of the past two weeks and in her place was Marlene Johanson the business executive.

She wore a Donna Karan suit—a smart cream linen short-sleeved tailored jacket, nipped in at the waist, which fitted her like a glove, teamed with a short straight black skirt that ended two inches above her knee. Sheer silk stockings covered her long legs, and on her feet were black Italian leather shoes with three-inch heels, increasing her height to six feet.

Her blonde hair was swept up and round in a smooth French pleat—not a hair out of place. Her make-up was simple but perfect. In her ears she wore plain gold Christian Dior earrings, and on the lapel of her jacket was a matching brooch. To complete her ensemble, she picked up her handbag along with a practical black leather briefcase.

She said goodbye to Paul in the kitchen and grinned at the look of stunned amazement on the faces of Aldo and Eta. Aldo was still casting surreptitious glances at her five minutes later as he helped her into the car, and when she directed him to stop at Signor Toni's in Amalfi he simply nodded.

The boardroom of Rossi International was on the top floor of a lovely old building in the heart of Naples' business sector. Signor Toni gallantly took her elbow as they followed a smartly dressed man, who had been introduced as the company secretary, through the large double doors to the boardroom beyond. Marlene stopped just inside the entrance and coolly looked around. A typical boardroom, she thought. All panelled mahogany and large elegant windows draped in the finest Genoa velvet. There was a huge table laid with blotters, writing materials and glasses for the water and wine on offer. No one had yet taken a seat, she noted, and wondered who would chair the meeting.

Her glance went further, to the bottom of the room, where there was a magnificent marble mantelpiece with an excellent portrait of the late Paolo Rossi above it. But it was the group standing there that gave her pause. She recognised the Contessa, Caterina and Carlo Andretti, and there were also four men whose names she had in her possession but whom she had never met before. One, she knew, would be the company accountant.

'*Buongiorno*, Contessa, are we ready to start?' Marlene asked in fluent Italian. And she almost burst out laughing at the look of astonishment on the older woman's face, and on those around her.

'You speak Italian!' she exclaimed.

Marlene nodded, holding the black eyes with her own glittering gold ones. 'Are we ready to start?' she repeated. 'I want this business settled quickly.' She was a commanding figure, stunningly attractive, all efficiency, and it helped that she was the tallest person present.

'No, we are waiting for two more members,' the Contessa shot back, recovering some of her self-control. 'And what are you doing here, Signor Toni? You never usually bother.'

'I am here to protect my investment. What else?' He shrugged nonchalantly. 'Oh! And we can start. The other two members have sold their shares.' Signor Toni took great delight in telling the Contessa this, and Marlene did not begrudge him the privilege. In fact she had arranged it with him on the way here.

It was ludicrously simple in the end. After the preliminaries were over, and the company secretary took the chair in place of the late Paolo Rossi, the Contessa took the floor and gave a long speech on how badly the company shares were performing. She suggested the name of Rossi be discredited, and put forward a motion to reorganise and rename the company. Signor Andretti seconded the motion, and then Marlene rose to speak…

In a few short sentences she revealed her findings, and the paperwork to back them up. The assets of the company were vastly underrated. It was the Contessa who had deliberately started the rumours, in all the right places, with the sole purpose of lowering the share price and panicking people into selling. In the meantime, Signor Andretti had quietly been buying them at a rock-bottom price through a number of holding companies—all of which had been set up with the intention of gaining overall control. Why the Contessa wanted to change the name of the company Marlene had no idea. And she let her gaze linger on each man present individually for a moment at this point, before succinctly pointing out that the Contessa had caused their holdings to be greatly devalued.

Pandemonium broke out. The vote was a foregone conclusion. Marlene, with Signor Toni's vote and the votes of two of the other men, who had obviously known nothing about the conspiracy, easily outvoted the Contessa and her cronies. The company accountant was dismissed on the spot—it was obvious he was involved—and details on how to proceed were thrashed out without any trouble. The Contessa appeared to have been struck dumb, as did Andretti, and the meeting began to break up.

Marlene told Signor Toni in an aside that she was going to find the toilet, and left the boardroom. Crossing the hall, she found the door marked 'Donne'. She walked into the powder room and, standing in front of the vanity basin, glanced at her reflection in the mirror. Her eyes were sparkling, her face flushed; she looked triumphant and she was... Suddenly another face appeared in the mirror, and she spun around to confront the Contessa.

The Contessa looked right through Marlene as though she wasn't there. But Marlene had one more niggling problem, and she could not rest until she had it solved.

'Tell me, Contessa, why did you do it? Why set out to discredit the name of Rossi? Your own daughter's name—your name, even though you never use it. What possible reason could you have? You are a shareholder in a hugely successful company that keeps you in luxury. I simply cannot understand why.'

The Contessa's face was frightening to watch. 'I tell you why.' Her dark eyes gleaming malevolently, she stared at Marlene. 'I hated him. I hated Paolo Rossi from the day I married him.'

Marlene clutched the vanity basin, white-knuckled with shock. The woman meant it. It was in her face. 'But...'

'You don't know, do you? You are just like him, with your golden-brown eyes, your superb business brain. But naïve...'

'You knew he was my father!' Marlene exclaimed.

The Contessa threw her head back and laughed out loud, the laughter verging on hysteria. 'You stupid girl—I knew before you were born. That surprises you?' She cackled again. 'Rossi was in England, sleeping with your mother. I…I was madly in love with Carlo Andretti—a man of breeding, good pedigree, but no money—and he was married,.with a child. A divorce was out of the question. I was pregnant, so we planned it between us.'

Her black eyes were venomous as she continued, 'Rossi came back to Italy full of his success in opening a London office, and Carlo invited him to stay at his home. He gave a party for him and I was a weekend guest. We got him drunk and a little more besides. The next morning he woke up in bed with me. He could remember nothing. Two weeks later I told him I was pregnant and he had to marry me. He wrote to your mother, breaking off the relationship, but Carlo had already intercepted a letter from her telling Rossi she was pregnant. Yes, I knew…'

As the implications of what the Contessa was saying sank in Marlene's eyes widened in horror. She had once likened the woman to Lucretia Borgia, and now she knew she'd been right. 'Then Caterina is…'

'I had to sleep with Paolo Rossi when I married him, but as soon as my child was born—ten weeks premature—' again she cackled '—I never let the man touch me again. Caterina is Carlo's daughter, but it is a secret. No one knows.' Giving Marlene a sly glance, she added, 'Not even Caterina. Promise—you have to promise not to tell.'

The woman was evil personified, Marlene thought, but still she told her what she wanted to hear. 'I promise no one will learn your secret from me.'

'Good, good. We should have been together, you know. We should have been a family. We should have had all the wealth.' As Marlene watched the Contessa's eyes seemed to lose their focus, gazing into some distant reality only she could see. The woman was mad, or very near it. 'And we nearly did. Carlo's wife died—did you know?' She turned back to Marlene, suddenly almost normal.

'Yes, I had heard,' Marlene said softly, humouring her.

'But she left all her wealth to Rocco, and he is too much like his mother. She was a brewer's daughter—no breeding… The fortune should have been Carlo's; she cheated him out of his rightful share. Poor Carlo. So I vowed to give him the wealth and status he should have.' She gave Marlene a cunning look. 'That was when I started my plan. I move in the highest echelons of society—a word to a banker here, an investment house there… It was easy. When the share price dropped Carlo quietly bought shares. We had it all worked out. Gain complete control, get rid of the hated name Rossi and replace it with Andretti. Then Carlo and I would marry.'

The amazing part was that it almost made sense, Marlene thought sadly. It all fitted. In the letter Paolo had left Marlene to read after his death he had explained how hurt he had been that her mother had never written to him, that if she had he might not have married the Contessa, baby or no. Of course he had never heard from her—because he had been staying in the home of Carlo Andretti and had never got the letter. Rocco had told her that he was about ten when he'd discovered his mother in tears at his father's infidelity. That was when the affair must have started. The time-scale fitted perfectly. Twenty-seven years later, and again the dates fitted. Paolo had noticed the trouble starting in the company a few months before he died. Just about the time when Rocco's mother had died, or very shortly after.

'He will marry me, you know.' The Contessa grabbed Marlene's arm and stared up into her face. 'The other women all meant nothing to Carlo. He did it to keep suspicion from falling on me.' And as Marlene watched in wide-eyed horror the Contessa ranted on. 'I did the same. I took one young lover because he was an architect. He was good—he did what I told him.' Another horrible cackle erupted from her mouth. 'He rebuilt the villa, destroying every trace of my hateful husband's common family.' She let go of Marlene's arm. 'And the villa is still mine. Now I must find Carlo—fix a date for the wedding.' Still mumbling incoherently, the woman walked out.

The horror, the tragedy of it all, all the wasted lives, brought tears to Marlene's eyes. As a young girl the Contessa had fallen in love with a married man, and because of status, pride—whatever one wanted to call it—she had blighted the lives of so many people. Marlene's own mother had married her cousin to give Marlene legitimacy, but she had only ever loved Paolo Rossi. Paolo's life had been blighted for years by a wife who cared nothing for him and would not let him touch her. Marlene remembered him telling her about a number of casual women in his life before he'd met her mother again and why he had needed them, but she had never quite believed him until now. And then there was Rocco, who had no relationship with his father to speak of…

She gasped. Rocco… 'Oh, my God!' Marlene exclaimed out loud, the sound echoing in the empty room. Caterina was his half-sister!

It was a very subdued Marlene who sat in the back of the car with Signor Toni on the drive back to Amalfi. Almost being caught by the Italian paparazzi as they had left the Rossi building had not helped her mood.

Signor Toni took her hand in his and squeezed it gently. 'Your father would have been proud of you today. You should be happy.'

She raised her eyes to his. 'I couldn't have done it without you. Thank you from the bottom of my heart,' she said sincerely, then added, 'But so much deceit is hard to comprehend.' A tear fell down her cheek, quickly followed by another, and when the old man put his arm around her to comfort her she found herself telling him all about her confrontation with the Contessa in the powder room. 'I can't believe such wickedness,' she ended, brushing the tears from her cheek.

'You are like your father. If he had a fault it was that he always looked for the good in people and sometimes missed the bad. I remember him as a young man, coming back from England for the first time. He came to tell me of the continuing success of our venture and that he had fallen in love with an English girl. He was happy and so full of life. Three weeks later he came back to tell me he was marrying the Contessa, and he would not explain why. Now I know... But you must not cry, my dear. Years later, when he had been reunited with your mother and he visited me again, I saw once more the happy young man of his youth.'

The car stopped outside Signor Toni's house, but he did not alight immediately. 'This week, meeting you and your brother has given me more pleasure than I can say. Don't let the Contessas of this world get to you. And come and see me again some time.' In a courtly gesture he lifted her hand to his lips and kissed it. 'Promise?' he said. And she did.

Drawing up outside the glass pyramid entrance of the villa, Marlene stifled a feeling of disgust. The quicker she got herself and her brother away from here the better, she thought.

After a quick, if rather late lunch with Paul, she said her goodbyes to Eta and, bundling her brother into the car, joined him on the back seat. It was a short drive to Rocco's home, and Marlene heaved a sigh of relief when Aldo stopped the car outside the entrance door. Ten minutes later she was standing in the bedroom Paul always used and looking down on his sleeping form.

The innocence of youth. He had crawled into bed to take a nap without a word of protest, after a promise that he could go swimming in the pool later. But Marlene felt restless, her mind a host of conflicting thoughts. Whether it had been wise to come to Rocco's home after all she had learnt that morning she was no longer sure. She debated calling a taxi and booking into a hotel for the night.

She sighed heavily and eased her feet out of the high-heeled shoes. Wise or not, she was too tired and too dispirited to start looking for a hotel for one night—no easy task at the height of summer and the tourist season. Suddenly the thought of returning to England in the morning seemed highly desirable.

Shrugging out of her jacket and skirt, she laid them at the foot of Paul's bed and, picking up the holdall that held their overnight needs, walked along to the bathroom. She felt dirty, contaminated by what she had learnt. In the context of human relationships, the story must rank as one of the biggest failures ever. Stripping naked, she got into the shower and turned on the spray. The plot would make a great Fellini-type film, she thought drily. It had everything—passion, deceit, betrayal, not to mention adultery. All it needed was incest… She stopped dead, turned off the water and got out of the shower. Her last thought had been too horrible to contemplate.

Quickly she picked up a towel and dried herself, then, taking her swimsuit from the holdall, she pulled it on. Not stopping, she hurried out and into the garden. She saw the swimming pool and dived in. She forced her tired body to swim length after length of the pool in a fast crawl, hoping to force the unwanted thought from her mind. But finally, breathless, she dragged herself out of the water and sank down on a nearby lounger.

She closed her eyes, but she could not close her mind. She saw once again Rocco in the herb garden with Caterina, saw the other woman caressing his chest. No, they couldn't have been lovers. She was becoming paranoid. Hadn't Rocco himself told her that he thought of Caterina almost like a sister? It was her over-fertile imagination. But a devilish voice inside her head whispered, Yes, but Rocco didn't *know* Caterina was his half-sister, did he?

The distant ringing of a telephone stopped her tortured thoughts, and, leaping to her feet, she dashed back inside to answer it.

The telephone was on an antique hand-painted table just inside the hall. She picked up the receiver and said breathlessly, '*Pronto.*'

'So you are there,' a deep masculine voice replied rather curtly. 'I wasn't sure you would be.'

'Yes—yes, I am,' Marlene said eagerly. The sound of Rocco's voice was somehow reassuring to her. 'Are you on your way?'

'Not exactly. Is Paul with you?'

'Well, yes, of course.' Just then she heard his little voice calling from the bedroom. 'In fact I think he's just woken up,' she said, with a smile in her voice.

'In that case I won't keep you. I rang to tell you I'll be late in getting back. I have a dinner engagement, so get yourselves something to eat, and, as you're probably tired after your busy day, go to bed.'

'Yes, all right,' Marlene said quietly. Even over the telephone she had recognised the drawling sarcasm in his tone. 'Is something wrong?' she could not help asking.

A cynical laugh echoed down the wire. 'Wrong? What could possibly be wrong, when I have a willing woman waiting for me and warming my bed? *Ciao.*' And he rang off.

Marlene shivered, and after replacing the receiver she

rubbed her bare arms. Someone walking over my grave, she thought, and went to get Paul.

She spent the rest of the day with Paul in the pool, and when she finally persuaded him that it was time to go indoors she bathed him. Dressed in his nightclothes, he followed her into the kitchen. It was a cosy room. The pine units formed a galley-style kitchen that opened onto the breakfast area, where a round pine table stood surrounded by ladder-backed wood chairs. On one wall was a dresser, holding a collection of blue china that matched the plates standing all along the picture rail that trailed around the walls.

Marlene smiled when she discovered that the freezer and refrigerator were stocked to capacity with a multitude of pre-cooked pre-packed meals, all labelled and obviously prepared by Rocco's absent housekeeper. The man was certainly not going to starve, or cook…even if he did live on his own for months. Deciding on pasta in a rich cream and ham sauce, she set it to reheat and laid the table for Paul and herself.

The food was delicious, and with ice cream to follow made a perfect supper. By the time they had finished Paul's eyes were drooping, and Marlene picked him up to carry him to bed. She passed the suitcases standing in the hall, and worried again about the wisdom of staying here. Even now she could still call a cab and leave.

By ten o'clock at night, she was beginning to wish she had. Bathed and ready for bed, wearing an over-large white T-shirt—a relic from her student days—with a message emblazoned across it that 'Achieving starts with Believing', she was curled up on a large soft-cushioned sofa in the elegant but homely lounge. Marlene looked around her and asked herself for the hundredth time what she was doing here. Paul was sound asleep in the other half of the house, and she felt totally alone.

It had seemed so simple yesterday, when she had decided to take Rocco up on his offer, even though she had been disappointed in his lack of support. As it happened, she hadn't needed his support—she was more than capable of looking after her own affairs—but that was not the point. Rocco didn't know that. With a sigh, she realised she was being totally unreasonable. On the one hand she was a super-efficient business woman, but at the same time she wanted her lover to lean on… How mixed-up could one get?

She tipped her head back against the cushions and, unfurling her long legs, stretched. God, she was tired! Closing her eyes for a moment, she debated going to bed.

Somehow, even after all the intimacies she had shared with Rocco, she still did not feel comfortable with the idea of crawling into his bed on her own. Plus, she knew that she was going to have to tell Rocco about the morning's meeting before anyone else did. She yawned widely and her eyelids drooped. She was asleep.

She didn't hear the door or the man walking into the room. The first inkling she had that she was not alone was when, on opening her eyes, she saw Rocco towering over her.

'Sleeping the sleep of the innocent, were you?' he asked mockingly, his dark gaze taking in her rumpled state.

Marlene's hand reached up and, still drowsy, she stared at Rocco, her golden eyes wide with mingled surprise and love. 'You're back,' she murmured. But he didn't take her outstretched hand.

'As you see.'

She pulled herself up to a sitting position and smoothed the cotton shirt down to her knees. 'Did you have a good trip?' she asked rather stiltedly. Her glance took in his broad-shouldered form, elegantly clad in a lightweight cream suit and a tan shirt. But his tie and the first few buttons of his shirt were pulled loose, and he had a distinctly dishevelled air about him.

'Such touching concern,' he drawled, looking down at her with a mocking smile. 'I suppose I should be flattered.' He arched one black brow. 'Given your busy life and sudden wealth and notoriety.'

'Notoriety?' she queried, staring at him. Silently he quite casually removed his jacket and let it fall on the arm of the sofa. His tie followed, but she could sense the barely controlled tension in him, and she stiffened as he dropped down beside her on the sofa. 'What do you mean?' she asked with a sinking heart. Somehow he had already heard about her triumph of the morning.

'You looked very good on the television news this evening. Almost unrecognisable to some who know you.'

She gulped. 'The television?'

'Yes, and very interesting it was too. The Contessa had arranged for the Press to be on hand, hoping to reveal her plans for Rossi International. Instead they got an almost incoherent interview from her and a brief picture of you being handed gracefully into a Mercedes by Signor Toni. An old man who never looked sideways at a woman until you appeared.'

'Oh, no.'

'Oh, yes,' said Rocco, and his voice hardened as he went on, 'I was right about you from the first. Your capacity to bemuse older men must be inbred. But then why should I worry, as long as you warm my bed?' And, sliding an arm around her shoulders, he hauled her towards him.

Curved against his side, the familiar warmth of his big body enveloping her, Marlene should have felt relieved but the opposite was true. She tried to put some space between them, but his arm tightened around her back, his fingers digging into the skin under her arm. 'I can explain,' she said huskily.

'There is no need.' With his other hand he clasped her chin and turned her face towards his. 'I know everything. I have just spent a very enlightening evening dining with my father,' he drawled silkily. 'And surprise, surprise—the owner of a pleasant country herb garden turns out to be a financial wizard with her own company and an international client base.' His black eyes looked mockingly down at her. 'Now, for some women that would be enough. But not you, Marlene.'

She swallowed, her throat tightening. 'I had no choice…' she began to explain. 'I promised Paolo I would try and save his company. I couldn't tell you—you must see that.'

'I see nothing,' he ground out from between his teeth, 'except a mercenary little bitch who set out to make a fortune and a fool of me at the same time.'

Her temper flared at the unfairness of his comment, but still she tried to justify her behaviour. 'I couldn't tell you the truth because you were too close to the other people involved.'

'And I wasn't close to you?' he snarled, his black eyes flaring with controlled anger. 'You lay in my bed, in my arms. I had y—'

She cut him off. 'I thought you said never to mix business with pleasure,' she reminded him.

'Did I?' he snapped as he dragged her across his knees, his eyes leaping with fury and something else. 'More fool me,' he bit out, and his mouth crashed down on hers in a biting, savage kiss, forcing her lips apart.

She tried to push him away, her hands shoving against his chest, but he was too strong for her. He pushed her back so her head fell against the other arm of the sofa and she was splayed across him. Grasping her hands in one of his, he forced them over her head, and with his other hand across her stomach he held her immobile.

'Get off me!' she cried, her voice shaking with panic as she registered his furious expression.

'Very appropriate.' There was a derisory gleam in his eyes as he read the motto printed on her shirt. '"Achieving starts with Believing". You'd better *believe* I'm going to have you, Marlene—because I am definitely going to *achieve* it.' And his head bent to kiss her again.

She struggled beneath him, her body bucking, then somehow she was flat on her back and his whole weight was pinning her down. It wasn't supposed to be like this, she thought frantically, even as her lips involuntarily parted beneath the pressure of his kiss.

CHAPTER TEN

'PLEASE, ROCCO,' Marlene cried, and with her hands free again she pushed against his chest. 'Not like this.' His lower torso pressed hard against her, making her aware of his arousal, while he leant back slightly, his elbows either side of her shoulders, and stared down into her flushed face.

'"Please, Rocco,"' he mimicked savagely. 'What pity did you show to the Contessa? I was right about you the first time I saw you. You are a devious, lying, mercenary little bitch.' His black eyes glittered with fury. 'You couldn't be satisfied with a share in the Rossi empire for your half-brother. You had to have it all. Never mind about the man's legitimate wife and child, you had to grind their faces in it. And I thought I knew you. I actually considered asking you to ma—' He shook his black head. 'You made a complete fool out of me.'

'No, no...' Marlene said desperately, realising Rocco did not know the full story. 'I—' And she stopped. How could she tell him that Paolo Rossi was her father without telling him that Caterina was his half-sister? 'What about Caterina?' she asked, suddenly desperately needing to know. 'Was she ever your lover?'

'Jealousy, Marlene?' he exclaimed in furious disbelief, jumping to a totally erroneous assumption. 'Is that what goaded you on? Well, you need not have bothered. I've never laid a hand on Caterina.'

'No, I'm not jealous—you've got it all wrong,' she said frantically.

'Wrong? My God, I have!' Rocco said savagely, and his hands moved to tangle in her hair, allowing the whole of

169

his weight to fall on her. 'So much for your damn lies,' he snarled, his handsome face, contorted with rage, only inches from her own. '"I know nothing about business,"' he mimicked. 'Like hell you don't. You've been running rings around everyone since I picked you up at the airport.' He laughed cynically. 'But at least I got something out of it,' he said, and, stroking one hand down her neck, he cupped her breast through the fine cotton of her shirt. 'I got to use your luscious body—who cares about your black heart?'

Marlene's breath caught in her throat at the insult, and she felt like crying at the injustice of it all. 'You don't understand—' She tried again, but his mouth clamped down on hers, kissing her with brutal aggression.

She struggled to get away, but he was too strong, too heavy. She tried to hit him, but in the tussle that ensued in one lightning movement he ripped her shirt over her head, and, catching her hands in one of his, wrenched them above her head again. Then he moved slightly, so she was trapped against the inside of the sofa.

'I understand all I need to,' he sneered, his hand stroking down over her naked body, shaping over her waist and hips. He thrust a muscular thigh between her long legs and moved against her in a parody of the sex act. 'This is what you like—your reason for being here.'

Marlene drew a shuddering breath and gazed up at him, futilely searching his face for a sign of any kind of affection. But the implacable determination in his black eyes told her all too clearly what he intended. He wanted to possess her with his body, humiliate her as he thought she had humiliated him.

'You know you do,' he said silkily, his fingers trailing up over her waist to her breast and flicking the rosy tip. 'And who am I to disappoint you?' he taunted.

To Marlene's shame, her traitorous flesh responded instantly to his touch. Never mind that he hated her. Never mind that he was simply using her. She could not disguise her need. And when he lowered his head, his mouth grazing over her aroused nipples, back and forward, she thought she would go mad with the effort to resist him.

'It's no good, Marlene,' he whispered against her breast. 'You want me.' He trailed kisses up her throat, and all the time his thigh moved rhythmically against her.

'Please—' she whimpered, not sure if she was asking him to stop or continue. But her plea was swallowed by his mouth covering hers.

If his kiss had been brutal again she might have held out. But, confusing her utterly, his mouth was gentle and his tongue circled her full lips, then probed the moist heat beyond. She closed her eyes and helplessly succumbed to the magic of his mouth, and when he finally let her hands go free she did not try to push him away, but reached for his head and plunged her fingers into his thick black hair.

She groaned her delight when he lifted his head and stared into her passion-glazed eyes, and then let his eyes sweep lower, over her naked form. Frantically she burrowed her hands up under his shirt, her fingers tracing muscle and sinew in feverish tactile pleasure.

'You are so luscious,' Rocco growled, and moved to suckle once more at her proud breasts.

She wasn't aware of the moment when he removed his clothes, but when he shifted slightly, sliding his hands beneath her and lifting her to meet the hard thrust of his manhood, she was aching for him. The blood coursed through her veins like quicksilver, igniting every nerve and fibre of her body. She was inflamed by the hard, pulsing heat of him to the very core of her being. She locked her long legs around his waist, her back arching up, urging him on. But Rocco had a different agenda.

'Softly, softly,' he rasped against the soft curve of her

throat, his hand slipping between their linked bodies, his finger stroking the nub of her passion. Marlene trembled on the brink but he would not be hurried. Playing her like a maestro, he took her to the edge over and over again, until every nerve in her body was screaming for release.

'Please...please,' she begged him, and he thrust hard and fast, and the climax hit them simultaneously, shattering in its intensity. Rocco collapsed on top of her, and for a while she floated in a mindless peace, the ragged sound of Rocco's breathing comforting to her ears. Then Rocco rolled off the sofa and stood up.

Her golden eyes soft with love, she watched as he pulled on his trousers. She knew she had a lot of explaining to do, but after the passion they had shared she was confident that this time Rocco would listen, and forgive her deception. But she was wrong...

'You can sleep in the room next to your brother tonight, and I'll arrange for you both to get to the airport in the morning.' He glanced down at where she lay naked on the sofa. 'And cover yourself. I've had enough for one night,' he opined, with no trace of emotion. And when the shock of his words froze her into immobility he added, 'You understand? Or shall I spell it out for you?'

Marlene understood all too well. What she had become in the last hour was a one-night stand. She scrambled into her T-shirt and looked up at Rocco with anguished eyes, incapable of saying a word. Then suddenly, for a split second, she saw a flash of the same pain reflected in his eyes, and it gave her the will to make one last-ditch attempt to explain. 'I don't know what your father told you, Rocco, but please let me try to explain—'

'Forget it, Marlene. It is over.' Turning, he walked away, flinging over his shoulder, 'Be packed and ready by eight. I don't want you in my home one minute longer than is necessary.'

*   *   *

Six weeks later, in the Johanson Herb Garden at two o'clock on a Monday afternoon, Marlene, with a basket on her arm, stopped by the rows of raspberry bushes and, reaching out, picked one of the juicy red fruits. She popped it into her mouth. They were ready for harvesting.

Methodically she worked between the rows, breathing in the clean fresh air and slowly filling the basket with fruit, glancing up now and then at the fluffy white clouds that drifted by, thinking how the change of seasons was coming. Soon it would be autumn, and soon she would have to make changes in her life.

She had got back from town half an hour ago, feeling restless and worried, and had changed into a pair of old blue jeans and a well-washed blue sweatshirt and headed for the garden. Now she hesitated and looked around her, and then down at the almost full basket, a sad smile on her face.

It seemed incredible that it had been in this spot, not even two months ago, that she had lain on the warm earth and watched Rocco Andretti stride down the garden. She dropped to her knees and placed the basket on the dry earth. The day itself was quite warm, with a gentle breeze rustling the leaves. Not unlike that first day, she thought, wriggling into a sitting position. She clasped her hands around her bent legs and rested her chin on her knees. Paul had gone back to school today, for the start of the autumn term, and she was alone. Alone with her thoughts…and with a hard decision to make. Should she contact Rocco Andretti again or not?

She closed her eyes and relived her disastrous last night in Italy. She shivered, but not with the cold. When she had finally picked herself up off the sofa and gone to the guest room, she had not slept a wink. At seven the next morning she had been ready to leave, with Paul dressed and waiting. She had been in the process of telephoning for a taxi when a cold-eyed, grim-faced Rocco had appeared. He had insisted on escorting them to the airport. The memory of the icy contempt in his eyes when he had left them standing in the departure lounge still had the power to make her shudder...

Opening her eyes, Marlene sighed. What was the use of reliving the past? She had cried all the tears she was going to for Rocco Andretti. The first week she'd been home she had done little else. But not any more. She took a deep breath. It would never have worked anyway. Who was it who had said, 'O what a tangled web we weave, When first we practise to deceive!' or words to that effect? she thought wryly. There had been far too much deceit, and too many secrets within secrets, for a relationship between herself and Rocco to stand any chance...

Picking up the basket, Marlene got to her feet, her mind made up. She had a good career, a good life, an adorable brother. It might be a small family but it was a loving one, and as for contacting Rocco again—when hell froze over sprang to mind...

The decision made, Marlene, head bent, attacked the fruit bushes with grim determination. The raspberries were not for sale; there were not enough of them. Usually she simply froze them and made the odd pie, but suddenly she had a craving for raspberry jam. There must be a recipe in one of the cookbooks her mother had been so fond of collecting, she mused as she neared the end of a row, and, lost in her own thoughts, she failed to hear the footsteps this time. She didn't realise she was not alone until she lifted her head.

'Hello, Marlene.'

The basket dropped from her nerveless fingers, scattering the fruit all over the ground. 'Rocco,' she whispered, amazed, as she looked at him.

He was standing in front of her, his tanned face seeming thinner and slightly pale. But his wide-legged stance, the large hands hooked into the pockets of well-cut denim jeans that clung to his muscular thighs and lean hips, the checked wool shirt emphasising his broad shoulders—all these reinforced the impression of a powerful, aggressive male.

Marlene took a step back and moistened her dry lips with her tongue. 'What are you doing here?' she demanded.

'I came for you.' He took a step towards her.

She stiffened. She caught the scent of his cologne—he was much too close—and she made to step back again. His hand reached out and caught her arm, and she tensed involuntarily.

'Marlene—the basket.' He glanced down at the ground and she followed his gaze. She had almost tripped backwards over it.

'Oh,' she murmured, brushing away his hand and stepping sideways. 'Well, as you can see I was busy, and it's your fault I dropped the fruit,' she said without preamble. 'So I suggest you take yourself off and let me get on with my work.'

'I know it's my fault, Marlene,' he replied, his voice clipped. 'Everything that has happened between us is my fault. I realise that now.'

Had she heard him right? Or were her ears playing tricks on her? She looked up into his eyes and there was no mistaking the sincerity in his dark gaze.

He jammed his hands back into his pockets as though he was afraid he would reach out to her if he didn't. 'Surprised?' he asked shortly. 'That I finally got over my arrogance, my raging hormones long enough to listen to the truth and now I want to apologise?'

'The truth?' Her lip curled. 'The truth according to your father and the Contessa.' She eyed him bitterly. 'No, thanks,' she said tightly, and, kneeling down, she picked up the basket and began gathering the fallen fruit. She could not bear to look at him; he was out of her life and that was the way she wanted it. But that didn't stop her pulse quickening when he dropped to his knees beside her and grasped her hand on the basket.

'Leave the damn fruit and listen to me.'

She eyed him scathingly, her temper rising. How dared Rocco walk back into her life just when she had decided to blot him out for good? 'Why the hell should I? You wouldn't listen to me, and now it's too late.'

He smiled—a grim twist of his lips. 'Because I love you.'

Marlene froze in the act of picking up a raspberry. Were her ears deceiving her yet again? He moved closer—so close that she had to look straight into his face.

'I am on my knees. I will grovel in the dirt if I have to,' he ground out. 'But you must give me a chance. Listen to me.'

Her mouth fell open, her golden eyes wide and unblinking. One hand still hung in the air; the other had a death grip on the handle of the basket. She was not imagining it. He had said he loved her. That he would grovel if he had to. How many times in the past few weeks had she dreamt of just such a scenario? The arrogant, overbearing Rocco on his knees to her. And now he was... But dared she believe him?

'I do love you, Marlene,' he said in a deep, dark voice, his gaze holding hers, his handsome face taut with barely controlled emotion. 'I know you must find it hard to believe, but please...' He caught her wavering hand in his. 'Please let me try to explain.'

She wanted to cry. She remembered saying the same words to him, and being ignored.

His fingers tightened around her hand. 'Damn it, Marlene—say something.'

She glanced around the garden in a daze, and then lifted her eyes to his. 'I...I don't think...' She couldn't get her thoughts into any kind of order. He was kneeling in the dirt, looking at her as if she was all he had ever wanted.

'You don't need to think.' He reached his other arm around her back and caught her up against him, his arms enfolding her as his mouth found hers and took it in a wild, passionate kiss.

Her fingers tangled in his black hair of their own volition. It had been so long, and she ached for his touch. She moaned when he lifted his head to stare down into her flushed face.

'You still want me, Marlene,' he ground out. 'You can't deny it.' They were knee to knee on the dry earth, and she looked at him and sighed heavily. 'I never tried to. It was you that…' He had chased her away without a backward glance.

'Let's get something straight right now,' Rocco said roughly. 'I never wanted you to leave. It was pride, male ego—call it what you will—that made me behave like an arrogant, conceited jerk the last night we were together, and I will never forgive myself for the way I treated you. But can't we put it all behind us and start again?'

Marlene rested her hands on his broad shoulders. 'It's not possible,' she said, hanging onto her self-control by a thread. 'With all that has happened.'

'Anything is possible if you want it enough—and God knows I want you in my life more than anything in the world.'

Her eyes lingered on his handsome face and a tiny kernel of hope fluttered in her heart. He looked sincere, but… She pushed on his shoulders and stood up. 'We'd better go in the house,' she offered, glancing down into his upturned face, a wry smile twisting her full lips. 'Grovelling in the dirt really doesn't suit you.'

Rocco leapt to his feet and hauled her hard against his

taut body. 'For you—anything,' he declared, and brushed his lips against hers.

She wriggled out of his arms, wishing it were that simple. Kiss and make up. But there had been too much hurt and heartache. He could still seduce her with a touch, a smile—the chemistry was as strong as ever. But she was wary now. He could also kill her with a single sentence—as she knew to her cost.

Marlene suddenly felt terribly nervous. Rocco was sprawled on the sofa in her living room, his long legs stretched out, the pale sun shining through the mullioned windows etching the harsh contours of his face, and she realised he looked exhausted. 'Would you like a drink? Coffee?'

Rocco shook his black head. 'Come and sit down,' he drawled, his eyes narrowing on her. 'I have to talk to you.'

Marlene swallowed, her pulse rate rising, but she did as he said and gingerly sat down on the edge of the sofa.

'I can't blame you for being wary,' he said quietly. 'The last time we were on a sofa together I virtually raped you.'

'No,' she denied vehemently. 'It was never that.'

'Wasn't it?' Rocco cast her a sidelong glance. 'Thank you for that, Marlene, but I still feel an absolute heel. You see, I had dined with my father, at his command, and of course he gave me a very edited version of the result of your morning's work. I was stunned to discover you were a financial wizard, and from there it was quite easy to believe you were a totally mercenary gold-digger—the poor Contessa outsmarted by a slip of an Englishwoman. But what angered me most was the realisation that I had asked you to trust me and you quite obviously hadn't. I had it all worked out—I went to Rome for informal talks with the chancellor of University College London, who was holidaying there. I agreed to spend the next year in London.'

Marlene's mouth fell open, her eyes wide with amazement as he continued, 'I saw you and I—and Paul, of course—living here during term-time and vacationing in Amalfi. I had it all organised and I was coming back to ask you to marry me, conceitedly believing your answer was a foregone conclusion—'

'I remember you almost said so,' Marlene cut in, recalling his bitten-off statement that fatal night. If what he said was true he had actually arranged his life around her, and her heart expanded with joy at the knowledge. When he had left for Rome he had told her to be waiting for him, had told her they were going to celebrate, but she had been too angry and resentful at his leaving to take any notice.

Rocco had cared about her. Still did... And but for her own folly they would have been engaged by now. 'Rocco.' She whispered his name, but he stopped her with a finger to her lips.

'Please, Marlene, don't say anything. Let me finish. My pride took a heavy battering that night. I bitterly resented the way you had turned me into a lovesick fool, and I was furious because I realised you didn't love me. How could you when you didn't trust me?' The look he gave her was full of self-mockery. 'I now know your reasons, but at the time I simply wanted to hurt you as I was hurting.'

Marlene instinctively reached out and put her hand on his thigh. 'No, Rocco, it wasn't your fault. I wanted to tell you the whole truth. I did try once, but...' her golden eyes smiled up into his '...that was just after the first time we made love, and after that I didn't dare in case you turned against me. Our relationship was so new. I didn't want anything to spoil it. I was a coward.'

Rocco's hand covered hers on his thigh and his dark eyes burnt down into hers. 'Is that the truth?' he demanded hardily.

Taking her courage in both hands, she told him how she

felt. 'Yes. You told me yourself you were not looking for a wife, just a lover, and I had no experience in that kind of relationship. I had only ever had one serious boyfriend and we only…' Fighting down the colour in her face, she determinedly carried on. 'We only did it once. Then I discovered he was picking my brains to get a partnership in the firm where we both worked instead of me.'

'The bastard!' Rocco exclaimed, angry on her behalf, and pulled her to his side so she rested in the curve of his arm. With his other hand tipping her chin, he added, 'Tell me who it was and I'll kill him.'

Marlene had to smile. 'That's exactly what Paolo said. But you can see why I was afraid to tell you the truth. My faith in the male sex was badly dented. And though I love you, and wanted to believe in you, I was…' She got no further as his mouth crashed down on hers.

A long moment later she stared up at him breathlessly. 'What was that for?'

'I love you, Marlene, and a moment ago you said you loved me. Did you mean it?' Rocco demanded, lifting his hand to stroke her burning cheek.

'I…I…' She hadn't realised she had given herself away so thoroughly.

'God! Don't go coy on me now, Marlene. I have to know.'

'Yes, I loved you,' she murmured, hypnotised by the expression in his eyes.

'Past tense,' he said, and, drawing her head to his, he rubbed his lips softly on hers, mouthing gently, 'You loved me once, Marlene. Let me try and make you love me again.'

For long moments there was silence, until Marlene needed to breathe or die from his kiss, and, leaning back in his arms, she said breathlessly, 'You don't need to try— I do love you.'

When he would have kissed her again, she held him back with a hand on his chest. 'But is love enough?' It was so easy to forget all that had happened in the past now she was held in his arms, but they had to talk—get rid of all secrets. 'It's six weeks since I left Italy. What made you change your mind about me now? Surely not your father?'

'The six longest weeks of my life.' Rocco husked, and, pushing her against the back of the sofa, he lowered his head.

'No,' said Marlene. It was too easy to fall into his arms with an avowal of love. She needed answers, needed to be able to trust him—now more than ever…

'OK, we have to talk. But I could think of better things to do.' Rocco grinned wryly. Half turning to face her, he squeezed her shoulder and, picking up her hand with his free one, laced her fingers with his. He looked down at their clasped hands for a second, then back to her lovely face.

'The reason it took me six weeks to get in touch with you does me no credit. When you first left I told myself I was well rid of you. I locked myself away in my house and drank myself into a stupor most nights, avoiding everyone. It was only when I finally went into Amalfi ten days ago and bumped into Signor Toni I realised what a fool I had been. I was going to ignore the man, but he wouldn't let me. He insisted on taking me for a drink and telling me the whole story. At first I didn't believe him.'

'You spoke to Signor Toni?' Marlene exclaimed.

'Yes, and when I left him I went straight to Naples and my father's house. After a rather drunken argument with my father—during which I learnt, by the way, that the Contessa has been admitted to a clinic for the mentally ill— I realised Signor Toni had been telling the truth, and the enormity of how badly you and your family had been treated sickened me to my soul.

'I know my own father betrayed the trust and good nature of his supposed best friend Rossi, and in doing so betrayed your mother. I know you are as much Rossi's daughter as Paul is his son. I know you set out to save your father's name, and I can't blame you for not trusting me with your true purpose. In fact I am amazed and thankful you let me anywhere near you with a name like Andretti.

'The apology hasn't yet been invented that can tell you how sorry I am at the way my family has behaved towards you and yours. But I swear I will do everything in my power to make sure no one ever hurts, deceives or insults you ever again.'

Marlene stirred restlessly against his side. She believed his declaration and his apology, but she still had one last worry. 'Caterina—' she began.

'I know now why you asked me if I had ever made love to Caterina,' he cut in, his dark eyes narrowing, his expression grim. 'She is my half-sister, and for that reason alone I could hate my father. He should have told me— especially once the girl was older. It was pure luck that nothing happened. But then again, maybe there is something in the genes. I always thought of her more as a kid sister than a woman, in any case.'

'I am sorry,' she said softly. It must be hard for a man like Rocco to know that his own father had been deceiving him all these years.

'There is no need. I think in the back of my mind I have always had a suspicion. I told you once that as a young boy I discovered my mother in tears, and if I am honest I have never liked my father since. I used to feel guilty about it, but as I got older I realised you can love people because they are your parents, but it does not necessarily follow that you have to like them. My father always had a mistress—dozens over the years.'

'The Contessa said the other women were just a

smokescreen so no one would realise they were having an affair,' Marlene interjected.

Rocco threw back his head and laughed out loud. 'My God, the woman really was deluded if she believed that. My father only ever had one goal in his life: to be wealthy and enjoy himself. He married my mother for her money and I was the requisite son to carry on his name. But in all honesty he was never a father to me. Paolo Rossi spent more time with me when I was a child than my father ever did.

'I don't know why I imagined our relationship would change after the death of my mother. Perhaps I felt guilty, as she left me her personal fortune. When I came back from South Africa I had the stupid idea of making it up with my father and splitting my inheritance—hence my attempt to help him by coming to England and meeting you.' He glanced sideways at her. 'That is the only favour he has ever done for me. He gave me the chance to meet you again.'

'And you hated me on sight,' she said.

Rocco lifted their clasped hands to his mouth and his brilliant white teeth nipped the back of her hand. 'I never hated you. I lusted after you. God, how I lusted after you. I didn't know what had hit me.'

She flushed slightly. 'Lust isn't love,' she said bravely.

He studied her lovely face with dark, intent eyes. 'I know—I was a fool. I was blinded by lust; I couldn't see past your luscious body. Which is why I behaved like a complete jackass.'

'And now?' Marlene dared to ask. 'Now you know the difference?' She still needed reassurance that he really did love her.

'Never doubt that I love you, Marlene,' Rocco replied, and, putting their joined hands against his chest so she could feel the heavy pounding of his heart, his expression deadly serious, he stared into her eyes. 'I think I have always loved you from the first time I saw you, but at the time I didn't believe in love.' One dark brow arched sardonically. 'Given my father and friends, it is not so surprising.'

'You asked me to be your mistress,' she couldn't help inserting.

'That was when I thought you had been Paolo's mistress—and you didn't disillusion me,' he chided gently.

Guilt made her blush. 'I was stupid.'

'No, you were only trying to protect your brother. Something else I love about you. When I discovered the truth from the Contessa I was angry, but on the Sunday after we made love for the first time I had great difficulty hanging onto my anger. By the Monday, when you walked into my house and into my bed, I had resolved to marry you. I decided no one else was ever going to have you but me, and the very next morning I set about making the arrangements. But—arrogantly—I still wasn't prepared to admit it was love.'

'So when…?' Marlene murmured, needing to know.

'The night I left you to go to Rome. I turned and looked back at you, with Paul in your arms, and I knew without any doubt or qualifications that I loved you and wanted you to be the mother of my children.'

It was what she had wanted to hear, and she had not the heart to deny him any longer. Overcome with emotion, she leant forward, slipping her arm around his back. 'Thank you, Rocco,' she breathed against his lips.

'No, I thank you, my darling,' he said, and, freeing her other hand, he hauled her hard against his chest, his lips nuzzling her neck and then her ear. 'When did you know you loved me?' he murmured, and she realised Rocco was just as insecure as she had been.

Tilting back her head, a beautiful smile illuminating her

face, she said casually, 'Well, it all started when I was grovelling in the dirt, weeding between the raspberry bushes, and I glimpsed this incredibly attractive man.'

'Seriously, Marlene.' He stopped her, his dark eyes soft and oddly vulnerable.

She raised one slender hand and gently traced the outline of his brow. 'I am serious. I took one look and I wanted you. Nothing like that had ever happened to me before, and after the first day in Italy I knew I loved you and always would,' she whispered softly, and pressed a soft kiss to his firm lips.

Rocco turned her in his arms, lifting her over his legs, and they kissed as they had never kissed before—openly, with love and tenderness, need and passion. Then he lifted his head and stared down at her flushed face, her lovely swollen lips, and said, 'You will marry me, Marlene? I won't insist you take my name—under the circumstances, you can keep your own—but marry me, and I solemnly swear I will look after you and Paul always and for ever.'

Marlene could have wept for her proud, arrogant lover. She knew what it must have cost him to say that she could keep her own name, and with equal generosity she responded, 'Yes, I will marry you, and I will be proud to be known as Mrs Rocco Andretti.'

For a long time there was only the occasional groan and whimper to break the silence in the sun-washed room.

'This is no good. I refuse to make love to my fiancée for the first time on a sofa,' Rocco rasped finally, sitting up and brushing back his thick black hair, his usual arrogance returning. 'Where is Paul?'

'At school. He'll be back at four.'

Rocco glanced briefly at the thin gold watch on his wrist, and then without a word he swung Marlene up in his arms and stood up. 'Show me the way to the bedroom, sweetheart.'

'I seem to remember you saying that once before and getting a bowl of fruit thrown at you.' Marlene chuckled, lacing her hands behind his neck.

Rocco stopped, an arrested expression on his handsome face. 'Which reminds me—what were you doing picking raspberries? Not the usual occupation of a financial consultant on a Monday, surely?'

'What about love in the afternoon?' she mocked lightly. 'You're going to take me to bed. Mind you, I'm no lightweight, and carrying me upstairs is a lot harder than along a hall.'

'In my present state, please don't mention hard,' Rocco growled. 'I need the exercise to stop me from exploding here and now...'

Marlene yawned widely, snuggled up against Rocco's huge, warm body spoon-fashion under the rose cotton sheet, with his large hand splayed across her stomach. She had never been happier.

'Tired, darling?' His deep voice feathered her shoulder, and his hand stroked from her stomach to cup her breast.

Turning around, she looked up at him with eyes full of love. 'Never too tired for you.' She grinned, but before Rocco could capture her mouth she stopped him. 'One little boy will be back very soon.'

'Damn.' Rocco grimaced. 'Foiled again.'

'Do you mind about Paul?' It suddenly hit Marlene that not every man would want to marry a woman with an almost four-year-old child to look after.

'God, no,' he declared, and, rolling over onto his back, he pulled Marlene on top of him. 'Don't ever think that. I love the little boy as much as I would love one of my own.' And, pulling her head down, he kissed her with passion and promise.

Lying on top of him, Marlene was aware of the renewed

stirring of his arousal, and she moved her hips against his hard thighs teasingly. She would have loved to give in to the sensual delight he promised, but he had reminded her of a more urgent problem. Rolling off him, she sat up. 'You asked me before why I was picking the raspberries', she reminded him.

'I don't care.' He slanted her a smug grin from where he lay flat on his back, his hands behind his head, looking like one incredibly satisfied, sexy male. 'Come back here and finish what you started.'

'No. Not until I've answered your question. You did say we had to be honest with each other,' she stated with mock humility, giving him a sly grin. 'I was picking raspberries because I had a sudden desire to make raspberry jam. In fact,' she mused as her stomach suddenly made a distinct grumbling noise, 'I'm hungry now. A cheese, cucumber and raspberry jam sandwich would go down a treat.'

'A *what*?' Rocco pulled himself up to a sitting position. 'The English are not renowned for their food, but that sounds disgusting.'

'Well, if you will assault a lady on a sofa totally unprepared…' She knew the exact moment she had conceived—their last night together in Italy. 'You might expect that six weeks later she'll have a few odd crav—' She didn't finish.

'My God! You're pregnant!' His arm curved around her shoulders, pulling her towards him, and, twisting his hand in her long hair, holding her face only inches from his, he demanded, 'Would you have told me if…?'

Marlene looked deep into his eyes and saw her own reflection and her own doubts mirrored there. 'Yes,' she said. 'But I only found out today.' She thought of her visit to the doctor, and her restlessness on her return, which had led her out into the garden. She recalled her decision not to contact him until hell froze over, and then Rocco's sudden appearance.

'I believe you because I need to. I feel bad enough that our child was conceived in anger. I couldn't stand the thought that you might never have told me as well.'

'Never say that. Our child was *not* conceived in anger. It might have started that way, but it certainly didn't end that way, as I recall. And I would have told you about the baby,' she reiterated firmly, and, closing the space between them, she pressed her lips to his, putting all her love and reassurance into the kiss.

He lifted his head and smiled down into her wide golden eyes. 'Thank you for that, Marlene. There have been enough lies between us already to last a lifetime—but never again.' Cradling her head with his hand, he breathed against her mouth, 'Our child—I never thought life could be so perfect.'

Marlene lifted her arms around his neck, a secret smile on her flushed face. They still had a lot of sorting out to do, a lot of adjustments to make, but time and love were on their side. Anyway, she told herself, crossing her fingers behind his head, it wasn't a lie. It was a miracle! Her private hell *had* frozen over… She was back in her lover's arms to stay…

Amanda Browning still lives in the Essex house where she was born. The third of four children – her sister being her twin – she enjoyed the rough and tumble of life with two brothers as much as she did reading books. Writing came naturally as an outlet for a fertile imagination. The love of books led her to a career in libraries, and being single allowed her to take the leap into writing for a living. Success is still something of a wonder, but allows her to indulge in hobbies as varied as embroidery and bird-watching.

Look out for more of Amanda Browning's sexy stories – coming soon in Modern Romance™

SEDUCED
by
Amanda Browning

CHAPTER ONE

MEGAN TERRELL caught the sound of a car driving into the yard and paused in the act of studying the drawings for the only boat currently being built by what had once been a small but thriving company. It had never been unusual for vehicles to come and go at the Terrell boatyard, but they had a tendency, these days, to bear creditors, not potential customers.

Frowning, she wondered if she had forgotten to pay a bill, but was sure she hadn't. Keeping track of their debts bordered on paranoia with her, so that she knew what had to be paid yesterday, and what could wait a little longer. Her stomach clenched. Unless Daniel— She cut off the alarming thought. Don't borrow trouble, their father had always said, and it was doubly valid now, when she had enough of her own to contend with.

'Sounds like visitors. Were you expecting anyone, Ted?' she asked the man who stood beside her. Ted Powell was the genius who turned her designs into the sleek craft Terrell's were renowned for. Once he had had a dozen men working with him, now there were only two. It was sad. She refused to think it was hopeless, however.

He shook his head. 'Not that I can recall, unless the German's changed his mind. It was a beautiful boat, Megan. One of your best,' he added, and she sighed wistfully.

It had been beautiful, and the commission had been worth its weight in gold. Only they couldn't afford to hire more staff, and the German hadn't been prepared to wait.

The cancellation had been a blow. Quite frankly, she had been relying on the commission to tide them over.

Megan shook her head, knowing better than to hang onto the slim hope. 'He was pretty adamant,' she recalled, and pulled a face at the sound of a car door slamming. 'I'd better go and see who it is. You never know, it could be somebody wanting us to build a fleet!' she joked wryly, before hurrying off.

Thank heavens for a sense of humour, she thought as she approached the door. It was essential in these days of recession when boats were a luxury most people had decided they could live without. However, just in case someone had won the pools and decided to allow Terrell's to share their good fortune, she pinned a smile of welcome on her face. With her first glimpse of the visitor, her eyebrows rose in surprise and her smile grew crooked. Lucas! The man standing propped against the wing of his car, dressed in an expensive silk shirt and casual trousers, was without doubt Lucas Canfield.

It was eight years since she had seen him in the flesh, but with the success of his computer empire giving him millionaire status, and looks a movie star would have envied, his face was splashed across the papers so often he was virtually a household name. Like washing-up liquid, though not as squeaky clean! Her eyes danced at the analogy, for he had always been unrepentant about his reputation with the opposite sex. The Lucas Canfield phenomenon had been a worthy target for her taunting until he had removed himself from her orbit.

Megan could see what women saw in him. He was as handsome as sin, and just as darkly seductive. He was also elusive, as they discovered to their cost. Lucas was a butterfly, flitting from one woman to the next, sampling each, staying a while before going on to the next unknown, and perhaps tastier morsel. She'd known it when she was eighteen and he seven years older. Now he was thirty-three, and nothing had changed.

Right this minute he had his long, muscular legs crossed at the ankles, and his arms folded over his powerful chest in a way she recalled as uniquely his. She'd long ago lost count of the number of times she'd squared up to him when he'd looked as relaxed as this.

At sixteen she had taken it upon herself to improve him, to save him from himself. Her shots could have been made of rubber the way they had bounced off him. She'd get angry, and he would laugh, teasing her about her own romantic ideas of love and marriage. The trouble was, it had been hard to stay angry with him for long. In the end she had given up her attempts, settling for a constant taunting, so that he should never forget that one female wasn't impressed.

She admitted to being impressed now, for he looked tanned and healthy, so vibrantly alive that he charged the air around him. His strongly etched, enticingly handsome face bore little sign of the passing of time, and was still framed by a shock of black hair. Then there were his eyes. Unforgettable eyes of such an intense blue that it would be easy for a woman to drown in them. Many had. The list was endless. And it was all done with so little effort on his part. Oh, yes, he was still Lucas, as rawly masculine as he had ever been.

The sound of feminine laughter distracted her from her study, and she caught her breath as a leggy blonde swayed into view and attached herself to Lucas's arm, hanging on like a limpet whilst he smiled down at her in a way Megan could only describe as lecherous. As she watched, Lucas lowered his head, pressing a lingering kiss to an inviting pair of lips.

Megan felt her smile slip as a small flicker of anger sprung to life, only to be instantly dismissed as her lip curled wryly. She shouldn't be surprised when she had just been thinking of him as the playboy he was. His picture was always in the society pages, and he was never alone. He had been photographed with some of the most beautiful women in the world. She didn't know how he found time to make his money, but he did, because he was as well-known for his corporate activities as he was for his more personal ones.

'How much longer must we wait? There's obviously no-body here, and I'm starving. Don't forget you promised me lunch, Lucas, darling,' the blonde pouted, and Megan got the impression that food wasn't what she was thinking about at all.

However, the interruption reminded her that she couldn't stand skulking in the shadows for ever, with the possibility of Lucas discovering her there. What he would say to that would probably burn her ears off. Their relationship had always been feisty, a kind of private war in which they used whatever weapons came to hand, normally verbal. Truth to tell, she had always kind of enjoyed their fights, even though she'd usually lost, and it occurred to her now that she had actually missed them. Perhaps that was why her heart was beating just a little faster as she prepared to step outside, because she anticipated a very lively exchange.

A tiny smile curved her lips as she moved. Lucas was the first to catch sight of her as she emerged into the sunlight. He straightened immediately, blatantly carrying out a lazy inspection of her person. Surprisingly, she felt the lick of it like a tongue of flame on her flesh, but before she could ponder what it meant he unleashed a smile on her that lit up his deep blue eyes in a way which heralded devilment of some sort, and Megan laughed, shaking her head despairingly. He hadn't changed.

'Hello, stranger,' she greeted him easily, pleased to see him, though she wouldn't boost his ego by saying so.

'Well, well, well, if it isn't little Megan all grown-up at last.'

Megan sent him an old-fashioned look. 'I was grown-up when you last saw me,' she reminded him drily.

'Ah, but you only had the promise of the beauty you've become,' Lucas contested, and, much to her surprise, Megan felt heat sting her cheeks at the fulsome compliment.

She told herself her reaction was simply due to the fact that she didn't expect kind words from him. Insults, yes, compliments, no. 'Stop it, Lucas. You'll be turning my head next!' she rebuked him, grinning.

In the next instant her smile slipped as she saw her brother come out of the office. He wasn't supposed to be here. Only days ago he had gone to a race meeting up north with his friends. Ice trickled down her spine as she computed the possible reasons for Daniel's presence. The logical one would be because he actually owned Terrell's, but logic had nothing to do with his behaviour these days. It was the unpalatable alternative which churned up her stomach. If he was back this early, it probably meant he had run out of money! She didn't need the inevitable argument that that would bring on top of losing a valuable commission.

'Good God, Lucas!' Daniel's stunned exclamation as he recognised the visitor echoed round the yard.

Megan bit back a demand to know what had happened because Lucas was Daniel's friend, and had been from her brother's first day at school, when Lucas, older by two years, had taken it upon himself to make the new boy welcome. It was a bond which had never been broken, and she couldn't jeopardise it with rash words. She would wait until they were alone.

Lucas detached himself from the blonde and moved towards his friend, his eyes and voice amused. 'You look as though you've seen a ghost. Is my turning up like this so unpleasant, Dan?'

Ignoring his sister, whom he must have seen, Daniel smiled broadly. 'Hell, no!' he denied, grinning delightedly, and held out his hand to the man he had hero-worshipped as a boy. 'It's good to see you, Lucas. Damn good,' he insisted as Lucas shook the proffered hand.

Megan watched them going through the back-slapping motions of male bonding, wishing, not for the first time, that Lucas had not moved away. He had always been a good influence on her brother. She could have done with that these last few months when Daniel had become like a rudderless ship, at the mercy of every vagrant tide or wind—the very last thing she needed with the recession damaging the business. Because she needed Terrell's. It was her anchor, her purpose, and Daniel was setting it on a direct course for the rocks.

'What took you so long to find your way back here?' Daniel asked, stuffing his hands into the back pockets of his jeans. 'Did you lose our address?'

Lucas accepted the criticism with a wry smile. 'I shouldn't have left it so long, but it's good to see you too, Dan. And the old place,' he declared warmly, reacquainting himself with the yard he had known so well as a boy. 'I have to admit I wasn't sure of finding you still here. A lot of good companies have gone to the wall these last few years.'

Daniel's laugh was off-key as he dragged a hand through his hair, and once again he avoided looking at Megan. 'Not us, thank God. We're on the crest of a wave. Things couldn't be better!' he declared, and Megan's lips twisted bitterly as she heard the outright lie. Not that she was surprised. Daniel certainly wouldn't want his idol to know the awful truth.

Lucas nodded. 'I'm glad to hear it, though it wouldn't have surprised me to hear things were rough,' he responded, and Megan held her breath, wondering how her brother would respond to the invitation.

Laughing dismissively, Daniel didn't quite meet his friend's eyes. 'We've been lucky, I guess,' he said, and finally turned to his sister. 'Hi, Meg. Isn't this great? You could have knocked me down with a feather when I saw him!' he exclaimed with an uneasy laugh.

He might well be uneasy, Megan thought acidly. He was hoping that Lucas's arrival would sidetrack her from his own unexpected appearance. She might have said nothing at all if she hadn't seen the flush on his cheeks, and recognised the cause. Daniel had started drinking several months ago, and she hadn't been able to stop him. It was another bone of contention between them.

'I thought you were in York,' she said staunchly, and angry colour rose up his neck.

'Not now, for God's sake, Meg!' he snapped, glaring at her, and she knew her assumptions about the early return were correct. Fortunately for him, she had no intention of airing their dirty linen in public, but she would not let it pass unacknowledged.

'Well, since you are back, Ted needs to see you. It's important, Daniel,' she insisted as she saw him about to object. 'I'm sure Lucas and his friend will excuse you for the few minutes it will take,' she maintained firmly.

Still flushed, Daniel produced a brittle laugh as he turned to his friend. 'Sorry, you know how it is. The place would fall apart without me! I'll see you later,' he promised before turning towards the shed.

Which left Megan facing Lucas and the woman. It was the blonde she turned to. 'I hope you'll forgive us for squabbling in front of you, but Terrell's has that effect on us, I'm afraid,' she apologised, only to receive a coolly distant smile for her pains.

'That's quite all right,' the blonde replied, sounding bored, and turned to smile up at Lucas. 'I'll wait by the car, darling. Don't be long. We have a date...remember?' With that pointed rejoinder, she cast another aloof smile at Megan, and left them.

Amused rather than put out, Megan stared after her. 'I'd be careful if I were you, Lucas. That pretty much sounded like she was staking a claim!' she drawled, turning back to him.

He was grinning, but there was something at the back of his eyes she couldn't identify. 'I'm always careful where women are concerned.'

Her brows lifted disarmingly. 'Mmm, I know. Safety in numbers, right?'

'Something like that,' he agreed easily, crossing his arms and taking his weight on one leg.

Of all the constants in the universe, Lucas was the one she was most sure of. 'You haven't changed, have you?'

'Unlike you. You look very sophisticated these days, Red. Very cool and in control.'

He was the only one who had ever called her that. It had irritated her as a teenager, but now she found that it sounded altogether different. Somehow darkly sweet and intimate. It sent a shiver along her spine, and she suddenly felt anything but cool.

'I work in a predominantly male field, so it wouldn't do my career any good to be seen as an emotional female,' she responded, hoping he wouldn't notice the inexplicable increase in her breathing.

Lucas's only evident reaction was to quirk one eyebrow. 'I'm surprised you're still here. I imagined you would have married long ago.'

Yes, he would think that, but a lot had happened since

he had been away. He couldn't have known his comment would hurt, and that she would have to grit her teeth to laugh and make the statement she was now known for. 'What? Hand myself over to some man? You must be joking!' It was a glib answer, one polished to perfection by years of use. 'I decided years ago that marriage wasn't for me, and nothing has happened to change my mind,' she added for good measure. Glancing up at him, she discovered that for once she had surprised him.

'That doesn't sound like the Megan I remember. She waxed lyrical about making some man happy and raising a dozen kids. The last I heard you were crazy about Chris Baxter. What happened to him?'

Megan was shaken by the soft question. She had forgotten that Lucas had left before she'd broken up with Chris. She had hurt him, and her only excuse was that she had been too young to use finesse. Too overwhelmed by events to limit the damage. She knew better now. Years later she had apologised to Chris, and he had forgiven her, but they had never again been friends.

'We split up,' she shrugged, as if it had been no big deal. 'It didn't ruin his life. He's married now, with two small children,' she pointed out lightly.

'They could have been yours,' Lucas declared next, and Megan had to glance down quickly, pretending to remove an imaginary speck of dust from her blouse, before she had the necessary control to look him squarely in the eye.

'No, they couldn't. I'm not mother material. They'd disrupt my life, and I prefer it the way it is.' One day she might even believe it, she thought wryly.

Lucas frowned, shaking his head. 'So you're a career woman now?'

Megan smiled over-brightly. 'Absolutely. I've outgrown those childish fancies. I'm not looking for the right man, any more than you're looking for the right woman,' she retorted, feeling herself back on safe ground.

Now his smile grew. 'Who says I'm not looking? I just haven't found her yet.'

Megan looked sceptical. 'You mean you'd give up your lifestyle for just one woman?'

'Like that.' Lucas snapped his fingers. 'Its been a longer search than I expected.'

'And you've seen no reason not to enjoy yourself in the meantime,' she mocked, struggling with a strange emotion which appeared to be knotting her stomach. 'I thought you were looking a little jaded. Perhaps you ought to slow down. You're not getting any younger, you know, Lucas,' she advised sardonically.

'Wherever did you get this idea that I'm some kind of super-stud?' Lucas laughed, a full, rich sound which curled its way along her senses and set them fluttering.

Megan registered her reaction with a sharp intake of breath. Out of a clear blue sky she suddenly realised she wasn't responding to an old friend, but to a virile man who possessed physical magnetism in spades. She was a little surprised to find herself no more immune than the next woman. For as long as she could remember, Lucas had simply been just Lucas. Now her brain was having to do some rapid readjusting to the novel idea, whilst her senses were already several laps ahead!

'Probably from the way you change your women as often as you change your socks,' she drawled with oodles of irony, glad she had learned to hide her feelings because Lucas would have had a field-day with them.

'You've been reading too many papers, but I find it interesting that you bothered to read about me at all,' he remarked and she laughed this time.

'I've always been rather partial to horror stories,' she returned drily.

'Some day someone is going to give you a well-deserved beating,' Lucas growled, and Megan laughed again.

'You're not going to reserve that pleasure for yourself?'

'Believe me, I would, if it wasn't for the fact that Dan would probably tear me limb from limb.'

She grimaced, knowing that these days Daniel was more likely to lend him a hand! Nevertheless, she grinned. 'That's what brothers are for,' she quipped, and out of the corner of her eye caught sight of the blonde's angry scowl. 'Er...your friend seems a little put out,' she murmured, and Lucas glanced from the humour in her eyes to his companion.

'You're right. I'd better go and soothe her ruffled feathers.' He glanced at his watch. 'Tell Dan I'll be back as soon as I've booked into a hotel.'

Megan was surprised. She had assumed this was a flying visit. 'You're staying down here?'

His teeth flashed as he smiled. 'For a while. Think you can put up with me?'

'In small doses I even quite like you,' Megan admitted, then cocked her head to one side as she heard a bell ringing. 'That's the phone. I have to go, sorry,' she apologised, already on the move, and waved her hand in his general direction as she hurried towards the office.

Inside, Megan dashed for the desk, grabbing up the receiver to gasp a rushed, 'Hello.'

The voice which came down the line was familiar and disappointing, and she realised she had still been hoping to hear from that wretched German. 'Oh, Mark, it's you,' she replied, unwittingly ungracious, and turned to lean her weight against the edge of the desk whilst they talked.

However, as she did so, she faced the window, from where, framed in perfect view, she could see Lucas and the blonde were locked together in a passionate embrace. Standing beside the car, oblivious to who might be watch-

ing, the blonde seemed intent on eating him up alive, and
Lucas didn't look as if he minded! Mere seconds later they
parted with patent reluctance, and she watched as they held
a short conversation before both climbed into the car and
Lucas drove off.

Megan experienced a curious mixture of emotions. She
really didn't care who he kissed, and yet seeing the blonde
draped around him had made her feel furious with him.
Which was totally ridiculous under the circumstances.
Good Lord, this was Lucas. The playboy of Europe! The…

'Hello! Hello! Megan? Are you there?'

With a gasp of contrition, Megan belatedly realised she
had left Mark dangling on the end of the line. 'Oh, good
heavens! Yes, I'm here, Mark. Sorry, but I…er…got distracted,' she invented hastily. 'Did you want something?'

'Just to check if we're still on for tonight.'

'Of course. I'm looking forward to it,' she responded
cheerfully, although it wasn't quite true. She had been dating Mark for a couple of months now, and though she liked
him well enough she had the uneasy feeling that he might
be one of her mistakes.

His chuckle was intimate. 'Good. I've chosen somewhere
quiet and romantic, where we can be alone,' he claimed,
and she stiffened, her thumbs pricking like mad. Oh, Lord,
not again!

'Oh, um, that sounds wonderful,' she lied as her heart
sank to her boots. Maybe she was wrong, but she really
didn't think so. She'd just have to play it by ear. 'Where
are we going?' she asked, and then spent an uncomfortable
ten minutes having her worst fears realised, before Mark
rang off, promising to pick her up at eight-thirty. It was not
going to be a pleasant evening, but there was no avoiding
it. Mark would have to go.

Feeling dispirited, she went to the washroom to freshen
up. They were in the middle of a heatwave, and the hu-

midity made her uncomfortably sticky. The cold water she splashed on her face felt wonderful. Finally reaching for the towel, she stood back to look at herself critically in the mirror.

What she saw was a twenty-six-year-old woman, taller than average, with a generously curved body, right now clad in jade trousers and a white silk shirt. Her riot of rich auburn hair framed a heart-shaped face whose main feature, in her opinion, was a pair of slanted green eyes. She failed to see the charms of a slightly retroussé nose and a generous mouth, even though they created a total picture which had men beating a path to her door.

A brooding reflection clouded her eyes, and she reached for her brush, dragging it through her hair. Fate had a black sense of humour. Nature had fashioned her to attract a mate, had endowed her with every feminine instinct to achieve that purpose, and she had wanted nothing more, until fate had stepped in. Now, whilst she enjoyed dating, she wasn't looking for a husband. As her group of friends began to pair off, she remained determinedly single.

Most thought she had ice water in her veins, but they were mistaken. She had had an affair once, and it had been a disaster. She had been at university at the time, and feeling particularly alone. She had gone into it for all the wrong reasons, and they had both ended up being hurt. She had discovered that sexual satisfaction was no substitute for emotional involvement. And, since that was all she could offer, she had resolved never to go down that road again.

She had developed an instinct for knowing which men wanted more than she had to give, and avoided them. Occasionally she made mistakes, but she rectified them quickly, gaining for herself a reputation for coldness. She didn't mind. She would not offer more than she could give, nor take more than she deserved. It was the creed she had chosen to live by. And if, as sometimes happened, she was physically attracted to a man, she ignored it, burying herself in her work until the feeling passed.

Her career had become everything—her family and her life. She intended to make Terrell's a world-renowned name for quality and innovation. Her pride in her work was all the satisfaction she needed. A reaffirmation which brought a glitter to her eyes, and she turned away from her reflection, heading for the door.

Back in the office, she glanced to where her drawing-board stood to one end of the room. She resisted the urge to tinker with a new design, turning her back on it to round the desk and sink down onto the seat. There was more than enough paperwork to keep her busy for the rest of the day.

In the beginning Daniel had taken more than an equal interest in the running of the boatyard, but these days she very rarely saw him pick up a paper unless she forced him to. It wasn't that she minded the work, but she did mind the change in him. She couldn't explain it. When he'd first received his inheritance, he had had such enthusiasm, but these last few months he had acted as if he couldn't stand the place. He didn't seem to care about anything except going to the races with his fast friends.

She found herself increasingly angry with him, helplessly so, because he refused to talk about it. The problem was, he wasn't a good judge of horses, and lost more money than they could afford. If he wasn't careful, they would lose the yard too. They must have a serious talk, and soon, if she could make him stand still long enough.

Not long afterwards, the object of her thoughts came through the door. Daniel dropped down heavily onto a vacant chair and rubbed a hand over his eyes. She refused to feel sorry for him, though the lines and unhealthy pallor on his face caused her concern. Unbidden, the memory of Lucas's lithe figure filled her mind. She didn't want to compare them, for that was unfair, yet there was no denying that Daniel was just a little bit less of everything than Lucas. Not as tall, not as muscular, and his handsomeness had a slightly weak quality to it.

Instantly she felt disloyal to have found Daniel wanting, but at the same time it served to remind her that loyalty was a rare commodity at the moment. Grimly, she crossed her arms, but when she spoke she simply sounded tired. 'How much did you lose this time, Daniel?'

Though it shouldn't have, her question appeared to take him unawares, rousing his anger. His temper had been on a short lead lately, too. 'No more than I could afford,' he snapped, then eyed the room irritably. 'Why are you always stuck in this tomb? It's turning you into a real bitch, Meg. I don't know how you stand it!'

She ignored the unflattering comment, knowing it to be a diversionary tactic. 'Just be thankful that I can. Somebody has to see that Terrell's runs smoothly, seeing as you've abdicated all involvement in favour of enjoying yourself with your so-called friends!' she retorted.

Daniel jumped up, ramming his hands into his jeans pockets. 'They are my friends!' he insisted angrily, and she sighed.

'No, they're not. They're just using you. Why can't you see that?' It was so clear to her. They would drop him as soon as the money ran out. Which might be all too terrifyingly close.

'Why can't you see that I'm not as stupid as you think? You're always complaining! You've never respected me, never thought I could know what I was doing!'

The accusation took her aback, and she caught her breath sharply. 'That's unfair! I did respect you.'

He didn't miss the qualification she had been unable to omit. 'Did?' he charged harshly.

It hurt her to admit it, but she wouldn't leave it unsaid if there was a chance that it could do some good. 'How can I respect you when you behave so foolishly? You just make me mad at you!'

'I had noticed,' Daniel said sourly. 'What exactly is it you don't approve of? My right to do what I like with my own money?'

Of course he had a point, but she would be failing in her duty if she didn't try to make him see sense. 'I just think—'

'I don't give a damn what you think,' he interrupted rudely, and colour rose in her cheeks as she lost her temper.

'I know. You don't care what anyone thinks, just so long as they don't stop you from enjoying yourself!' she declared disgustedly.

His fist thudded onto the desk. 'Its my life, for better or worse! What the hell business is it of yours how I live it?'

Megan shoved the chair back as she shot to her feet. 'It's my business because you're my brother, Daniel, and I care what happens to you. Beyond that, this is my livelihood too. I have to see the results of what you're doing and it sickens me!' she returned, alarmed at the violence of the argument, for it was so unlike Daniel to raise his voice.

His face was mottled and angry. 'You get well paid for any inconvenience!'

She paled, cut to the quick. 'Dear God, Daniel, how dare you say that to me? I work damn hard to keep this business going, without any help from you.' Without pay, either. She'd been robbing Peter to pay Paul for months, and there was none left over to pay Megan! She was living off her own dwindling assets, which he would have found out if he had had the interest to do the accounts. She hadn't told him yet, but the day was fast approaching when she would have to.

His head went back at her accusation. 'Believe me, I'm truly grateful,' he said ungraciously, and her lips parted on a sharp intake of breath.

'You know, Daniel, this business won't be able to support your lifestyle for ever. You can't keep gambling with your future this way.' And mine, she added silently. 'You're pushing everything to the edge. What happens when you go over it?'

If she'd thought that would reach him, she was wrong. 'Then you can say "I told you so",' he sneered, and turned accusing eyes on her. 'What did you do with Lucas—scare him off too?'

She smothered an urge to snap back. 'No, he had to go. He said to tell you he would be back later.'

'Lucas was always more than a match for you, wasn't he?' Daniel taunted nastily. 'Well, as I'm not supposed to be here, I'm going back to the house,' he declared challengingly, and shouldered a surprised Ted aside as the man unfortunately attempted to enter the room at the same time as he was leaving it.

Megan sank down on her chair, finding she was shaking. They'd never argued like that before, never, and she wasn't afraid to admit that it had alarmed her. Daniel had always been a gentle soul. Weak, yes, but gentle. For him to act so out of character meant something was badly wrong.

Ted turned from watching Daniel's exit to study her. 'What was that all about?'

Megan sighed heavily, raising her hands in a gesture of futility. 'I can't even talk to him any more. He just doesn't listen.'

Ted humphed. 'That crowd he hangs around with are no good,' he pronounced gently.

'I know. He didn't used to be like this. I'm hoping that if only we can get him away from those ghouls he'll change.'

'Maybe. I'll make no bones about it—Daniel's too easily led. You do your best, love, but you're still only his sister. He needs to face someone with a bit of fight in them. Someone he'll respect, and who won't let him take the easy route,' Ted stated firmly, and Megan nodded.

'Unfortunately, people like that don't grow on trees.' She grimaced despondently, and Ted scratched his head wryly.

'No, but they own telephones,' he chuckled, making Megan frown.

'OK, I'll fall for it. What do you mean?' she asked drily.

Ted shook his head at her, despairing of her intelligence. 'I mean Lucas, of course. Daniel told me who the visitor was, and it occurred to me that he was always good with your brother. Daniel always looked up to him. Why don't you get Lucas to talk to him?' He let the thought sink in.

Megan's eyes widened. He was right. She had said it herself only a short while ago. But… 'How can I? Daniel would never forgive me if I told Lucas all about him.' She sighed, hating to see such a good idea go west.

'Daniel's anger won't last, but once Terrell's is gone it's gone for good!' Ted said gruffly, his hand on her shoulder tempering the blow. 'Think on it. Meanwhile, here's a list of supplies. I was ordered to give it to you.'

Megan couldn't help laughing as she took the paper. 'Surprise, surprise.'

'So, where is the man? I didn't see a car outside. Has he gone?'

'Only to a hotel. He drove off with his playmate some time ago,' she returned drily, and Ted shot her a look.

'Playmate?'

Megan's lips curved in amusement. 'The ubiquitous blonde. Like that charge card, you'll never see him without one!'

'Aye, he was always one for the ladies, was Lucas,' he replied with a laugh as he left again.

Megan propped her chin on her hand. Ted had never spoken a truer word, especially about Lucas's influence over her brother. Or, to be more accurate, her half-brother.

They had had the same father but different mothers. And thereby hung a tale. The situation had given Daniel a birthright to waste, and herself an inheritance so cruel, there was no room for tears.

She pushed the knowledge back into the recesses of her mind, refusing to think about it. However, she would give Ted's suggestion some thought. When you'd gone through every other means available without success, you were willing to consider anything.

In the meantime, work beckoned. With a sigh, she picked up her pen again, reaching for the nearest ledger, and for the second time that day was halted by the sound of a car. She recognised it this time, though, and went to the door. Lucas was just climbing out.

'Back so soon?' she asked sweetly, and Lucas grinned, making himself comfortable by resting his arms on the car roof.

'I didn't want to miss a minute of your sparkling company, Red.'

'It's just as well I know better than to believe you,' she responded drily. 'If you're looking for Daniel, he isn't here.'

Brows raised, Lucas glanced at his watch. 'Short day?'

Megan crossed her arms and leant against the doorframe. 'Every now and then he gives himself time off for good behaviour. You'll find him up at the house.' Hopefully sleeping, and not drinking, she added silently.

'Thanks,' Lucas said, preparing to get back in the car. 'Why don't you join us?'

She could just imagine what Daniel would have to say to that! 'You know what they say—two's company, three's a crowd. You'll be able to talk more freely without me there. You must have lots to catch up on,' she refused politely.

'Don't you want to hear what I've been doing?' he taunted.

'Oh, I think I've got a pretty good idea!' she exclaimed sardonically, and he laughed.

'You're wrong, you know, but, if it pleases you to believe what you read, so be it,' Lucas declared, and with another of his blinding smiles, which left Megan rooted to the spot, he climbed into the car, started the engine and drove off.

She shuddered, scorched by a heat far stronger than the sun. When it came to dangerous weapons, Lucas's smile should be registered as lethal! Turning back into the office, she knew she would have the devil's own job trying to concentrate on anything as mundane as work. Reaching her desk, she picked up an invoice, resolutely ignoring the memory of eyes and a smile which seemed to be having the strangest effect on her.

CHAPTER TWO

IT WAS CLOSE to midnight when Mark brought his car to a halt outside the house, converted from two cottages, which Megan had shared with Daniel since their father died. It was a hot summer night, and the lounge windows were still thrown wide, muted light shining through them. Megan wished she were inside, not sitting in the sporty convertible, waiting for trouble.

The date had rung warning bells from the start, for not only had Mark chosen a secluded restaurant but he had presented her with flowers too. Her misgivings of earlier had been slowly consolidated, taking her appetite away. Although he didn't say so, she knew Mark took their relationship more seriously than she had thought, and this was his bid to take it a step further. Now, when he took her in his arms to kiss her goodnight, it was with a depth of passion he hadn't shown before. She didn't resist, but she didn't respond either, and when that fact finally got through he eased away to frown at her.

'Megan? Is something wrong?' he asked, puzzled, and Megan closed her eyes momentarily, bracing herself.

'Yes, Mark, I think there is,' she began gently but firmly. 'I like you very much, but…' She hesitated, reluctant to cause hurt. It shouldn't have come to this. Usually she read the signs, and could put an end to the association before there was any danger of misunderstanding. But she had been so preoccupied lately, she had totally misread the situation.

Beside her, Mark had tensed. 'But?' he queried shortly, and she knew that tact was going to get her nowhere. She would have to be blunt.

'I don't want an affair.'

In the reflected light, she saw Mark smile and her heart sank. 'I know that, honey. I don't want an affair either.' He reached out, fingering a stray lock of her hair. 'Oh, Megan. I think I'm falling in love with you,' he declared huskily, and ice settled in her stomach.

Licking dry lips, she tried to be gentle. 'Don't fall in love with me, Mark. You'll be wasting your time.'

'Let me be the judge of that,' he countered huskily, clearly thinking she was playing hard to get, and Megan knew that subtlety simply would not work.

Turning in her seat so that her hair pulled free and his hand fell away, she eyed him squarely. 'Listen to me. I'm sorry, but I don't love you, Mark. I won't ever love you. I like you a lot, and enjoy your company, but I'm not looking for more than that. I'd like to continue seeing you, but only if you can accept my rules.'

He heard her out in silence, and she could feel him withdrawing from her. 'And if I can't accept them?'

Megan felt her heart sink further, for she knew this was going to be one of the bad times, but her expression remained firm. 'Then this is goodbye.'

She could feel his anger surging towards her, and something nasty flickered in his eyes. 'You know, I didn't believe it. They tried to warn me, but I argued them down. Now I see you really are the heartless bitch they said you were, aren't you?'

She had heard worse, but she flinched anyway. So much for love. Gathering up her bag and her poise, she sent him a cool smile. 'I'll take that as no, then, shall I?' Climbing out, she shut the door with care. 'Goodbye, Mark. I'm sorry it had to end this way.'

He gunned the engine before delivering a parting shot, and she had to strain to hear what he said over the noisy revving. 'My mistake. I thought you were simply wary of involvement, but now I see you don't have anything to give a man. I pity you, but I figure I'm well out of it!'

Even though she had expected it, Megan still caught her breath as she stared after the departing tail-lights, feeling weary to her bones. His words hurt and tears stung the backs of her eyes, but she blinked them away because she was never going to feel guilty again for allowing someone to believe things which were not true. However, such confrontations always left her that little bit more diminished, so it was as well they didn't come along too often.

With a sigh, she turned to go inside, and it was then that she saw the shadow outlined in the lounge window. It moved as she did, and she frowned as she walked indoors, not liking the idea of having been overheard, and yet grateful that Daniel was at least home before her for once. Tossing her bag onto the hall table, she entered the room on her left.

Stretching and running her fingers through her hair, she kicked off her shoes. 'This is a nice surprise, Da...' She got no further, because at that point she discovered that the man in the room wasn't her brother at all, but Lucas. Her lips parted in shock and her rounded eyes darted to the window, as if to confirm what she already knew.

Now standing by the fireplace, with his arm resting on the mantel, Lucas observed her in amusement. 'I found it very edifying,' he remarked, confirming her suspicions. 'Do you always discard importunate suitors so delicately?'

Pale with shock, Megan realised her hands were still raised, and hastily lowered them to her sides, using the precious seconds to recover. It had been bad enough imagining Daniel hearing what had transpired. To discover that it was Lucas was unsettling. Not that she cared what he thought. Her reasons were as valid as ever, and she would not explain, even if she could have.

So she shrugged, pretending an insouciance she was far from feeling right then. 'Only those who won't take no for an answer,' she said blithely, flinging herself gracefully into the corner of the couch and crossing her legs with a slither of silk.

Lucas's eyes followed her down, lingering to caress the shapely curves of her calves with an intensity which brought a tiny gasp to her lips. Megan felt a tingle of warmth ignite in the pit of her stomach. Her eyes widened. She couldn't recall the last time she had experienced such an instantaneous kick of desire, but it wasn't so long that she had forgotten what it felt like. The surprise came in feeling it now, with Lucas. Unbidden, a tingle of anticipation sent a delicate shiver over her skin.

'Determined to keep all men at arm's length, Red?' Lucas's mocking query pierced her bemusement, and with a swift mental shake for allowing herself to be so easily distracted Megan manufactured an equally mocking smile.

'I'm a modern woman. I reserve the right to choose who I want to have affairs with,' she responded lightly, though in truth her 'affairs' were in the singular. Which could hardly have been said of the man who stood before her.

As she spoke, one part of her brain noted that the elegant dinner suit he wore could not hide the sheer power of the man. She had always known he was handsome, but she had registered his physical magnetism clinically, not receptive to the signals he sent out. She was tuned into them now, though, with a vengeance, and it made the hairs stand up on her skin.

'Making sure you only choose those men you can control, no doubt,' Lucas remarked coolly. 'What are you afraid of?'

Thick lashes dropped to veil her expression from him.

'Afraid' was such a timid word, meant for fanciful things. Her terrors had substance, but she had the power to control them—an awesome power that she could never, ever abdicate, for it was, quite simply, a matter of life and death.

That brought a grim smile to her lips as she looked up, taking his question as it was meant—at face value. 'What are *you* afraid of? You're conspicuously unattached yourself. You must have your own rules about how close any woman is allowed to get.'

He acknowledged that with an inclination of his head. 'True, but my method of parting is less Draconian. That poor fool outside bared his soul to you, and you ground it in the dirt. Where's your compassion?'

She stared at his austere face without flinching. He was making a value judgement, and she couldn't blame him, based on what he had heard. She had sounded heartless, but to tell him she had only been cruel to be kind would lead to demands for explanations, and she had decided long ago that she would apologise for nothing. In a harsh world, only the strong survived. And she *would* be strong. There was no other course for her.

'He didn't love me,' she said evenly. 'And even if he did he won't tomorrow.'

Across from her, Lucas shook his head incredulously. 'How did you get to be so hard?' he asked, and she almost laughed.

With years of practice and determination she had built a shell as hard as nails, but underneath… Tonight's episode was evidence enough that she was still vulnerable. Sometimes she wondered if there would be anything worthwhile left inside when the wall became complete. Would it be an empty shell of a life? How ironic. How…

But she would not think of that. Not now. Not ever. 'Where's Daniel?' she asked, ignoring the question and thereby sealing his opinion of her. She told herself she didn't care.

After the briefest of pauses, Lucas accepted the change of subject with a twist of his lips. 'I haven't the faintest idea.'

That had her sitting up straighter. 'What do you mean?' Surely if they had gone out together he would know where her brother was?

'I mean I have no idea where he spent the evening. I was otherwise engaged,' he informed her, and Megan was on her feet in an instant.

'But…if you weren't with Daniel, what are you doing here?' she asked, anxiety making the question sharper than she intended.

Lucas hesitated, frowning himself as something occurred to him. 'Dan didn't tell you, did he?'

All sorts of dire possibilities as to what she didn't know danced across her mind, and she clamped her arms about her waist, bracing herself for trouble. 'You may as well tell me the worst,' she invited in a flat tone, which brought his blue gaze to lock questioningly with hers.

'You sound as if the world might have come to an end,' he said with the faintest hint of a laugh.

She didn't smile. If Daniel had gone off to another race meeting, it might very well be the end. 'I'm too tired for games, Lucas. Just get it over with, will you?' she snapped, then sighed heavily. It was no use blaming him for Daniel's shortcomings. She waved a dismissive hand. 'I'm sorry. I…' The rest tailed off helplessly, and Lucas took pity on her.

'When I met Dan this afternoon, he invited me to stay here,' he explained concisely, and Megan blinked at him stupidly.

'That's it? I thought…' She took a steadying breath, and produced a rather tired smile. Never mind what she had thought, she had been mistaken, and the relief was heady. 'I ought to know Daniel would do something like that without consulting me!' she exclaimed wryly, and Lucas frowned.

'You have some problem with me staying here?'

Only in so far as it gave her another mouth to feed and another body to clean up after. They had dispensed with the housekeeper months ago, and not unnaturally everything fell onto her broad shoulders. By not telling her, Daniel had probably been paying her back for what she had said earlier. If he expected her to complain, he was mistaken.

'Not at all. You're very welcome to stay, Lucas, though you'll have to give me a moment to make up the spare bed.'

'There's no need. I'm quite capable of making my own bed, if you'll show me where the sheets are kept,' he countered, walking towards her, and as he did so Megan caught sight of a smudge of pink by his mouth. It was the same colour the blonde had worn earlier, and she realised with whom he had been 'otherwise engaged'.

It was automatic to reach up and rub the revealing smudge away with her thumb. 'How careless of you to leave the evidence showing. There, that's better. That shade of pink does nothing for you, you know,' she taunted silkily, and would have moved away, only she suddenly found her wrist caught in a loose but unbreakable grip.

Lucas's blue eyes glinted wickedly. 'Perhaps I left it for you to find, Red,' he said softly, and though her heart gave a wild lurch she quirked her eyebrows tauntingly.

'Now why would you want to do that?' she countered, hoping he didn't hear that touch of breathlessness in her voice.

His smile was slow and seductive. 'Why, to see what

you would do, of course. A person's reaction can be very revealing.'

Her stomach did a reverse flip before settling again. 'And what did mine reveal?' she challenged, tinglingly aware of the heat of his touch and the warmth of his closeness. She was all at once very wide awake, with all senses functioning.

'That you think I'm as shallow, if not shallower, than the women I take out.'

Megan grinned and tipped her head to one side. 'I did notice you had found another blonde clone,' she remarked by way of confirmation.

Lucas's eyes glittered as he raised an eyebrow questioningly. 'Blonde clone?'

Finding the exchange wildly exhilarating, she looked right back at him. 'My, you must be in a bad way if you haven't noticed they all look alike. They even have the same names, like Sophie, Stephanie or Sylvia,' she remarked, and his lips twitched as he released her wrist.

'I had no idea you'd made such a close study of the situation.'

Megan sighed elaborately, hiding the fact that her flesh still felt the imprint of his. She favoured him with an old-fashioned look. 'It's hard not to when your picture, plus "friend," is plastered across the newspapers almost daily. By the way, I hope you fed what's-her-name tonight, thus sparing us from watching her try to make a meal out of you in public!'

'You saw that, did you? Watching is never as much fun as participation. A very…affectionate woman, Sonja.'

'Ah, Sonja!' Megan exclaimed sardonically. 'How very…Nordic.'

A devilish gleam entered his eyes. 'Only by name. By nature she's pure Latin. Didn't you enjoy the show?'

Now that he mentioned it, no, she hadn't. 'It made me

think of the tigers in the zoo at feeding time, when they pounce on their food and tear it apart with their teeth!' she declared, with a delicate shudder of distaste.

Lucas's lips curved appreciatively at the analogy. 'You think I should fear for my life?'

Her eyes danced. 'I'd say you should fear more for your freedom.'

He pretended to consider that. 'You think she intends to have me?' he asked, and Megan laughed.

'Have you? She already thinks she's got you! If I were you, I'd be feeling very nervous right now. If you listen hard enough, I'm certain you'll be able to hear church bells ringing!' she enlarged with a liberal amount of unholy enjoyment.

Lucas grinned, and the gleam in his eyes deepened. 'You'd really enjoy seeing me caught, wouldn't you, Red?'

She grinned right back at him. 'I find the idea quite poignant. The biter bit, so to speak.'

His teeth flashed whitely as his smile broadened. 'It's a wonder you haven't thought of having a go yourself.'

'I may be stupid sometimes, but I'm not insane!' she riposted neatly, though her heart actually started to race at the very idea.

'I'm surprised you didn't say desperate,' he commented drily.

'I was trying to be polite,' she lied brazenly, and Lucas threw back his head and laughed, causing her to watch him in fascination.

After a moment or two he recovered his poise and observed her with his head tilted to one side. 'You know, Red, I'm glad you haven't changed too much. You're still as fiery as your hair. It would have been a shame to see all that vibrancy subdued. You're much more entertaining this way.'

Megan rounded her eyes at him. 'More entertaining than Sonja?' she probed.

'Within reason. Sonja's talents are more...womanly,' Lucas said softly, and his remark was all the more deadly for it.

The enjoyment died out of her so swiftly that it was quite shocking. She simply hadn't been expecting the cloaked attack, had allowed the novelty of her awareness of him to make her drop her guard. With a faint laugh she glanced down at her hands, was surprised to find that they carried a fine tremor, and dug deep for her composure before she looked up again, smiling with icy humour.

'You think Mark's right, don't you? That I'm missing something quintessentially feminine.'

Lucas shrugged. 'Most men would prefer more warmth and less frostbite,' he conceded and Megan unexpectedly saw red.

'It's amazing!' she exclaimed angrily. 'If I appeared to promise something and then didn't deliver, you'd call me a tease. Because I chose to say no, you call me cold.'

Lucas studied her fierce expression with interest. 'Oh, I wouldn't say cold exactly. More cold-blooded. You have to be in control, and no quarter is given to anyone who oversteps the mark.'

Baldly put, but true. She wasn't prepared to compromise on that part of her life. If you avoid involvement, you can't cause pain—a maxim she kept to herself.

'There is no point in having rules if you don't obey them,' she insisted, and drew a frown from him.

'How can there be rules in love? You never know when it's going to strike,' he countered, and she smiled, seeing the opening.

'Precisely my point. I don't want love to strike, and my rules are there to make sure it doesn't. There's no room for love in my life. Love means marriage and a family. I don't want children. I'm not the maternal sort. And I certainly don't want to be tied to one man for life. Love is a trap, and I want to be free to do anything I please with my life.' There were so many lies in there, she ought to have had her fingers crossed, but Lucas didn't know that.

He took her at her word. 'Interesting. There's just one thing you've forgotten. Life has a way of scuttling the best laid plans.'

She knew that only too painfully well, which was why she left nothing to chance. 'Not mine. I have no intention of being taken by surprise. My life is exactly the way I want it,' she said with the utmost conviction, sounding as cold-blooded as he had accused her of being. Raising her chin defiantly, she met his look and damned him to criticise her.

'I take back what I said—you certainly have changed, Red,' Lucas uttered with a shake of his head.

And not for the better, obviously. She had expected his condemnation, but not the hurt it brought with it. She had thought she was beyond that, but apparently not. She shrugged it off with an unrepentant laugh. 'Oh, dear, I appear to have shocked you!' she exclaimed, pretending an amusement she was far from feeling.

Lucas didn't laugh this time. If she'd been asked to describe his expression, she would have said it was regretful. 'I'm trying to equate the warm, lovely girl I used to know with the woman standing before me now.'

Megan found she had to turn away to swallow the lump of emotion which blocked her throat. Walking to the window, she reached out to pull it shut. 'Did you expect me to stay a child for ever?' she asked as she drew the curtains and faced him again.

He was watching her as if she was a particularly tricky puzzle he was determined to crack. 'No, but to go to such extremes is unusual. What happened to you, Red?'

How strange. Nobody else had ever asked that. They had simply accepted everything she said and did. It upset her to find Lucas so perceptive, but it was too late for confidences. So she frowned as if she didn't understand. 'Nothing happened. I just grew up.' And made some decisions about her life which had been painful but unavoidable, she thought.

Artfully she stifled a yawn. 'It's getting late. If you come with me, I'll get the sheet and duvet. You don't mind using a duvet, I hope? I know that some men simply can't abide them.' She was babbling, but she didn't care. She had had just about all she could safely take of the conversation.

'The duvet will be fine,' Lucas confirmed, watching her carefully, so that she felt rather like a specimen under a microscope. He indicated that she should go before him, and she did so with relief.

Leading the way upstairs, she went to the laundry cupboard on the landing and handed him the sweet-smelling covers.

'Are you sure you can manage?' she asked politely, and Lucas nodded.

'I'll be fine. Goodnight, Megan,' he said sombrely, and headed down the corridor towards the spare room.

'Goodnight, Lucas. Sleep well,' she called after him but if he heard he made no sign. Biting her lip, she went downstairs again to secure the house, leaving only one light glowing in the hall before collecting her things and going up to her room.

Once inside, she threw the window wide and sank down onto the window-seat. All things considered, this had to be one of the worst evenings of her life. First Mark, then Lucas. Separately the confrontations would have been bad enough, but back to back... She felt exhausted. No matter how convinced she was of the rightness of her actions, defending them always left her feeling drained. Tonight had been especially wearing, for, although Mark only knew her as an adult woman, Lucas had a lifetime of memories to compare her with.

It was funny how neither her father nor Daniel had remarked on the woman she had become by the time she'd returned from university. Only Lucas had found the change out of character. She found that she didn't like him thinking less of her, but there was no way to alter that. Not without revealing too much. She had her pride. She did not want pity. She refused to feel sorry for herself, and would abhor having anyone feeling sorry for her. That was an inherent part of her rules.

She had been eighteen years old when she'd made them. One day she had been looking forward to university, followed by love, marriage and a family. The next, everything had changed. That year her mother had developed cancer, and, as so often happened, within months they had lost her. Megan had barely got over the shock of it when another had followed in the form of a letter. What Kate Terrell had never been able to tell her daughter during her life had been revealed to her in the scrawled lines she'd read in the solicitor's musty office.

A stunned Megan had learned that Kate Terrell had had a genetic disease. It was hereditary, and there was no cure. Passed down through the female line, it was not life-threatening to Megan or any daughter she might have, but it would be fatal to a son. Boys rarely survived infancy.

Curling her feet under her, Megan folded her arms about her waist, arming herself against the memory. She hadn't wanted to believe it, but when she had gone away to university she had consulted a doctor, and that was when the nightmare had begun. She had had tests, and they had confirmed her mother's story. She had the gene and would pass it on to her children. Too stunned to react then, in the following months she had gone through every emotion possible between anger and despair. Hating her mother for not telling her. Hating the world for being so unfair.

Megan rested her head back against the panelling and closed her eyes. She remembered the doctor insisting that she could go ahead and lead a normal life—it had made her want to laugh and cry. For how could she ever have a normal life? To her that meant a husband and family. Children. Knowing what she knew, how could she have them? How could she condemn a daughter to go through what she was going through? How could she carry a son under her heart for nine months, and then slowly watch him die?

Peace had only come with the acceptance that there was nothing she could do about herself, and carrying on the way she was would only make her ill. The past was unchanging, but she could do something about the future. She had seen very clearly what she must do. She would not gamble with her unborn children. She would end the misery here, by making sure she was the last of her line. It was a choice only she could make. She wasn't a martyr. She hadn't enjoyed the pain of her decision, but she'd known it was the right one, and it had given her the peace she'd sought.

That it also meant she would never marry was something she'd accepted unflinchingly. If she couldn't have it all, she would rather have nothing. No regrets, no recriminations, her commitment would be to her career. She had lived by her decision, and only once had she given in to her loneliness, her need for closeness, and had an affair.

Toby had loved her but she hadn't loved him. He had thought he could change that, and for a while she had let him try. But she had always known there was no future for them, and that by allowing him to think otherwise she wasn't being fair. The pain and guilt had been hard to live with, even after she had ended the affair. She had made it a rule after that never to get involved with anyone.

Sighing heavily, she combed her fingers through her hair.

Lord, she hated hurting anyone, but she couldn't take without giving, and because she couldn't give she wouldn't allow herself to take. So she kept everyone at bay because it was safer that way. Sometimes things went wrong, like tonight, and sometimes she met the unexpected. Like this attraction she was feeling towards Lucas... It was certainly startling, but she had been attracted to men before and nothing had come of it. This would turn out to be the same, she was sure. So she would ignore it, and when Lucas left, whenever that might be, things would be back to how they were.

Bolstered by that sound piece of common sense, Megan stretched her weary bones and finally prepared for bed.

THE NEXT DAY dawned bright and sunny and, refreshed, Megan donned a white vest-top and pleated khaki shorts which showed off an expanse of tanned flesh gathered from hours of messing about on the water. As she slipped her feet into a pair of trainers, she hoped she might find time for some sailing this afternoon, though she wouldn't hold her breath.

On her way down to the kitchen she looked in Daniel's room, and wasn't surprised to find the bed undisturbed. Telling herself she wouldn't read more into it than she had to, she skipped down the stairs, sniffing the air. The scent of coffee perking wafted up to her. Frowning, because it was still early, she pushed open the kitchen door to find Lucas seated at the table sipping at a steaming mug.

He glanced up as she halted in surprise, his eyes running appreciatively down her slim figure to her long, tanned legs. A smile curved his lips.

'Very nice,' he complimented softly, and Megan felt a resurgence of that tingling awareness skitter over her nerves.

'You don't look so bad yourself,' she responded, which

was an understatement, because in rather disreputably faded jeans and a body-hugging black T-shirt he was a sight to please a woman's sore eyes. And her eyes, she realised wryly, must have been very sore, because the day had suddenly and unexpectedly taken on an extra sparkle. She crossed to the refrigerator with her pulse just a little heightened. She was beginning to see why those women ignored the danger signs. There was something about Lucas which could make you not give a damn.

'Have you had breakfast?' The prosaic question settled her pulse back to normal.

Lucas twisted in his seat to follow her with his eyes. 'I was going to, then I recalled you had a tartar in charge of the kitchen and thought better of it,' he explained, watching her remove eggs, bacon, butter and milk.

Megan tutted and reached down a saucepan. 'Bella was a very nice woman. Unfortunately she's no longer with us, but I can assure you this housekeeper is not the jealous type, and will cook you scrambled eggs and bacon if you're interested,' she said, facing him again.

She didn't know whether to be flattered or not by his surprise. 'You?'

'I do know how to cook, so you can be sure I won't poison you accidentally,' she warned, tongue-in-cheek. 'So, eggs and bacon?'

Humour-lines crinkled up by his eyes at her allusion. 'They're fine by me,' he agreed instantly, and watched how effortlessly she went about the task. 'Is there anything I can do to help?'

She sent him a doubtful look over her shoulder. 'If I can trust you not to burn it, you can make some toast. Bread is in the bin and the toaster is over there.' She nodded to her left.

For the next few minutes the scene was quite domestic as they worked together in perfect harmony. Megan's heart gave a curious little jerk as she recognised the fact, then she told herself sternly not to start reading anything into it. They had always got on when they weren't fighting. Which meant a fight was probably waiting just around the corner.

'What happened to your housekeeper?' They were sitting down eating the food they had prepared when Lucas returned to the subject.

Pausing with a forkful of fluffy egg halfway to her mouth, Megan shrugged. 'We decided we didn't really need her. Daniel is hardly ever here for meals, and the house isn't so big that I can't cope with the cleaning,' she lied, and felt him staring at her lowered head as she concentrated on her food.

'Why pay for something you can do yourself, right?' he remarked lightly, making her look at him suspiciously, wondering if he had guessed the truth.

But from his blandness, he apparently hadn't, and she relaxed. 'Absolutely,' she agreed, remembering how the economy had helped for a while.

'It's fortunate you're a good cook.'

It would have been all the same if she weren't! 'Perhaps scrambled eggs and bacon is all I'm good at,' she countered.

'Oh, I'm sure not,' Lucas argued with a nuance she had no trouble interpreting, and her heart missed a beat.

'If that's a sample of your much vaunted technique, I'm surprised it gets you anywhere!' she mocked, but he only grinned.

'There are a lot of women who would disagree with you about that.'

She sent him a pitying look. 'Heaven only knows what those poor deluded women see in you,' she despaired, and began collecting up the dirty crockery.

Lucas held out his plate, but when she took it he refused to let it go. As she was bending over the table, the manoeuvre brought his head mere inches away from hers. 'You'd have to kiss me to find out,' he said invitingly, and, despite herself, her heart kicked against her breast as if trying to escape. She looked at his mouth and her stomach lurched. Lord, but he was potent, she thought, and managed to keep her composure by a monumental effort.

'I'll pass, thanks,' she replied, wincing inwardly at how husky her voice sounded, then almost forgot to breathe when she saw his eyes drop to her mouth.

'You're sure? I wouldn't mind obliging,' he added persuasively, and a tingling sensation passed over her lips, as if he had actually touched them.

Releasing the plate, Megan straightened up. 'Since you're in such an obliging mood, you can oblige me by doing the washing-up. Hot water is in the tap, detergent is on the drainer, and you'll find rubber gloves under the sink if you want to protect your lily-white hands!' she taunted, heading for the door with a wide grin on her face.

There was a bounce in her step as she grabbed up her bag and car keys, and she realised that she had almost forgotten how to really laugh. She had always enjoyed sparring with Lucas, and having got the better of him just now added an extra zest to the day.

She was humming as she drove her ancient Fiat into the yard, and Ted's lugubrious face twisted into a grin when she joined him in the shed moments later.

'You seem perky.'

Megan grinned. 'I left Lucas doing the washing-up,' she explained.

'Got him on a string already, have you?' Ted chortled. 'I guess we can expect fireworks to light up the place again.'

She didn't say anything, just smiled. Things had changed with Lucas's arrival, and perhaps Ted was right and he would bring them luck. Time would tell.

SHE SAW VERY LITTLE of Lucas and Daniel over the next few days. They went out early and came back late, and she hoped good things would come from the time they spent together. She would have been happier if they'd gone out in the evenings too, but there they went their separate ways. She had no doubt what Daniel was doing—nor Lucas for that matter. No doubt the sexy Sonja was keeping him busy! Not that it bothered her. He could do what he liked, and it allowed her to get a grip on the fledgling attraction she had succumbed to.

A week slipped by without incident. Megan began work on a new design. As she sat at her drawing-board, her eyes traced the sleek lines. The craft would cut through the water so perfectly that Megan knew she could sell it if only they had the funds to build it and show it. She frowned. If she just altered this…

She didn't hear the footsteps approaching, and it was only when a shadow blocked out her light that she looked up to find Daniel beside her. Her smile faded as she took stock of his morning-after appearance. His clothes were clean: it was his face which looked wrinkled. Aware that he rarely sought her out unless he wanted something, she tossed down her pencil.

'You've come to the wrong place, haven't you? This is a boatyard,' she greeted him sardonically.

'I know what it is,' Daniel answered testily, transferring his gaze from her to the paper. 'Mmm, not bad.'

Megan brushed her hair back, her eyebrows rising at his grudging praise. 'Yes, well, I try to keep my hand in just in case a miracle happens,' she responded mockingly. 'What can I do for you? Or are you here to work?'

His eyes clashed with hers then darted away again. 'I need the key to the safe.'

Megan froze. The only things inside were the medals her great-grandfather had won in the First World War and her mother's jewellery. He knew that as well as she did. 'They belong to me, Daniel,' she reminded him.

Daniel's jaw clenched mutinously. 'You'll get them back, I swear! I only want to pawn them.'

She turned back to the drawing and began to re-trace a perfectly good line. 'No! You know if I let you take anything I'll never see it again.'

'I give you my word you will, Meg,' he swore, with a nervy edge to his voice which brought a tight smile to her lips.

'I'm sorry, Daniel, but your word isn't worth much these days,' she told him as she swung round to face him again.

Daniel dragged a hand through his hair. 'Thanks for the vote of confidence!' he snarled, and met her unflinching look. He swore silently. 'What happened to loyalty, Meg?'

'I expect you bet it on a horse that's still running! I don't understand you any more. You were going to have the best boatyard in the country. How can you let it all slip away?' she asked bluntly, hoping for an honest answer, but he merely looked stubborn.

'I work to live, not live to work!'

It was remarks such as those which made her so angry with him. All the anger and disappointment of the last months spilt over in an angry tirade. 'How dare you say that so glibly? What about our last two workers who put their faith in you? What do I tell them when I lay them off?'

Daniel didn't care for her tone. 'It won't come to that,' he protested, catching her arm.

'It already has, or are you too blind or too stupid to see?' she challenged, shaking him off.

Daniel flushed. 'Lay off me, Megan!' he growled harshly, grabbing up her mug of pencils and throwing it at the wall. 'Just lay off me, all right?' he ordered, and in a manner she was fast coming used to, he stormed out.

Megan found she was shaking. Daniel's actions had actually alarmed her to that extent, and she suddenly realised there was more to this than she'd thought. She didn't know what, but the icy lump in her stomach was warning enough. Her heart lurched. Oh, Daniel, what on earth have you got yourself into? she cried silently.

CHAPTER THREE

'PROBLEMS?' Lucas's lazy drawl came from behind her, and she spun round to find him in the doorway, his shoulder propped comfortably against the frame.

Taking a deep breath, she crossed the room to clear up the mess Daniel had made. 'Go away, Lucas!' she snapped, wondering how long he had been there and how much he had heard. Finishing the task, she set the sadly dented cup back in its usual place.

'Do you often fight?' he asked, and Megan winced at the realisation that he had witnessed that much at least.

'Don't you have anything to do besides poke your nose into other people's business?' she retorted, abandoning her drawing and going to the desk. Her hands were still trembling too much to draw a straight line, even with a ruler.

'Not right now,' Lucas replied smoothly.

Picking up a pile of folders, Megan carried them to the nearby filing cabinet, set them down on the top and proceeded to file them.

'You have the hide of a rhinoceros! What you saw was just a difference of opinion. We have them all the time,' she lied, watching him move away from the door to study her design.

'In that case I suggest you buy unbreakable furnishings or you'll have lost everything in a week!' he drawled back, without taking his eyes from the board. 'She's going to be beautiful,' he praised, tracing a line with his finger.

Megan smiled wryly, warmed by the unsolicited comment. 'Thanks. Now all I need is someone to commission me to build her.'

Lucas glanced up curiously. 'That shouldn't be a problem, surely? Dan said you were doing well.'

She heard the unspoken query and her lips twisted. 'He was ever an optimist. There's a recession on, you know.'

'I had heard something about it,' Lucas agreed as he wandered over to the desk. He ran a cursory eye over the ledgers she had spread out there. 'Since when have you been in charge of the books?'

'Since our accountant complained about the army of ants which kept running riot over the pages,' she quipped, accurately describing her brother's atrocious handwriting.

Now Lucas shot her a quizzical look. 'Still that bad, hmm?'

She laughed, and caught his acknowledging smile. Her breath lodged in her throat. Lethal, she thought, not for the first time. 'He should have been a doctor,' she declared, filing another folder, sorting a mis-file at the same time.

'And whilst you're designing boats and keeping the accounts, what does Dan do?' Lucas enquired mildly.

It was on the tip of her tongue to say, Spends money we can ill afford to lose, but thought better of it. 'Daniel is in charge of promotion. Somebody has to go out there and get people to buy,' she explained, wondering just what the two men had talked about these last few days. Certainly not Terrell's, by the sound of it.

As she reached for the next folder, she found that Lucas had crossed the room silently and was there before her. His hand skimmed off the file and opened it for his lazy perusal. Fortunately it was only the sail-maker's account, so he wouldn't learn much from it. She sent him a speaking look, which, naturally, he ignored.

'That doesn't sound like Dan's sort of job to me,' Lucas observed, and she grimaced.

'No, he'd much rather be out on the water, but he knows this is just the beginning. We're all dependent on each other. I design the boats, Ted will build them, and when we've made enough money Daniel will race them.' It was perfect. Daniel had always craved thrills and excitement, and this idea had really set him buzzing.

'Sounds ideal,' Lucas conceded. 'So why do I get the feeling there's a "but" in there somewhere?'

Megan saw no point in beating about the bush. 'It's all taking a little longer than we expected,' she admitted ruefully.

Lucas didn't need it spelling out to him. 'And Dan's beginning to get restless,' he pronounced, tossing the file back on the pile.

'I was hoping spending time with you would recharge his batteries,' she said, although she doubted it after their latest row.

'Perhaps this afternoon will help. We're taking the *Sea Mist* out for a run.'

The mention of the yacht their father had built brought a glow to her eyes. She had nothing but happy memories of golden days spent on the water. 'She could do with it. I'd give a fortune to be going with you!' she exclaimed wistfully, and Lucas smiled down at her.

'Why don't you? There's plenty of room.'

Tempted, Megan looked up right into his eyes, and had the distinct impression that she was already on the water—and in danger of drowning! In the next instant she was shaking her head and taking a step backwards. Boy, oh, boy! No wonder women toppled like ninepins. His charisma was breathtaking. It had certainly acquired the unhappy knack of stealing her breath away!

'Daniel wouldn't like it. Besides, I have too much to do here,' she said, abandoning the filing to take her seat behind the desk. 'Is that what you came to tell me?'

'Partly. I actually came to ask you to have dinner with me.'

If she'd been given a million years to think, she never would have come up with that. 'Been stood up, have you?' she asked, not bothering to hide her amusement at the idea.

Lucas's eyes took on a gleam of devilment and he didn't deny it. 'Keep me company and you can gloat to your heart's content,' he offered.

Megan sat back and crossed her arms, liking the idea of enjoying herself at his expense. 'Well, well, who would have thought that the Don Juan of Europe would be so strapped for company that he would be forced to ask me for a date?' she exclaimed, deciding she also liked the way his eyes sparkled with amusement.

Lucas grinned, and whimsically she felt she could understand how Red Riding Hood must have felt on first encountering the wolf! 'Of course, if you're too scared to agree, Red...' he began, and her brows rose.

'Are you actually daring me, Lucas?' she asked softly, and he laughed low in his throat.

'Would I?'

Since when had he had a voice like rich, dark chocolate? she wondered with a tiny shiver. 'You'd do anything if it was to your advantage,' she said baldly, and he laughed again.

'Is that a yes or a no?'

'It's neither. I'm wondering why you haven't asked my brother,' she hedged neatly.

'I did, but Dan's got a prior engagement.'

So much for hoping that spending time with his old friend would wean him away from the new! Though her heart sank, she made her voice light. 'In that case I'd better take pity on you, hadn't I? On one condition, though.'

His lips twitched as he suppressed a smile. 'Which is?'

'That we go somewhere there won't be any cameras. I

don't want to wake up tomorrow to find my photograph splashed across the tabloids and me described as your latest woman!' she proposed drily.

Lucas inclined his head. 'I promise you the utmost discretion. And if by chance a reporter should turn up I'll insist that we're just good friends,' he retorted, tongue-in-cheek, and Megan groaned.

'Don't do me any favours!' she snapped, and he laughed as he headed for the door.

'I'll see you in the hall at eight.'

Megan closed her eyes, aware that she was looking forward to the evening more than she would have expected. A bubbling laugh escaped as she grinned to herself. It would be interesting to see just how the Lucas Canfield machine went into operation.

AT A QUARTER to eight that evening, Megan made her way downstairs. She stopped before the hall mirror, and smiled at what she saw. She had taken great care with her appearance, an imp of mischief making her pull out all the stops. After all, it wasn't every day that a woman was taken out by the legendary Lucas Canfield! She had braided her wild mop of hair into a French plait, which drew attention to the delicate structure of her cheeks and jaw. Then, using the minimal amount of make-up to the greatest effect, she had turned her eyes into mysterious green pools, and given her lips that just kissed pinkness.

She had chosen to wear her little black dress, with its tiny straps and figure-hugging lines, because it flattered her and gave her skin the creaminess of alabaster. She hoped it would knock his eyes out, and felt a kick of excitement at the idea.

Hearing a door slam upstairs, Megan darted away from the mirror, not wanting to be caught preening. She made her way through to the kitchen at the back of the house.

Ted was at the sink washing up his dinner things. He lived in a cottage just down the lane, but a fire had virtually gutted his own kitchen a month ago, and Megan had insisted he use theirs until the rebuilding was done. As he was doing the work himself, he turned up at odd hours to eat the supper she left for him in the microwave.

He glanced round, eyes widening when he saw how she was dressed. 'Where are you off to?'

Megan pulled out a chair and sat down at the table. 'I'm going out to dinner with the world's sexiest man. According to several magazine polls, he has the wickedest smile and the cutest backside,' she told him, grinning as his brows rose.

Ted sniffed. 'Sounds like a prat to me!'

Megan giggled, feeling more exhilarated and expectant than she had for a very long time. 'You've no soul, Ted. Nine out of ten women would have recognised Lucas from that description.'

'Lucas?' Ted's startled expression crinkled into a grin. 'I bet that made him spitting mad,' he declared, and they both burst out laughing.

'It's his fault for getting such a reputation,' Megan pronounced. 'Do you remember what it was like before he left? No woman was safe!'

Ted sobered. 'Aye, I remember, so just you be careful, girl. I'd hate to see you get hurt.'

Megan was warmed by his caring. 'Lucas can't hurt me,' she reassured him.

He raised a soapy hand warningly. 'Any woman can get hurt. You're no exception.'

There were all sorts of hurts, but the one he worried about was the one least likely to affect her. She kept her own counsel, though, and went over and squeezed his arm. 'Don't worry, I'll be careful,' she promised. 'Anyway, Lucas and I are like chalk and cheese. We never agree about anything.'

'People who say that usually end up married to each other!' Ted pointed out humorously, and her smile faltered just a little.

'Not us. I don't ever intend to get married,' she said firmly, but he only shook his head.

'Who knows what the future has in store for us?'

Megan turned away, masking the bleakness in her eyes with lowered lashes. 'Who knows?' she repeated shortly. She knew. Had known it since she was eighteen years old. Nothing had changed, nor ever could. There was no mystery, just plain, cold fact.

She shivered and glanced up, staring straight into a pair of shocking blue eyes which were regarding her oddly. Her nerves leapt and her throat closed over. Lucas had appeared from out of nowhere.

'Are you practising for the SAS or something?' she snapped, jerked out of her calm by his silent approach. Why did he have to creep about the place like that?

'Next time I'll cough loudly to announce my presence,' Lucas declared drily, walking over to Ted with his hand held out. 'Good to see you again, Ted.'

This was the first time their paths had crossed since Lucas had arrived, and Ted responded with a smile and a grip like a clam. 'You too, Lucas. Looks like you've done well for yourself.'

'I can't complain.' He nodded towards the sink. 'I see Red has got you well trained.'

Ted scowled. 'This is all she'll let me do. I had a small fire back at my cottage, and she insists I eat here until it's repaired. Won't take any money, so the washing-up is mine.' He sent her a glare which was supposed to remind her that he was still angry about not paying his way.

Megan narrowed her eyes back at him. 'I have to cook anyway, so don't say another word. I want to do this.'

Ted's expression softened. 'You're a right mother hen, fussing over me like I'm your only chick. What you need is a family of your own to cluck over.'

Megan knew he meant it kindly, and didn't know how his words hurt her. Nor would she reveal it. If her smile didn't reach her eyes, he didn't know it. 'I've enough to do with you and Daniel,' she quipped, and turned pointedly to Lucas. 'We're going to be late,' she warned, and Ted rolled his eyes.

'Uh-oh. When she gets that look in her eye, a wise man heads for cover. You'd better come down to the yard for a talk, Lucas. It's been a long time since we had a chat.'

'Too long,' Lucas agreed. 'I'll be there.'

'Look forward to it,' Ted nodded. 'Now, it wouldn't do to keep the lady waiting any longer.'

'Not when she's got a temper on her to match her hair,' Lucas agreed, and stood aside to allow Megan to lead the way out.

'I'll lock up on my way out, Megan,' Ted called after her.

'OK, Ted. See you tomorrow.' Pausing in the hall to collect her shawl and bag from where she had left them on a side table, she turned to find Lucas looking her up and down with masculine appreciation. Prickles danced over her skin, and to hide it she summoned up a dose of mockery. 'I hope you approve. I didn't want to ruin your reputation by appearing dowdy.'

His blue eyes danced. 'I'm impressed. I won't have eyes for any other woman tonight,' he declared smoothly, and although Megan had heard the same words any number of times on this occasion she found that it brought her out in goose-bumps.

Masking her surprise with the ease of long practice at

hiding her feelings, she let her own gaze study him. Lucas was…heart-stopping. The dinner suit did with subtlety what jeans did so blatantly: hint at the latent power of the muscular body beneath. No wonder women queued up to go out with him. He was all male, pure power and virility.

And, however much it went against the grain, she knew in all honesty that she wasn't proof against it. She was strongly attracted. He appealed to her on a physical level, but that was nothing new. Attraction was one thing, doing something about it entirely another. She had common sense enough to know that there would never be anything between herself and Lucas. It was inconceivable, she thought with a whimsical smile.

'I'm sure you're already aware that you look as handsome as sin,' she quipped as she let herself out of the door and waited for him to join her.

'Does that mean you think I'm vain?' he asked ironically, taking her elbow and steering her down the path to where his classic Jaguar waited.

Megan laughed and met his blue gaze. 'I would never be so rude. Besides, vanity is in the eye of the beholder!'

His expression became quizzical. 'I thought that was beauty?'

She allowed her lips to curve wryly. 'It all depends on your perspective. What *you* see when you look in the mirror might be beauty, and therefore vanity, whilst what *I* see when I look at you is entirely different,' she proclaimed brightly, and felt warmth bubble up inside her when he laughed.

'God help me, I know I'm going to regret it, but I have to ask. What *do* you see?' Lucas challenged as he reached round to open the passenger door for her.

Amusement danced in her eyes as she turned to survey him with every appearance of seriousness. 'You're quite good-looking, in a…battered sort of way.'

Lucas winced. 'You make me sound like an old suitcase that's gone round the world one too many times! I have to hand it to you, Red, you certainly know how to cut a man down to size.'

'It's good for your ego,' she declared humorously. 'Somebody has to make sure you don't believe all that flattery,' she added, climbing inside the car and taking an appreciative glance round at the handsome interior.

'So you've appointed yourself the guardian of my morals?' he queried mildly, shutting the door and going round to take his own seat.

Megan fastened her seat belt. 'Why not? I've always seen you very clearly.' She'd never been blinded to his faults by his good looks and charm.

Starting the car, he cast a brief glance at her before pulling out into the road. 'And disliked what you saw.'

Megan watched his hands on the wheel. They were very competent. She had no doubts about him handling the powerful car. Whatever he did had his full attention—even his women! 'I won't be a hypocrite and deny that you're good to look at. It's your attitude towards women that leaves something to be desired.'

Lucas took his eyes from the road for a second, sending her a grin. 'I thought the trouble was that I desired them all!' he taunted, before concentrating on his driving once more.

She sent him an exasperated look. 'Don't you have any conscience at all?'

'Apparently not. What I need is a Jiminy Cricket. Care to take on the job?'

'No, thanks. It would be a thankless task, with very little job satisfaction. You'd never listen.'

He chuckled. 'Perhaps you underestimate yourself.'

Megan shook her head. 'I have no influence on you.'

'Probably because you're going about it the wrong way.

Try cajolery instead of a blunt weapon,' Lucas advised, causing her to turn and study his profile to see whether he was serious or not. There were crinkles beside his eyes and mouth which told her he wasn't.

'Now you're spoiling my fantasies!' she complained. 'I had visions of you stretched unconscious at my feet.'

'Well, now, if we're swapping fantasies—' Lucas began wickedly, and she interrupted him swiftly.

'We're not,' she declared repressively, which only made him laugh.

'Coward.'

Megan found herself smiling as she turned to look out of the window. Catching her reflection, she sighed. Damn him. Even when she had been seriously disgusted with him, he'd always managed to make her laugh. It was so irritating!

'So, tell me, Red, what have you been doing with yourself these last eight years?' Lucas asked, after a while.

'You mean besides blighting the lives of all the local men?' she countered sardonically, and he shot her a narrow-eyed look.

'It's all a joke to you, isn't it?' he condemned shortly, and Megan shrugged.

Of course it wasn't, but she wasn't about to explain why. Instead she said musingly, 'I find it strange that if a man had made a similar statement about women you'd merely have laughed. Do I detect a double standard?'

Lucas didn't take his eyes from the road. 'I wouldn't have laughed,' he said firmly, and Megan snorted sceptically.

'Says the man who goes through women like a hot knife through butter! How you ever manage to fit in work heaven only knows. I'm assuming, that is, that you do work?' she goaded drily.

'Oh, I manage to write the odd letter or two.'

She looked at him mockingly. 'You mean you can re-member what pen and paper are? I should be careful—you might overdo it and have to retire to bed!'

Lucas chuckled, a rich sound which made her flesh tingle most unsettlingly. 'If I had to retire to bed, I wouldn't go alone,' he informed her.

'That I can believe. I'm sure Sonja would oblige,' she drawled, recalling the woman's…eagerness.

'I'm sure she would,' he agreed silkily, a reminiscent smile curving his lips. 'However, being an airline hostess, she might well be on the other side of the world, so I'd have to find a substitute.'

'There shouldn't be any shortage of those! The queue would probably outdo Harrods' January sale!'

'It's nice to hear you think so highly of my…prowess,' Lucas came back softly, and she couldn't help but laugh.

'Sorry to disillusion you, Lucas, but it isn't that I think highly of you, rather that the IQ of the women you take out has got to be in single figures!' she countered smartly, but only succeeded in making him grin.

'You're never short of a sharp remark, are you, Red? You'd better be careful you don't cut yourself. After all, I'm taking you out tonight, so what does that say about your IQ?'

Megan waved a hand airily. 'That doesn't count. For one thing, I'm not blonde. More importantly, dining with you seemed slightly more enjoyable than cleaning the oven—a chore I'll put off at the slightest excuse.'

His soft laugh set the hairs rising on her skin. 'You know something, Red? You're one of the few women who can genuinely amuse me.'

Her eyebrows shot up. 'Really? I thought I made you angry.'

'You do that too. Your cavalier handling of men is hardly likely to endear me.'

'Ditto your use of women,' she returned coolly.

'So we have something in common after all,' he responded mildly, turning the car into the drive of a very exclusive country club.

Not quite, she thought. His actions had no purpose other than his own pleasure, whilst hers were a necessity. She would not raise false hopes, even if sometimes she felt very lonely indeed.

She stared up at the ivy-clad structure. It looked very expensive, the sort of establishment you had to be a member of to visit. 'I didn't know this place existed,' she murmured as they parked in the first available space.

Lucas turned to her with a faint frown as he switched off the engine. 'Dan recommended it. I assumed you'd been here before.'

Megan felt her face tighten. If Daniel frequented this sort of place, no wonder they were in trouble. Her heart sank, even as she managed to stop her smile from slipping. 'He must wine and dine potential customers here. Now I know why his expense account is so huge!' she joked, though joking was very far from her mind. To suspect the sort of place her brother was using was one thing, to know, another. She climbed out of the car knowing she would always have this picture in her mind now.

Lucas joined her, taking her elbow in a firm hold but not immediately making a move to enter the building. 'You've gone very quiet. Is something wrong?'

She could have groaned. Didn't he miss anything? 'I was marvelling at the lengths you've gone to for one little meal,' she taunted, and began walking towards the front door.

Lucas fell into step beside her. 'Impressed?'

'It's quite taken my breath away!' she exclaimed drolly, and he gave a bark of laughter.

'Good. It means I'll be spared your particular brand of

sparkling repartee for a while,' Lucas shot back pithily, making Megan smile.

'How unkind! Not to mention ungentlemanly!' she complained, her eyes recovering some of their lost sparkle.

'You have the knack of making me forget to be a gentleman. However, I ease my conscience with the knowledge that there are times when you're very far from being a lady,' Lucas returned smartly.

She suspected a double meaning, but chose to ignore it. 'I'll have you know I stopped climbing trees years ago.'

'That's a shame. I used to enjoy catching a glimpse of your long legs in those very short shorts you used to wear!' He sighed regretfully, really stealing her breath this time. When he glanced at her, his eyes gleamed like the devil. 'You have, as the Americans would say, legs to die for.'

Megan felt those selfsame legs turn decidedly wobbly as they walked inside. She knew he had said it on purpose to put her off balance, but even so it made her feel hot inside to know that he admired her legs. She sought her brain for a snappy reply, but a man in evening dress came to meet them and the moment was lost.

'Good evening, sir, madam. You'll be dining?'

Lucas relieved Megan of her shawl and handed it to the man. 'I've a table booked for eight-thirty.'

'The restaurant is to your left. I hope you enjoy your meal.' He nodded at them both and disappeared.

Lucas glanced towards an archway from which issued bursts of laughter. 'The bar sounds crowded. We'll go straight to our table, unless you object?'

Megan was happy to accede to his idea. She had recovered her poise now, and was determined to get her own back. Lucas's teasing had always managed to find a way through her defences when they were young, and it appeared that eight years had made no difference. However, she was no longer a child, and her weapons were sharper. She was determined to give as good as she got.

The restaurant turned out to be part of a nightclub. Discreetly lit tables encircled a dance area which already had one or two couples gliding around to the music of a live band. Around the walls, plants and partitions gave some tables a semblance of privacy. Perfect for lovers, she mused wryly, and wasn't surprised to follow the waiter to a secluded table.

'We have the champagne you ordered chilling, sir,' he told them as soon as they were seated. 'I can serve it now, unless the lady would prefer something else?'

Lucas quirked an eyebrow her way. 'Megan?'

'The lady would like a stinger, please.'

Lucas ordered a Manhattan for himself, and the waiter nodded, handed each a large padded menu and departed. As soon as they were alone, Megan set her elbows on the table and rested her chin on her cupped hands. The Lucas Canfield machine had just gone into motion, and it brought a wry twist to her lips. He was certainly smooth. The result of years of practice.

'Champagne? All this undivided attention could quite easily go to a girl's head if she wasn't careful.'

Lucas sat forward, so that the room between them was drastically reduced. 'Ah, but we both know how careful you are, Red. When it comes to the warmer emotions, your head will ever rule your heart.'

It wasn't said to be unkind. To Lucas it was a simple statement of fact. How could he know that it was only true because there were some risks she was not prepared to take? Someone had to be strong. To say enough was enough. It ended here, with her, and to hell with what anyone else thought!

Megan met Lucas's steady blue gaze. 'Are you sure?'

'I'm never sure of women. They can always surprise me,' he returned drily.

'Even me?'

'Let's just say I know you better than most women, so it would be highly unlikely.'

'How diplomatic of you,' she laughed, allowing her attention to drift around the room. 'I suppose you take all your women to places like this?' she remarked as she encountered a ferocious glare from a bottle blonde sitting a few tables away. She was taken aback at first, but her eyes swiftly began to dance with amused speculation. 'Tell me, are you forever running into old flames? Like that one over there?' Megan tipped her head in the blonde's direction.

Lucas took a brief glance round. 'Ah.'

Sensing a problem, she raised her brows and smiled sweetly. '"Ah"?' Mentally rubbing her hands, she waited for what she expected would be a jealous confrontation.

Lucas was fully aware of her enjoyment. 'That's Mona, a friend of Sonja's.'

The penny dropped and her smiled widened. 'Oh, I see. You had a date with her tonight, didn't you? And you cancelled it, saying...?'

His teeth gleamed whitely as he smiled back unrepentantly. 'That I had a business meeting.'

Megan decided that the evening had just gained added appeal. 'And Mona now knows it wasn't and will tell Sonja. My, you do have a problem, don't you? I had no idea how exciting a rakish lifestyle could be.' She made no attempt to hide her glee, and her sympathy was loaded with irony. 'Is there anything I can do to help? Do you want me to go and explain that I'm just a good friend?'

Observing her with some amusement, Lucas put up a restraining hand. 'Spare us. I can do my own explaining. I know how to handle women like Sonja.'

Megan's smile took on a scornful curve. 'I wouldn't

doubt it for a second. Lord knows, you've had enough practice.'

Lucas's reply was thwarted by the arrival of their drinks, and he had to wait until the waiter had gone to respond. 'Considering your own less than perfect treatment of men, do you think you have the right to be so disapproving, Red?'

She might have guessed he would throw that in her face. 'I don't use men the way you use women, Lucas. You care no more for them than you do for your car,' she condemned, but that only produced a wider smile.

'On the contrary, I see my car as a work of art, and treat it accordingly,' he corrected smoothly, making her hackles rise.

Of all the arrogantly chauvinistic remarks she had ever heard, that took the cake! 'Women are more than bodies to be polished and admired!' she retorted scornfully, then caught the gleam in his eye which told her he had deliberately thrown out the bait she had taken so easily.

Lucas watched the heat die out of her. 'You do like to lead with your chin, don't you?'

He was as slippery as a snake, and he knew her too well! 'That doesn't alter the fact that your reputation hardly does you credit.'

'I'm not responsible for what the Press choose to write, or for what you choose to believe,' he told her levelly, sipping at his drink.

'Meaning that the reports of your prowess have been greatly exaggerated?' she challenged, and his blue eyes gleamed devilishly.

'How can I answer that without sounding big-headed? Let's just say when I want a woman to purr she does.'

Though she knew darn well he was goading her, Megan felt a shiver run down her spine, and disgust had nothing to do with it. He had a way of saying and doing things which played havoc with her senses. She savoured her own drink before attempting a reply.

'Just remember, cats that purr also have claws. You're going to come a cropper one day.' And how she'd like to be there to see it!

'Something tells me I shouldn't look to you for solace when the time comes,' he remarked, with wry amusement.

Megan opened her mouth to agree, but a discreet cough announced the arrival of the waiter once more. 'Would you care to order now, sir?'

Lucas picked up the menu and raised an eyebrow at her. 'Shall I order for you?' he asked, and Megan nodded. Usually she preferred to choose herself, but it would be interesting to see what Lucas would pick out. He reeled off a selection in the original French, and within minutes the waiter had disappeared as silently as he had come.

Megan was impressed in spite of herself. He did it all so naturally that he commanded respect from staff who were long past being impressed. 'Do you always order for your dates?' She couldn't believe that women really liked having the choice taken away from them.

Lucas sat back, the better to observe her. 'Only when asked to. I don't force myself on women in any fashion.'

It pleased her to hear it, and, really, she hadn't expected him to be that sort anyway. It didn't stop her provoking him, though. 'I thought you might be afraid I would order the most expensive dishes.'

'Would you have?' he challenged, and Megan dropped her gaze to her glass for a moment before meeting his eyes again, her own revealing amused honesty.

'I admit to being tempted, but I decided that being ill would harm me more than your pocket, so if you've chosen oysters, smoked salmon or caviare they'll have to go back because I don't like them,' she informed him lightly, taking another sip of her drink.

There was a certain fondness in the smile he gave her. 'I'm glad you finally learned not to cut off your nose to spite your face. You can relax, Megan. I seem to recall you were always partial to fish, so I ordered Dover sole.'

Megan sighed. If she was noting his faults, she would have a very short list! 'You speak French very well.'

His face softened. 'I had a good teacher. And, before you ask, yes, it was a woman, and no, not in the way you mean. My mother was half-French, and she insisted I learn both languages as a child. Then I spent my holidays with her mother, my grandmother, when I was allowed to speak nothing but French. Fortunately I found it easy, and as I grew older I discovered I had a knack for languages. Which came in handy when expanding our market into Europe.'

Megan listened with genuine interest, vaguely recalling a very elegant woman who used to call for Lucas sometimes. 'I think I remember your mother. She was very beautiful.'

'She still is, though her hair is more grey now.'

'I recall your parents left the area soon after you did. Wasn't your father some sort of scientist?' Like most children, what she had known of her friends' families had been sketchy at best.

'He was a research chemist. Very hush-hush. He died several years ago, and my mother decided to go back to France. As my work takes me abroad regularly, I see more of her now than I used to. She's happy, but she misses Dad. They had a good marriage. I envy them that.'

She saw the way his face softened, and felt as if her heart was being squeezed. For a fleeting instant she saw herself with the sort of marriage he meant. Saw herself loving and being loved. With children and shared laughter. Things she hadn't allowed herself to think of for a very long time. She felt their loss so keenly, she wanted to cry. Only by biting her lip did she manage to blink away the threatening moisture. She didn't have time for this, and 'what if's were pointless. They were no match for facts, and that was what she had. Cold, hard, ruthless facts—and the strength of will to do what was right.

It was that same indomitable strength which had her raising her glass with a smile. 'A toast. To happy families,' she declared with a toss of her head, and drained the little which remained in her glass.

Lucas followed suit, but his expression was dubious. 'I thought you didn't believe in such things?'

Megan studied her empty glass, recalling clearly the conversation they had had that first night. 'Of course I believe in them, for other people. I intend to remain independent.'

'Free of encumbrances?'

A faint smile twisted her lips. 'Don't sound so disapproving. You're still unencumbered and you're older than I am!' she exclaimed lightly, though, as always, the mention of family made her heart heavy.

'I told you—I haven't found the right woman yet,' Lucas countered easily.

Megan gave an unladylike snort. 'Not for want of trying! Oh, Lucas, you can't really expect me to believe you're a romantic?'

His blue eyes glittered back at her. 'I've warned you before about jumping to conclusions about me.'

She looked sceptical. 'Yes, but love…'

'Love has been known to move mountains.'

'So has dynamite!' she quipped back instantly, but he remained serious.

'Laugh if you want to, but, whether they admit it or not, everyone needs love.'

Megan's heart gave a painful lurch. Oh, yes, she needed love. Sometimes she felt so lonely, it was as if she had an aching void inside her. Then she would recall why she would never fill it, and painfully she would shore up her defences.

Now she hid her resignation behind an incredulous smile.
'Even you?'

Lucas inclined his head gravely. 'Even me. I know that,
if I keep looking one day I will find the one woman I'll want
to share my life with,' he admitted easily, and his sincerity
was something she couldn't argue with.

She was shaken, she admitted to herself, and because of
it she couldn't find it in her to mock him. Though it went
against all she knew of him, she believed him. And the
knowledge brought an unknown wistfulness to the curve of
her lips as she stared at him. 'I hope you find her, Lucas,'
she said gruffly, then, uncomfortably aware that he was looking at her oddly, she made a business of looking round for
the waiter. 'I'm starving. Aren't you?' she declared over-
brightly.

'Thank you,' Lucas said softly, and she sent him a startled
look.

'What for?'

There was a strange expression in his eyes which she
couldn't name. 'For being honest.'

Colour washed into her cheeks. 'I…' She stopped her instinctive denial and sighed. 'You meant it, and I couldn't
step on your dreams,' she said truthfully.

'You could have done. I find it interesting that you didn't.'

'Well, don't read anything into it which isn't there. I had
a noble impulse. Don't make me regret it,' she warned
shortly. She didn't want him probing into her motives. Lucas
had the sort of incisive brain which cut through masking
trivia to the important matter hiding inside. He could easily
discover her armour for what it was, and then he would go
on to destroy it in order to find what she was hiding.

That must not happen. For what would be amusing to
him would devastate her. Her armour was all she had, and
she would protect it to her last breath. She wanted no man's
pity, and especially not Lucas's!

CHAPTER FOUR

WHETHER LUCAS HAD taken Megan's hint or not, he turned out to be an ideal dinner companion. He put himself out to relax and amuse her, and it wasn't long before her equilibrium returned and she found herself enjoying both the food and the company.

The conversation became lively as they went from topic to topic. Much to her surprise, Megan discovered they had the same taste in music and literature. Her guard dropped, and for the first time in what seemed like for ever she found she was really enjoying herself. When he launched into a series of anecdotes told with a dry, sometimes wicked sense of humour, laughter bubbled out of her.

She realised with a pang that she had missed his sense of humour. He was telling her about a friend of his who had come to grief on a skiing trip, and she found herself watching the way his eyes crinkled up as he laughed, and listening to the dark magic of his voice. His eyes danced, inviting her to share the joke. He laughed with pure enjoyment and her heart began a crazy dance in her chest.

Simultaneously warning flares went off in her brain, and with a sense of incredulity Megan became aware that she was in very real danger of falling under the spell of his charm. The dismaying thing was that he had won her over without even trying, because Megan Terrell was no more than the proverbial thorn in his side. The sister of his best friend. A pest.

The knowledge sobered her. She didn't need the com-

plications of a one-sided attraction. She didn't want to be
attracted at all. But she was, and she had only one way of
dealing with it. She must ignore it. Starved of fuel, the
feeling would die a natural death. Helped by the fact that
Lucas did not feel the same attraction. Aware of the danger,
she could remain on the outside looking in, and enjoy the
show.

When the sweet trolley arrived, Megan was once more
in control of her wayward senses. With her brain fully functioning, she allowed Lucas to choose for her, accepting the
generous slice of chocolate gateau with a wry laugh.

He glanced at her with brows raised. 'Something
wrong?'

'Not really. I was laughing because I think I've discovered how you do it,' she explained lightly.

'It?'

With a long-suffering sigh, Megan rested her chin on one
hand and sent him a smile. 'Trap usually intelligent women.
First you flatter their egos with single-minded attention,
next you disarm them with laughter, and finally you seduce
them with the sensual delight of food. Very simple. Very
effective,' she enlightened him breezily as she cut a spoonful of cake and raised it to her lips.

She had to admire the swiftness of his brain. After a
fleeting instant of surprise, Lucas looked across at her with
eyes full of appreciative humour. 'I had no idea you were
taking notes.'

'I'm thinking of writing a book. You know the sort of
thing. *Seduction—the Canfield Way.*'

'I'm sure you can find a better subject for study than
myself,' he argued, watching her enjoyment through
hooded eyes.

Megan held up her hand. 'There's no need to be so modest. I imagine you have a very low failure rate,' she insisted,
warming to the idea, hoping to discomfit him. Toying with

another spoonful of the delicious cake, she began to raise it to her mouth. Halfway, she happened to glance across the table, and discovered that Lucas was watching the manoeuvre with an intensity which gave her an odd little thrill, chasing her breath away and increasing the beat of her heart.

It was then that an imp of devilment took hold of her, for, instead of retreating, she carried the spoonful to her mouth, deliberately savouring the texture on her tongue. She waited, scarcely breathing as a rush of excitement kicked in her stomach, then he transferred his gaze to her eyes. Wry amusement didn't quite mask the sensual warmth she saw there.

He sat back, crossing his legs comfortably. 'Taste good?' he asked huskily.

'Delicious,' she conceded, wondering if she had taken leave of her senses. Those were not the sort of games you played with a man like Lucas.

'You're a tease,' he accused, with a shake of his head.

'And you're an unprincipled flirt,' she responded instantly.

He grinned. 'Some would say in that case we deserve each other.'

Megan raised her brows pointedly. 'It's a proven fact that very few people get what they deserve. If they did, you would have been boiled in oil long ago!'

'You're a bloodthirsty little thing, aren't you?' Lucas marvelled. 'Beautiful but bloodthirsty.'

Though her brain urged caution, she found she was enjoying the exchange too much to stop. 'Ah, a compliment. Should I swoon?'

Lucas's lips twitched. 'I wouldn't advise it.'

'I thought your women were expected to keel over on command?' she challenged mockingly.

He rubbed a thoughtful finger along the bridge of his

nose. 'It's optional. For myself, I'd hate to see you flop face first into your chocolate cake.'

Megan couldn't stop the laugh which gurgled out of her. 'You have a point. Perhaps I should start purring instead?' she asked dulcetly.

His blue eyes glittered brightly as he studied her mobile face, which was alight with mischief. 'Only if you want to,' he said softly.

She sighed, abandoning the sweet and wiping her lips with her napkin. 'The trouble is, I never did manage to master the technique of doing that. Sorry. You'll just have to wait for Sonja to oblige.'

He didn't have to laugh; the way his eyes glittered was proof enough of his amusement. 'It wouldn't be the same. There is an alternative. Perhaps I could teach you to purr?'

The *double entendre* made her nerves leap. 'I wouldn't put you to so much trouble.'

'Oh, it wouldn't be a bother, it would be a pleasure,' he riposted silkily, clearly enjoying himself, and Megan found to her surprise that she liked amusing him.

'Mmm,' she acknowledged drily. 'That's what I thought!'

This time Lucas laughed aloud, studying her as if he had never quite seen her before. 'Having fun?' he asked at last, and Megan sighed.

'Actually, I haven't enjoyed myself so much for a long time,' she admitted, and knew, with a sense of despair, that it was true. Trying to keep Terrell's afloat took all her energy, so that she had little left for enjoyment these days.

'Hmm, I'd take that as a compliment if your enjoyment wasn't at my expense,' Lucas responded sardonically. 'However, I'm prepared to overlook it if you dance with me,' he offered as he stood up.

She supposed she should have taken umbrage at his assumption of her acceptance, but Megan saw no real reason to refuse. She loved dancing, and she had every reason to suppose that Lucas was a good dancer, seeing as he had taught her in the first place. Besides, it was only a dance. She rose to her feet.

'Don't tread on my toes,' she warned teasingly.

He smiled into her eyes. 'Trust me,' he said, and led her onto the floor.

The thought that struck her as she turned to him was that she did trust Lucas. He was one of the most trustworthy men she knew. She was warmed by the knowledge as he drew her into his arms, and as a consequence her defences were lowered, heightening her perception of herself and the man who held her.

She knew at once that this was different. She had danced countless times with her hand on a man's shoulder, his arm braced around her, guiding her. She had been held close, so that there was scarcely room for a wisp of air to pass between their two bodies. Yet this was not the same. It was light years from being the same.

Awareness took on a totally new dimension. Slowly her fingers flexed, taking in the texture of the cloth which stretched across the broad span of his shoulders. Lucas was strong and powerful; he made her conscious of her own softer curves being flattened against him.

A tiny sigh escaped her lips as something very basic struck her. Their bodies fitted together so well, it was as if they had been made for each other. She felt protected, sheltered, and knew that there was nothing in this world she would rather do than rest her head on the shoulder which lay so invitingly close. Something expanded inside her, and without thought her eyelids fluttered down, and at once her body softened, melting against his as she drifted with the music.

When she felt his hand move in a lazy glide up her spine,

pressing her closer, she wanted to sigh. Nothing had ever felt so right.

Lost to the world, she barely registered Lucas's muffled, 'Hell!' an instant before somebody cannoned into her from behind, making her eyes fly open as she stumbled. Lucas prevented her from falling with a fearsome grip on her arm. She would have bruises tomorrow, she mused wryly. Glancing around, she realised the floor had filled up, and she hadn't been aware of it.

'Are you OK?' he asked, glancing down at her, and Megan nodded.

'Where did all these people come from?'

Lucas looked amused. 'I had the feeling you were nodding off,' he teased, then frowned as they were bumped again. 'This is impossible,' he muttered tersely. 'We'd better go back to our table.'

Megan was happy to fall in with the suggestion. Her mind was whirling as they struggled through the milling couples. She hadn't been nodding off—she had been miles away. Lucas had felt so safe that she had been able to forget her fears and worries for a small moment of time. He'd always been good at that, so there was nothing to get alarmed about, she told herself. She had simply been able to relax because she had known he would make no demands on her. There was nothing else to read into it. Nothing at all.

All the same, she decided it would be a good time to take a break. It was very hot inside, and she needed to cool down anyway. So when they reached their table she didn't sit down, but picked up her bag.

'I'm just going to freshen up,' she explained when she met his questioning look. 'Why don't you order some more drinks? I won't be long,' she promised as she turned and walked away.

Crossing the busy foyer, Megan was searching for the

right door, when a roar of male laughter from above made her glance up. A group of men stood on the landing, her brother amongst them. Of course she now knew that Daniel came here, but, with the nightclub downstairs, what could there be on the first floor to hold his interest? This could be her first clue as to what was troubling him, she realised, and she altered course to mount the sweeping staircase, determined to find out.

As she reached the landing, the group began to disperse into a room to their left. Hurrying after them, she caught Daniel's arm before he disappeared. He turned at once, surprise turning to horror when he saw her.

'What the hell are you doing here?' he demanded in a shaken tone, and her heart sank as she examined his ashen face.

'I was about to ask you the same thing,' she said huskily, aware of a nameless anxiety clawing at her. What was wrong?

One of the other men had turned in the doorway. 'Come on, Danny; stop nattering and get yourself in here. We've no time for skirts tonight!' he ordered, giving Megan a cursory glance of dislike before vanishing inside.

She had met him once and the dislike was mutual. *'Danny?'* she queried disbelievingly, and Daniel coloured angrily.

'It's what my friends call me.'

Considering he had hated that diminutive all his life, she was surprised he allowed the use of it. 'If they were your friends, they'd know you hate the name.'

'Don't start, Megan. It's only a name, so why should I let it spoil my fun?'

Megan felt her throat close over, too aware of her anxiety to be angry. 'Fun is supposed to make you happy, Daniel, not like this. Won't you please come home and talk to me, tell me what's wrong?' she pleaded, and felt him tense under her hand.

Daniel's jaw clenched mutinously. 'There's nothing wrong. How many times have I got to tell you that how I live my life is my business?'

Her thumbs were pricking badly, and she knew she had to replace her burgeoning anger with reason. 'Not just yours. You're squandering away everything our family worked so hard to build.'

A guilty colour stained his cheeks at that. 'So what? Terrell's is mine now, and I can choose to do what I want with the proceeds.'

Which reminded her of something she hadn't had time to tell him. She'd been waiting for an appropriate moment, but there was no time like the present—if it would help. 'There might not be any proceeds much longer. The German cancelled his order,' she said bluntly.

There was a second when he seemed to sway, but then he had control of himself once more. Only his voice held a betraying quiver. 'That's his prerogative.'

Her anger was despairing. 'And you don't give a damn!'

Daniel laughed raggedly, shaking off her hand. 'You're wasting your time trying to make me feel guilty, Meg,' he told her shortly. 'I suppose Lucas brought you here, so why don't you go back to him and stop spying on me?' he ordered. Turning his back, he walked into the room and shut the door on her.

Megan stared at the silent wood in shock, her mind filled with the brief but telling glimpse she had caught of well-patronised gaming tables. Gambling. Her blood ran cold, and she realised she was trembling. Daniel wasn't just living beyond his means, he was gambling! Not penny ante stuff, but the real thing. No wonder there was no getting through to him. He was hooked, and, like so many gamblers, hoped for the big win which would retrieve his fortunes. The trouble was, he wasn't just taking himself down, he was taking her with him!

Though he wasn't aware of it, she had invested her own money in the business, so that there was very little of her own inheritance left. She had never resented the money, only the way it was being wasted. But this was something else. Something far more serious, if she was right and Daniel was hooked. He would need help, and she didn't know if she was the one to give it. Even supposing he would accept it. All she knew for certain was that this was beyond her scope.

Descending the stairs on shaky legs, this time she found the powder room with little trouble. The coolness of the peach-coloured room was a haven, to which several other women had come to freshen up. Megan moistened some pieces of paper towel and sat down at one of the vanity mirrors, pressing the pads against her warm cheeks. If she'd been the sort to give in to hysteria, she would have been lying on her back drumming her heels against the floor, she thought wearily.

Her lashes dropped and she suddenly felt very tired.

'Finding Lucas too hot to handle?' a biting voice challenged from beside her, and Megan blinked her eyes open to find that the woman called Mona had taken the next seat.

Lowering her hands, Megan tossed the paper into the waste basket. She sensed trouble, and whilst she knew that the sensible thing to do would be to get up and leave she had never run from a fight. A quick glance round proved that the room was empty now, save for the two of them, so she didn't have to pull her punches. Opening her bag, she took out a lipstick.

'Not at all. I've always been able to handle Lucas,' she returned sweetly, setting the cat among the pigeons.

Mona turned on her chair to bring herself closer to Megan. 'You'll never keep him. You don't have what it takes!' she declared spitefully, and Megan felt her hackles rise.

She produced a sultry smile. 'Strange, I've had no complaints so far. Lucas seems more than satisfied,' she rejoined. What utterly charming people Lucas knew! She had no conscience about defending a mythical romance from this unwarranted attack.

Mona's face lost any charm it might have had. 'Listen, you little tramp, I'm warning you to stay away from Lucas. Sonja is a friend of mine, and Lucas belongs to Sonja!'

Any number of people could have told Mona that she had just made a very bad mistake. Megan paled with anger. Nobody had ever called her a tramp before, and without any justification. Just who did the Monas and Sonjas of this world think they were that they could talk to her like that? Her chin lifted pugnaciously. If the woman wanted a fight, she could have one—in spades.

'Really? Does he know that? Lucas has always given the impression of belonging solely to himself.'

Tell-tale heat stole into the other woman's cheeks. She knew Megan was right, but refused to give way. 'You lured him on. There's no other way he would break a date with Sonja to go out with you. But mark my words. He might have you tonight, but that's all you're going to get!' Mona threatened nastily.

'Which is more than you'll ever have. You want him for yourself, don't you? But I bet he's never even looked at you, has he?' Megan made a wild guess, and knew she was right when the other woman turned pale.

'Bitch!' Mona snarled, and, with a flounce, rose to her feet and left the room.

Megan expelled an angry breath. That had been very unpleasant, though she was glad she had routed her enemy. The thought of Lucas with that woman made her shudder. Thank goodness he had better taste, although Sonja hadn't been much nicer. What did he see in them, or was that a naïve question? Her lips twisted. Probably. Not that it mattered; she wasn't interested in Lucas; she had just been defending herself.

She refused to listen to the tiny voice which said she had enjoyed squashing the woman too much to be totally disinterested. Taking a deep, calming breath, she slipped her lipstick back into her bag and made her way back to the nightclub.

She paused inside the doorway to get her bearings, but had no trouble picking out Lucas. She had the disconcerting feeling that she would always know exactly where he was, even in a crowded room. She began to make her way towards him, and that was when she realised he was talking to a woman seated at the next table. Her eyes narrowed. No, not just talking. From the way the woman was laughing, he was flirting with her quite outrageously. He couldn't be left alone for five minutes!

Anger made her quicken her step, until that tiny voice demanded to know what she was doing. What on earth was she getting angry about? She had no claim on Lucas, and didn't want one. What he did was none of her business. Her step faltered. It was a timely reminder, and a resigned smile curved her lips as she got her perspective back.

As if sensing her gaze, Lucas glanced round, his blue eyes meeting her mocking green ones. He must have read something in them, for his brows rose questioningly. I've just had a nasty exchange because of your roving eye, she thought, and here you are chatting up the nearest available woman!

She dropped her bag on the table and sat down. 'I'd be careful if I were you—the knives are out tonight,' she warned ironically, smiling coolly at the brunette, who was still hoping to regain Lucas's attention. The woman promptly turned her back.

Lucas's lips twitched. 'Been fighting, have you? I wondered why you were gone so long,' he observed, his voice
carrying a betraying wobble.

Megan picked up her drink, debated whether to throw it
at him, and decided that drinking it would do her more
good, even if it wouldn't be as much fun. 'I've just had a
very interesting conversation with a friend of a friend of
yours,' she informed him wryly.

Lucas stilled in the act of raising his glass to his lips.
'Ah. I detect Mona's heavy hand. You'd better tell me what
happened.'

'I was warned off you, in no uncertain terms.' Megan
smiled reminiscently, with all the friendliness of an angry
tigress.

'I shouldn't imagine that went down too well,' Lucas
surprised her by saying quite grimly.

Taking a sip of her drink, Megan pondered the fact that
he actually sounded annoyed on her behalf. 'Like a lead
weight,' she admitted ruefully.

'I'm sorry,' Lucas apologised, making her give him an
odd look. 'You shouldn't have had to go through that.
Mona took far too much upon herself.'

Well, well, well, Megan thought wonderingly, feeling
better about the whole thing. She had never expected Lucas
to champion her, but maybe she had done him an injustice.
'It doesn't matter. I got my own back.'

There was wry humour reflected in his blue eyes. 'I'm
sure you did.'

Megan finally laughed. 'I was tempted to tell her you're
no great catch!' she told him slyly.

'I'm surprised you didn't,' he remarked, sipping at his
own drink and looking pleasantly relaxed.

Megan looked at him quite soberly. 'Frankly, she
wouldn't have believed me. To people like Mona and Sonja

you're the glittering prize. They'll have to learn the hard way that all that glistens isn't gold,' she sighed.

Lucas's laugh was harsh with cynicism. 'They don't expect gold. So long as the diamonds are real they'll have no regrets.'

Though she had vaguely guessed as much, she was still shocked. 'That's the most mercenary thing I've ever heard!'

Lucas shrugged dismissively. 'It happens to be true. I'm a very wealthy man, with a reputation for being generous when an affair is over. Women like Sonja see an affair with me as an insurance policy against hard times.'

Megan shuddered with distaste. 'If you know they see you like that, how can you go out with them?'

'As a rule, I avoid the Sonjas of the world like the plague. My relationships have always been with women I like and respect, who know as well as I do that the affair will last as long as it is mutually beneficial. I've remained friends with them all.'

It sounded reasonable, but cold. Part of a different world she was glad she didn't inhabit. 'Then why Sonja, if she doesn't fit in?'

Much to her surprise, Lucas looked discomfited. 'She was the flight attendant on the plane back from Hong Kong last month. I needed a companion for a charity do, and she was free that night. She was good fun, and we went out a few times. When I knew I was coming down here, she asked if I could give her a lift. Her family live not far away. That was to be the end of it.'

Megan had to bite her lip to stop herself grinning. He didn't sound at all happy with the way things had turned out. Sonja wasn't the dumb blonde he'd expected. She had claws and was intent on getting them well into him. 'Something tells me Sonja has other ideas!' she said cheerfully, and Lucas shot her a fulminating look.

'Think it's funny, do you?' he growled, then laughed

reluctantly. 'Unfortunately, you're right. I'm afraid Sonja will have to go.'

'Do you think it will be that easy?' Megan asked, grinning all the more for he was allowing her to, at his expense.

'Probably not,' he admitted ruefully. 'There's bound to be a scene. Do you want to come and watch? No doubt you'd enjoy it.'

She pretended to think about it. 'I could render first aid. I have a badge.'

'And I know where you'd like to stick it!' he declared drily. 'On second thoughts, I'll go on my own.'

'Spoilsport!'

Grinning himself, Lucas drained his glass. 'I know you'd like to see blood, especially mine, but this time you'll be disappointed. Are you ready to go?'

She was. More than ready. It had been the strangest evening. Rather like an extended roller-coaster ride, all highs and lows. Lucas settled the bill, then they went to collect her shawl. As he draped it around her shoulders, Megan yawned.

'Sleepy?' Lucas asked, keeping his arm about her shoulders as he helped her down the steps and across to his car.

'A little, but I enjoyed myself tonight,' she confessed with the faintest hint of surprise.

Lucas picked it up. 'Even though you didn't expect to.'

'Well, you must admit it was chancy. All we ever do when we meet is fight,' Megan pointed out as he held the door open for her to climb in.

Lucas closed it after her and walked round to claim his own seat. 'Ever wondered why?' he probed, starting the engine.

She smiled faintly. 'Not particularly, though I suppose you have some wonderful theory,' she quipped easily.

'We fight, Red, because we like it,' Lucas countered smoothly, making her nerves twang. She had thought the same thing herself only the other day. 'What do you think that means?'

'That we're both masochists?' she ventured as they began to move and the darkness settled around them like a glove. The world shrank to the small space they sat in.

'It adds spice to our relationship,' Lucas corrected her, and Megan found her eyes drawn to where his hands rested on the steering wheel. They were long-fingered and capable as he manoeuvred the car with perfect control. They would have the same control as they roved over a woman's skin, bringing her to life. Bringing her pleasure.

She jerked straighter in her seat, alarmed at where her musings were taking her. Such thoughts were out of bounds. Especially when linked to Lucas. 'There's just one thing wrong with your theory—we don't have a relationship,' she pointed out coolly.

'Not yet,' he agreed, never taking his eyes from the road.

Megan felt her nerves jump. What did that mean? If he had the notion that she might somehow be available, she would put him straight at once. 'Not ever. I don't want a relationship with you.'

He laughed. 'I don't want one with you, either,' he said, and she wondered why his agreement didn't make her feel more secure.

They fell silent for the remainder of the journey. Though she tried not to be, she was very much aware of every move Lucas made. When his thigh muscles flexed she couldn't help wondering how his strength would feel against her softness. Her stomach lurched. Lord, she had to get a grip and stop fantasising like this about a man whose reputation with women made headline news. Even had she not had good reason not to get involved with anyone, she would never become Lucas's latest diversion.

When Lucas finally drew the car to a halt outside the house, she turned to him with a cool smile. 'Thank you for a lovely evening,' she said politely, and would have reached for the door release if Lucas hadn't swiftly leant across to stop her.

'It isn't quite over yet,' he told her softly, and her breath caught in her throat at his sudden closeness. It was impossible to see the colour of his eyes, but she could see them glittering.

The car seemed to be crackling with electricity, and her heart skipped several beats. 'What does that mean?'

'It means I think I ought to give you a little more information for your book,' he enlightened her silkily, his voice stroking over nerves never reached before.

Just when she needed them most, her wits seemed to go begging. 'Book?'

She sensed his smile. 'Mmm, you know. *Seduction—the Canfield Way*?' he prompted, using his free hand to brush a strand of hair off her cheek.

Megan jumped, regretting the whim which had made her tease him with that imaginary book. 'I think I've done enough research for tonight,' she argued far too breathlessly, and tried again to open the door, but Lucas wouldn't be budged. All she managed to do was bring herself so close to him that she could feel the brush of his breath on her cheek.

Her throat closed over and her lashes fluttered betrayingly. It was dark and they were alone. All she had to do was turn her head the merest fraction for their lips to touch. A tiny voice asked if it would really be so bad. Her sharply honed instinct for self-preservation said it could be catastrophic.

'I disagree. I think I should kiss you. Purely in the interests of science, of course,' he declared, and when she gasped and moved that fraction to look at him he brought his mouth down on hers.

Her first instinct was to fight him. She did raise one hand

to push him away, but it remained clenched at his shoulder as sweet, hot sensations throbbed to life in the pit of her stomach and she found her will to fight draining out of every limb. Her mind went into a tailspin. As her defences crumbled with pitiful ease, he disarmed her with the tantalising brush of his lips over her own, inviting her participation with the soft stroke of his tongue.

Like a diver deprived too long of air, long-suppressed emotions battled through to the surface. All sense of danger was swamped beneath a wave of sensuality. She suddenly couldn't think, could only feel herself coming to life, and she craved that resurrection with a hunger which brought a moan to her throat as the teasing went on and on. Her head fell back, and there was no other option in the world for her than to part her lips and invite him to deepen the kiss.

With a growl of satisfaction his mouth opened on hers, his tongue gliding in to take possession, and her skin began to prickle with a white heat. It was as if she had been plugged into a circuit which gave her a positive charge of electricity. All she was conscious of was the stroking of his tongue on sensitive flesh and a compelling need to respond. She couldn't help herself. Her fingers skated up to his nape, finding the lush locks of hair, and clung on as her tongue duelled with his. Her eyes closed as her body melted against him, and her sighing moan filled the air.

At her capitulation, Lucas shifted, pulling her across him until she was cradled in his lap. Her whole body seemed to be pulsing, needing more, and she moved against him. Lucas groaned, and she felt his body surge against her, his arousal thickening her blood and sending it coursing through her veins. He drew her close, and the sensual exploration finally became a demand. Her senses swam and her free arm went around him, holding on as she responded with a wildness which, though it was a stranger to her, was

so much a part of her nature. Uncaring, she flung herself
willingly into the storm which raged around them.

As kiss followed kiss with breathtaking intensity, Lucas's hand traced a searing path down her back to the luscious curve of her hip, halting when it met the silky stretch
of flesh below the hem of her dress, making her heart thud.
Then slowly it began to rise again until it found the swell
of her breast. Megan held her breath, then groaned as he
took her into his palm and her nipple hardened into an
aching point. It wasn't enough. She wanted him to touch
her, and, as if he had read her mind, in the next instant he
was pushing the tiny strap of her dress aside to ease the
bodice away.

Yet instead of administering the touch she longed for
Lucas tore his lips from hers and buried them against her
neck with a groan.

Feeling deprived, Megan took a painful breath. 'Lucas?'
she asked questioningly. Why had he stopped?

Lucas raised his head with a sigh. 'This is getting a little
out of hand. If I don't stop, we'll end up making love in
the car, and I haven't done that since I was a teenager!' he
said wryly.

Sanity returned then, like an icy flood, taking the heat
from her, leaving her cold with shock. Dear God, what had
she been thinking of? Suddenly she was aware that she was
still draped around him, and with a gasp of dismay she
scrambled back to her own seat. Righting her dress, she
had to swallow several times in order to be able to speak.

'That's nonsense. It wouldn't have gone that far!' she
exclaimed thickly.

'Wouldn't it?' Lucas challenged huskily from the shadows of his own seat. 'I didn't want to stop, and, if you're
honest, neither did you.'

Megan couldn't deny it. She hadn't wanted to stop. Her
body still ached with need, and she knew that if he touched

her again now she wouldn't resist him. She was shocked by her uninhibited response, and her inability to control it. Control was her life.

She fought for it now, and achieved partial success, in that she was able to find something to say. 'Well, now I *know* I've done enough research for one night.'

Lucas laughed throatily. 'If there's any point you're not sure of, I can run over it again,' he offered, making heat rise in her once more.

She felt as if she'd been run over already. 'No, thanks; I've already got more than I bargained for.'

'I'll second that,' he retorted wryly. 'I think it's cold shower time for me. Not that I should be surprised. This was always on the cards.'

The rueful statement brought her head shooting round. 'What do you mean?'

Lucas shifted in his seat, the better to see her. 'There's no point in pretending it's not happening, Red. We've been aware of each other since the moment we met again.'

Her gasp was audible. She had known about herself, but, like a naïve idiot, she hadn't realised Lucas felt it too. And, having just gone to pieces in his arms, she'd look like an even bigger fool if she tried to deny it.

'It shouldn't be happening,' she insisted gruffly, her heart thudding sickeningly fast.

'Tell me about it!' Lucas exclaimed drolly, sounding much more normal. 'I got one hell of a shock when I realised I was strongly attracted to the girl who had taunted me unmercifully for more years than I cared to remember,' he went on huskily.

'Then why couldn't you just remember that and leave me alone?' she charged, knowing it was unfair to put the blame on him, but doing it to salve her pride.

Lucas shook his head. 'Because you set my heart thumping and my skin tingling. I'm a man, not a machine. I wanted you, Red. I still do. Every bit as much as you want me.'

Megan stared at him, knowing it was true. She'd never felt such a powerful need, and it made her tremble inside. But that only served to make her forgotten common sense reassert itself. She might want him, but she would not have him. She would make that very clear.

'Then you'll just have to want, because this is as far as it goes!' she declared tightly, and fumbled for the lock.

Lucas made no attempt to stop her this time. She clambered from the car, slammed the door and raced up the steps on legs which threatened to fail her. She prayed that Lucas would not follow her. She desperately needed to be alone to think. When she reached the sanctuary of her room, she dived inside like a rabbit into its hole and collapsed against the solid wood.

Oh, Lord, she was in trouble!

CHAPTER FIVE

MEGAN PACED UP and down her room, feeling distinctly edgy. It was late. Earlier she had showered in a vain attempt to relax, but she had merely ended up cleaner and no less restless. Nevertheless, she had slipped into the T-shirt she used to sleep in and climbed into bed—and lain awake for ages. In the end she had given up and taken to pacing instead.

What on earth had possessed her to respond to Lucas with such abandon? Being attracted wasn't new to her. She had subdued it successfully more than once, so why had the strength of purpose she valued so much gone begging tonight? She had fully intended to resist, but somehow she hadn't been able to. The second he had touched her she had become powerless, overwhelmed by an attraction so powerful that denial had been the last thing on her mind.

Reaching the end of the room, she leaned her forehead against the wall and groaned aloud. That was why she knew she was in trouble. She had never felt this pull with any of the other men she had been drawn to. She had believed herself to be in total control because she had been able to dismiss them. Now she knew better because the truth had jumped up and hit her. There was no comparison. She had found it easy to quell the stirrings of need because those men hadn't made her feel the way Lucas did.

With one kiss he had shown her how wrong she was. She hadn't wanted the others, but she did want Lucas. It was like an ache inside her. An emptiness which needed to be filled, but only by him. No other man would do. Her eyes closed, and she took a shaky breath. The most terrifying thing, though, was realising she could have him, because Lucas wanted her too. His admission had shaken her and thrilled her at the same time. The knowledge that the feeling was mutual made her tremble inside even now. Swallowing hard, she began to retrace her uneasy steps.

For the first time in her life she was truly being faced with temptation, and part of her longed to give in. Lucas was dangerously alluring, his pull strong. She had lost herself in his arms tonight, forgetting everything. Nothing had seemed to matter, save that the wonderful things she was feeling should go on. And they could, if she were to have an affair with him. He was used to women finding him attractive, used to exploring mutual feelings. He probably thought she was too. But she wasn't.

Finding herself level with the window-seat, she sank down onto the cushions, more anxious than she could remember feeling for a long time. Tonight had brought her into direct conflict with her own rules. That was partly the cause of her restlessness—for the first time since university she was being tempted to break them. Lucas took her to places nobody else had, and she knew that if she showed him the slightest encouragement he would follow up what had happened tonight. And whilst a wanton part of her was inclined to do just that, the saner part urged caution.

Was it worth destroying her hard-won peace of mind for the fleeting benefits of sexual satisfaction? No sooner had the question entered her mind than the answer followed it. No, it wasn't.

The tension drained out of her as sanity returned. The chill of reality made her shiver. Finding herself susceptible to Lucas's potent maleness had opened her eyes. She had discovered she was not the person she had thought herself to be, but nothing else had changed. Sex was not the an-

swer. Experience had taught her that, and so she must fight
this unexpected attraction, and conquer it.

She knew that facing Lucas again wouldn't be easy. She
couldn't pretend that nothing had happened, but she could
make good and sure it didn't happen again. She would keep
her distance from now on, and Lucas would get the message. She was not available as a diversion.

As IT TURNED OUT, it was two days before she saw Lucas
again, because he was called away on business. Cowardly
though it was, she welcomed the respite. Not so welcome
was the fact that Daniel had become even more elusive, so
she'd had no chance to speak to him either.

That was how matters stood as Megan drove back to
Terrell's after a depressing meeting with their bank manager. She had the car windows down, allowing the warm
air to rush in at her. Daniel should have gone, and his
absence hadn't pleased the manager, but as Daniel hadn't
come home last night, as usual, the job had been left to
her. She hadn't been in a conciliatory mood herself, having
overslept, yet somehow she had managed to persuade the
man to extend their overdraft.

A small victory, but it had improved her mood as she'd
returned to her car. Shrugging off the jacket of her trouser
suit, she had tossed it onto the back seat and rolled up the
sleeves of her silk blouse, before setting off on the return
journey.

It was a beautiful day, with enough breeze to make it
perfect sailing weather. To her left she could see a lone
sailor out on the river, and envied him his freedom. She
couldn't remember the last time she had been able to just
take off. A mile further, and with a twist of the road, she
got a better view, and her lips parted in surprise. Closer,
she recognised the craft as Daniel's dinghy, and although

he was tacking away from her she knew he must be bringing her in to the tiny landing at the head of the creek.

She didn't stop to marvel that he was actually around at
this time of day. This was a gift horse she wasn't going to
look in the mouth. She needed to talk to him, and there
might not be a better time. Pressing her foot down, she
raced to get to the tiny beach before him.

Daniel's car wasn't in the yard when she parked there,
but then he had probably sailed down from the house. Ignoring the shed where Ted would already be hard at work,
she cut off along the path through the trees which led to
the beach. From the sound of whistling, she knew he had
got there ahead of her. At least he sounded as if he was in
a good mood, and she hoped that was a promising sign.

However, as she rounded the last bend in the path, and
the trees opened onto grass leading down to a sandy beach
with a small landing-stage, one glance was enough to reveal
not Daniel but Lucas. He must have returned whilst she
was in town.

He hadn't heard her arrive, which was just as well, for
seeing him so suddenly like this had taken her breath away.
In jeans, with the checked shirt he must have started out
wearing tied around his waist by the sleeves, his hair
mussed and his cheeks flushed, Lucas looked vitally alive.
Busy with the sail, he moved with instinctive male grace,
exuding power and confidence. The tanned flesh of his back
rippled as he worked, and to Megan he looked barely
tamed, as free-spirited as the flapping canvas, always threatening to break free. Something hit her below the ribs with
the force of a blow, and she found herself watching in
helpless fascination.

A feeling of vulnerability assailed her, because, heaven
help her, he called to her. He called to her in a way no
other man ever had. She was compelled to admit to herself
that looking at him gave her immense pleasure, and in do-

ing so experienced again that wild stirring of the blood. Her throat ached. How could one man make her feel so incredibly alive that he tempted her to break all her own rules?

She didn't know how, she only knew he did, and that made him all the more dangerous. Even now a wayward part of her was urging her to go forward, but she resisted, knowing that it only confirmed her need to keep her distance. Though it seemed to take an effort, she turned to go.

'See anything you liked?' Lucas's silky question floated over the air to her, making her jerk round again.

Colour washed in and out of her cheeks as she realised he had known she was there all the time. Unable to retreat now, she took a couple of steps towards him. Had she seen anything she liked? Dear heaven, she had liked everything far too much! 'I thought you were Daniel,' she pointed out defensively.

Lucas's head finally turned towards her, and he eyed her with a faint smile lingering around his lips. 'For about five seconds. But don't worry. I don't mind you looking. I enjoy looking at you, too. You're very easy on the eye,' he responded softly, and her stomach lurched at the easy compliment. She shouldn't have liked it, but her senses were refusing to cooperate with her brain. Whenever she came within feet of Lucas she stopped being a thinking human being and became a seething mass of emotions.

She watched him finish what he was doing and step onto the landing-stage. Her throat tightened. He looked too damned alluring, and she wished he would put his shirt on and shut temptation away. However, he showed no intention of doing so, and Megan decided it was time to make her position quite clear.

'Stop it, Lucas. I'm not interested,' she ordered shortly, and he flashed her a knowing look.

'You were interested the other night,' he observed, setting her nerves twanging as vivid memories assailed her. Having made sure the craft was secured, he walked towards her.

Lord, how she wished that night had never happened; then she wouldn't be trying to defend an indefensible position. 'Don't play games with me. I'm not in the mood,' she returned quellingly, trying to make it sound as if she meant it, but to her own ears merely sounding petulant.

It didn't work, anyway. Lucas ran his tingling blue gaze over her and inclined his head enticingly. 'I know a sure-fire way of getting you in the mood. Want to try it?' he invited, moving another step closer.

Megan had expected him to tease her, but he was being deliberately provocative, and with sudden insight she knew he had been expecting her. Maybe not here and now, but sometime. He had known she would come to deny anything and everything, and he wasn't going to let her. The other night she had aroused the hunter, and unless she could persuade him he was following the wrong scent he would use all his skills to trap her. It didn't help that she was hampered by her own wanton senses, but it made her more determined to win.

'No, I do not want to try it!' she exclaimed tautly. 'You're being ridiculous. Remember all the reasons why this shouldn't be happening.'

His brows rose mockingly. 'Is that what you did? Is it working?'

That hit her confidence at its weakest spot. Because, no matter how she tried, reminding herself of the distance her rules demanded, it wasn't working. Unable to hold his gaze, her eyes dropped, and he laughed huskily. Realising what she had given away, Megan abruptly put some distance between them, needing the breathing space. 'I told you the other night that that was the end of it,' she pointed out unevenly.

Lucas took his weight on one leg and eyed her averted face consideringly. 'Look me in the eye and say that.'

Taunted, Megan swung to face him, her lips parted to snap out the words, but he was far closer than she expected, and her throat closed over, making it impossible for her to get the words out. Instead she found herself staring at him helplessly whilst her senses rioted in response to his nearness. Lucas could have said anything then, but to her amazement his lips twisted into a wry smile.

'I know the feeling,' he admitted huskily, holding her eyes, and she knew he was as disconcerted by this unexpected attraction as she was. However, it was clear that he was willing to go with it. To test it and see where it would take him. 'Strange the way things turn out,' he remarked, walking around her to lean against the nearest tree.

Megan shifted to face him, feeling unreal. In a way she envied him his ease with his own sexuality, but it didn't alter the fact that she could not allow herself the same luxury. There were good reasons for her not to get involved with him, or anyone, and they hadn't changed.

'There's nothing here for you, Lucas,' she asserted as strongly as she could.

'Let me be the judge of that,' he countered softly, and colour rose in her cheeks as his intense blue eyes began a lazy inspection of her from head to toe. His gaze was a caress, designed to get a reaction, and her body responded without her volition. Megan felt her nipples tighten into hard buds, and knew they were pressing blatantly against her silk shirt. She didn't dare cross her arms as she was tempted to, for then he would know exactly what reaction he was getting.

Yet when his eyes finally met hers again it was obvious that he knew. 'I dreamt about you these last few nights,' he informed her in a husky drawl which touched her nerves and set them tingling.

She knew she had given him ample cause to think she might be willing to be seduced, which meant that she was fighting an uphill battle, but she couldn't stop until she had made him accept that she meant what she said. So far all she had done was undermine herself. She had to get a grip and fight this unwanted attraction to the last breath. It would help if he put his shirt on, but the mere mention of it would be more ammunition to him. She would have to try and ignore that broad expanse of male flesh.

'Nightmares can be scary,' she sympathised, with a flash of her old spirit, and he smiled in a way which set her heart tripping.

'Would you have comforted me, Red?' he taunted, and she shivered when his eyes dropped to her lips and remained there, so that it almost felt as if he was touching her. Her palms went damp as she acknowledged that he was good at this. Slowly but surely, curling tendrils of electric awareness were wreathing the air between them, with nothing more than a look.

Stiffening her resolve, she made herself remember that he was good because he had had plenty of practice. She was just another in a long, long line. 'I would have thrown cold water over you and let you fend for yourself!' she retorted, and he threw back his head and laughed.

Which didn't help her at all, because she liked the sound of it far too much. Plus he looked so carefree, she was tempted to join him! Lord, this was crazy!

'I find arguing with you strangely addictive,' he declared when he had sobered again.

Megan wanted to groan out loud. This was not what she wanted to hear. Instead of warning him off, everything she said was being used against her. 'Lucas, be sensible!' she implored again, but he shook his head.

'There's a time and place to be sensible, and this isn't it. We're attracted to each other.'

She swallowed painfully, unable to deny it. 'I don't want this.'

His smile was softly derisive. 'Do you think we have much choice?'

Megan caught her breath. He made it sound…ordained. As if the gods had spoken and there was nothing they could do. She shivered, shutting her mind against that primeval part of her which recognised his statement. 'Of course we have a choice. We can simply turn our backs on it and pretend it never happened!'

Lucas pushed himself away from the tree and prowled towards her with leonine intent. Megan backed away instinctively, unfortunately coming up against another tree which blocked her retreat. Abruptly she found herself with nowhere to go. All she could do was wait as he came to stand in front of her. His hand reached out, and she breathed in sharply as with one finger he traced the fullness of her bottom lip.

'Can you? Because I don't think I can. Like I said, I didn't sleep very well last night,' he said huskily.

Megan felt that touch in every part of her. It was as if by it he had taken total possession. She could no more run than a one-day-old chick could fly. More, she wanted to slip the tip of her tongue between her lips and taste him, and that shocked her because it meant that with a few kisses he had unlocked a wealth of sensuality which she hadn't realised she possessed. Certainly her one brief affair hadn't stirred her this much. Nobody had ever tempted her the way Lucas did. Nobody had ever driven her mindless with the passionate longing of his kiss.

There was all that and more right here, right now, and she felt she was caught in quicksand, struggling hopelessly to be free. She didn't know how to fight it, knew only that she must, and that gave her enough strength to twist her head to one side and force his hand to fall away. It was a small success and she hurried to bolster it.

'Perhaps you should have given Sonja a ring,' she retorted shakily, but only managed to draw a laugh.

'I'm afraid Sonja wouldn't do. You see, all I could think about was the sweetness of your lips.'

Her throat closed over as his words conjured up the moment in vivid colour. 'It was just a kiss, Lucas, nothing special,' she denied thickly, licking her lips and inadvertently getting the taste of him she had wanted only seconds before.

His eyes followed the movement, and he groaned softly. 'If that's so, then you won't mind kissing me again just to make sure, will you?' he challenged, moving to prop his hands against the tree at either side of her head, effectively trapping her.

Megan immediately found it incredibly hard to breathe. She wanted to push herself free, but knew she dared not touch him for fear that her hands would betray her as they had that night. 'Damn you, Lucas, let me go or I'll hit you!' she cried in desperation.

'That isn't what you really want to do,' he declared softly, taking her breath away. 'Deny it as much as you like, but we both know something special happened that night, and I've been waiting ever since to kiss you and make it all happen again.'

She was floundering and she knew it. 'You're wrong. Nothing happened and nothing will,' she asserted in a hopeless attempt to freeze him off. 'Carry on with this and you'll only make me despise you.'

'A lot of sour words pass through those lovely lips of yours, Red, but I know now they taste like nectar. It's something I could very easily become addicted to.'

Dear Lord, why was it that everything he said had the power to set her nerves jangling? How was it possible for one man to turn her world upside down in so short a time? 'This is crazy!' she declared faintly.

Lucas's smile faded, banked fire reflected in his eyes. 'The other night you turned to flame in my arms.'

The husky sound of his voice was sending tremors up and down her spine, weakening her knees and her resistance. She knew she had to do something to break free, otherwise she might do something else far worse. 'That was a mistake,' she insisted thickly, and he smiled slowly.

'A statement like that can't be allowed to pass, so let's put it to the test, shall we?' he suggested, and closed the gap between them.

'No, Lucas!' she protested desperately, bringing her hands up to push him away, but he caught them easily and forced them back against the tree.

'Megan, yes!' he countered with a husky growl, lowering his head.

Caught between the muscular planes of his body and the tree, there was nowhere for Megan to retreat to, and she groaned helplessly in her throat as his mouth found hers. She tried to resist the soft touch of his kiss, the sensual glide of his tongue along her closed lips, but even so small a contact started a conflagration inside her. Heat curled upwards, setting her nerves sizzling. When she wanted to be strong, her muscles seemed to weaken, turning traitor to her mind.

Then his mouth left hers, trailing along her jaw to her ear, making her shiver as his tongue traced the sensitive skin before foraying down to where her pulse beat frantically in her throat. She uttered a stifled gasp as his tongue stroked the spot, and bit her lip as his lips lowered to the open V of her blouse. Her breasts tightened, her nipples hardening to aching points which so craved his touch that when, in the next instant, his lips found one peak through the silk blouse, she couldn't stop her body arching into him.

She gasped again, and with a growl of triumph his head rose and his mouth found hers again. She had always been lost, she realised, right from the very beginning, and now there was no thought of fight in her. Her lips parted to the insistent pressure of his tongue, and when her own tongue melded with his he released her hands and slid his arms round her, drawing her tight to his strongly aroused body.

The knowledge that he wanted her was dizzying, sending all thought of self-preservation to the four winds. There was only now, and the feel of his hands and lips on her. Her own arms were around his neck, her small hands sliding into his hair and clinging on tightly. Lucas groaned and she shivered as one large hand pulled her blouse free and slipped underneath to run up and down her velvety skin.

When he lowered her to the grass, she didn't resist but welcomed the weight of him. His kiss deepened, becoming more and more demanding, and she returned it hungrily, a willing victim of her own need. The rights and wrongs of what she was doing were light years from her mind.

Beneath her blouse, his hand found the front fastening of her bra and released it, pushing it aside to fasten on the jutting mound of her breast, and Megan cried out at the intense pleasure which swept down through her body to increase the throbbing ache deep inside her. His thumb flicked back and forth, circling and teasing until pleasure was almost pain.

Lucas lifted his head then, and she opened dazed eyes to stare up at him. 'Sweet heaven, what you do to me! I want you, Megan. I've never wanted any woman as much as I want you right now!' he growled, and her heart lurched.

Had he not spoken, she doubted that she would have come to her senses, but he had and his words were like a douche of cold water. She froze, her heart thudding wildly as she dragged in air. It wasn't true. He wanted her the same way he wanted those other women, he just used the words to get what he wanted. Well, he wasn't going to get her!

Lucas felt her stillness and his eyes searched her face. 'What is it?'

Green eyes clouded with anger met his. 'Let me up,' she ordered coldly.

For a second he looked as if he was going to argue, then with a sigh he rolled away and sat up. Free to move, Megan scrambled to her feet, her legs about as useful as those of a newborn foal. She refused to look at him as she righted her clothes with more haste than accuracy. She knew that she had just had a narrow escape, no thanks to herself. If he hadn't mentioned those wretched women…! She ground her teeth in self-disgust.

Lucas was on his feet too, watching her curiously. 'What happened? You were with me up to that point,' he declared, sounding so cool and in control that she wanted to slap him. What other proof did she need that this was nothing out of the ordinary for him?

Megan glared at him. 'It was getting a little crowded down there!' she snapped, nodding towards the flattened area. As she saw him frown, her lip curled. 'With you, me and all your other women!' she enlightened him, only to see amusement curve his far too attractive mouth.

'Jealous, Red? I'll remember that for next time,' he had the gall to say, and she fumed.

'There will be no next time, and I most certainly was not jealous!'

His eyebrows rose. 'Then why are you so angry?' he asked softly, neatly taking the wind out of her sails.

Why *was* she angry? It was nothing to her who he had gone out with. He meant nothing to her. Nothing. Yet the reminder of the existence of those women hurt, a small voice taunted her. Only because he was attempting to add her to the list, she argued, and set her jaw. 'If I'm angry, then it's because I didn't appreciate being given that old line!' she shot back.

To her annoyance, Lucas refused to react the way she wanted him to. Instead of looking shamefaced, he had the nerve to look serious. 'It wasn't a line, Red. I meant it. The truth is I've never felt like this before.'

Despite herself her throat closed over. 'You can't really expect me to believe that?' she challenged with a shaky laugh.

Lucas dragged his hands through his hair, unwittingly drawing her eyes to his chest. She had to swallow hard and look away. 'The most I expect from you is a fight, but I don't mind that. Deny it all you like, but what we have here is a pretty powerful combination. I'm not going to walk away from it, or allow you to.'

Her heart lurched. 'Is that a threat?'

His expression softened to somewhere between sensuality and tenderness. 'No, it's a promise.'

For a moment all she could do was look at him as she turned to jelly inside, then from somewhere she found the spunk to stiffen her spine. 'I won't sleep with you.'

'Maybe I want more,' he suggested.

Megan shook her head. 'I won't have an affair with you either,' she declared as firmly as she could, considering he was turning her inside out.

'Why not? It would be good between us.'

She knew it, but it was not a good enough reason to abandon the rules she lived by. 'It's still no.'

'I'm not going to give up trying to persuade you to change your mind,' Lucas returned, and she smiled grimly.

'I never thought you would. I can't stop you, but you'll be wasting your time.'

'Time will tell,' he said irritatingly, and finally untied the shirt from his waist and slipped it on. Catching sight of her fiery eyes, he traced a finger down her cheek. 'OK, Red, if

I can't interest you in an affair, how about coming out with me this afternoon?'

The gentle touch and the change of subject threw her. She didn't know what to make of him. He seemed to be able to turn his emotions on and off at will. One minute he was trying to persuade her into bed, the next he was inviting her out as if nothing had happened.

She blinked at him. 'In the boat?'

His look grew wry. 'I don't think so. What you and I need is company, not finding ourselves alone in a tiny boat,' he said mockingly, and she realised then that he was just as churned up as she was; he just managed to hide it better. Strangely enough, that comforted her.

She took a steadying breath. 'What were you doing with the dinghy anyway?'

'Dan gave me the use of it, and as it was a perfect morning for being on the water I decided to sail down instead of using the car,' he explained.

'To ask me to go out with you, I suppose?' she asked unsteadily, and jumped when he took her chin in his hand.

Lucas stared down broodingly into her startled eyes. 'That was my intention, until we got sidetracked. I had this urge to be with you, and I didn't want to give you any more time to think. I want your company, Red, so what do you say?'

He was twisting her in knots. His touch was gentle, and he sounded sincere. She was tempted. She knew she was supposed to be keeping her distance, but would it really hurt to go with him? Wouldn't it do her good to get away from the problems which surrounded her for a while? Her conscience told her these were all just excuses, but somehow she couldn't make herself listen. She wasn't going to go mad. She wasn't going to kick over the traces. She was simply contemplating spending the afternoon with an attractive man who wanted her company.

Because you want to be with him, no matter what, an inner voice informed her, and she ignored that too. One afternoon wasn't going to compromise her.

Easing back a step, so that his hand fell away, she cleared her throat. 'Where would we go?'

Lucas took a deep breath before answering, as if her reply had been important to him. 'Some friends of mine moved down here six months ago. They've invited me over for the afternoon.'

'They wouldn't be expecting me,' she pointed out, and he pulled a wry face.

'No, but, like you, they'd expect me to turn up with someone. Peggy nags me about it all the time. She wants me to settle down and raise a family of my own.'

'You, with children? I don't believe it,' Megan scoffed lightly. But she did believe it. She had a vivid mental picture of him with blue-eyed, dark-haired children, and she envied him. Envied him so much it was as if a vice had clamped about her heart.

Lucas tutted. 'It may not be your ideal, but I'd like to have half a dozen.'

Megan found emotion suddenly welling into her throat, and had to swallow hard to shift it. Because the subject hurt, she made light of it. 'Six? Wouldn't your wife have anything to say about it?'

'OK, I'll amend that to at least two. I know what it's like to be an only child, and, while it has certain advantages, it really isn't much fun.'

Megan cast him a frowning glance. 'You were lonely?' she asked. Somehow she had always had the idea that Lucas was perfectly happy in his self-sufficient way.

He sent her a teasing look. 'Feeling sorry for me, Red?'

She tipped her chin at him. 'And if I am?'

'Join me this afternoon. You can't do anything about my childhood, but you can brighten up my afternoon.'

A curling tendril of warmth sprang to life in her stomach at the idea that she could do anything as special as brighten his day. It wasn't true, and it only showed how dangerous Lucas was that part of her actually wanted to believe it nevertheless. It went some way to filling the huge emptiness inside her. Which was frightening. She had learned to live with the hole by ignoring it. Now, suddenly, she was very much aware of it, and of a yearning need to fill it.

And that brought her up short, because there was nothing she could fill it with, and she didn't want to remember the pain. Dismayed to find herself thinking of things that she had hoped were long buried, Megan shivered. To spend the afternoon with him would be sheer folly.

'Sorry, but I've got too much to do,' she refused shortly, heading for the path back to the yard.

Frowning, Lucas fell in step beside her. 'Doing what, precisely? Have you suddenly been inundated with requests for yacht designs?' he challenged, shooting her down so swiftly that she winced and sent him a daggers look even as she kept on walking.

'Thanks, I needed reminding!'

Lucas sighed, catching her arm to halt her in her tracks. 'You'll weather it, Red. You're too good to go under,' he declared, and his confidence in her brought a flush to her cheeks.

'Maybe you could try telling that to Daniel,' she said wryly, and Lucas frowned.

'I thought the problem was just the recession,' he said, making her sharply aware that she had almost said too much.

'Oh, it is,' she confirmed with a laugh, but Lucas didn't smile.

'I've noticed he doesn't seem to be around much.'

Megan caught her breath. 'Yes, well, there isn't an awful

lot for him to do.' As ever she made excuses for her brother, though she knew he wouldn't appreciate them.

It was Lucas who started them walking again. 'You know, you could get a job with any of the top companies on the strength of your work. You don't have to rely on Terrell's. I'm acquainted with several of the executives personally and would be glad to put in a word for you.'

She was truly lost for words for a moment, because it was a very generous offer. She was beginning to realise there was a great deal more to Lucas Canfield than she had suspected. Her voice, when she spoke, was gruff. 'Thanks, but Terrell's is my home. I...' Need it, she had been about to reveal, then changed her mind. 'I couldn't leave it.'

Lucas nodded. 'I can understand that, just as I can see the worry is wearing you down. You need a break, Megan.'

She couldn't help but smile drily. 'You're saying your offer is purely altruistic?' she queried, and he laughed ruefully.

'No, but if I promise to keep my hands to myself will you come?' he argued persuasively, making her hesitate.

She knew she shouldn't. Lucas was dangerous, and she was far too susceptible, and yet... 'Well...'

'Come on, Red, you know you want to,' he urged as they emerged from the trees into the sunlight.

She turned her face up to it, realising she hadn't seen more than the inside of the office for weeks. Lord knew he was right, and she needed the break, so why not?

'All right, I'll come,' she said swiftly, before she could change her mind, and hoped she wouldn't live to regret it.

Lucas glanced at his watch. 'Fine. I've got to sail the boat back before the tide changes, so why don't you drive back to the house and change into something more summery? I'll meet you back there as soon as I can, OK?'

'What about lunch?' she asked. She had skipped breakfast because of the appointment, and was already feeling the pangs of hunger. Lucas waved that away.

'That's taken care of. Jack's manning the barbecue. They'll be expecting us about half past one,' he declared, and with a wave of his hand he set off back the way they had come.

Megan stared after him, worrying at her lip, wondering if she was being wise. She couldn't remember ever feeling this churned up inside. So embattled by the conflicting emotions inside her. Probably because there had never been any conflict before Lucas. She had no experience to go on; all she could seem to do was stagger from one emotional upheaval to another, hoping to survive intact. Maybe putting herself in the way of another upset wasn't the wisest thing she had ever done, but it was too late now. Whatever happened, she would have to live with it.

CHAPTER SIX

JACK AND PEGGY LAKER lived in a thatched cottage which had roses climbing the walls and was surrounded by a sprawling cottage garden awash with colour and scents. Peggy, a pretty woman in her late twenties, came to meet them as they drove up. Lucas waved to her as he came round to help Megan out of the car.

'What have you done with them, Peg? Tied them to a tree somewhere?' he asked, grinning, and the woman laughed.

'What, and spoil their treat? I haven't been able to keep them still since they heard you were coming.' A yell split the air just then, and Peggy rolled her eyes. 'Here come the little darlings now,' she said, with despairing fondness.

Megan, as amused as she was confused, turned in time to see two miniature tornadoes tear round the side of the cottage and hurtle themselves at Lucas. He fielded them with a roar, swinging them up and round to cries of 'Uncle Lucas! Uncle Lucas!'

Transfixed, Megan watched as the five-year-old twin boys gripped Lucas around the neck with unbridled affection. An affection which was fully returned, judging by the grin on his face. He looked so right with them, so natural, she thought.

'He'll make a wonderful father,' Peggy observed from beside her, glancing speculatively from Megan to Lucas and back.

Megan found that her throat had become so tight, it was hard to speak. 'He adores them,' she said huskily.

'They adore him,' Peggy added softly, watching as Lucas lowered her sons to the ground and allowed himself to be dragged off. He cast an apologetic grin over his shoulder as he went. 'They'll be all over him, and he'll love every minute of it. Sometimes I think he's just a big kid himself. By the way, in case you hadn't realised, I'm Peggy. The terrors are Martin and Michael. And you must be Megan. Lucas has told us all about you.'

'He has?' Megan exclaimed in surprise.

Peggy quickly slipped her arm through Megan's and urged her to follow the path Lucas and the boys had taken. 'Don't worry, it was nothing bad. He's very fond of you, you know. You're as lovely as he said you were, and I don't doubt just as wonderfully talented. You design boats, I'm told. I'm hopeless at drawing myself, but Lucas says your designs are amongst the best he's seen.'

'High praise indeed,' Megan murmured drily, whilst inside she felt warmth spreading through her at the idea of Lucas speaking well of her to his friends. However, what brought colour to her cheeks was the uneasy feeling that Peggy was putting a vastly different interpretation on her being here with Lucas, and she hastened to put her right. 'He always did give credit where it was due, but it's not personal.'

'Hmm, that's exactly what he said too,' Peggy remarked with amused satisfaction. 'Now, let's see what mischief they've got up to, and I'll introduce you to Jack at the same time.'

Megan allowed herself to be led off, knowing that Peggy had only been more convinced by the denial that there was anything between herself and Lucas. She wondered what the woman would say if she explained that all Lucas wanted to do was get her into bed. Not that she would say anything of the sort. Let Peggy imagine what she liked; she would have to change her mind when nothing came of it.

Her husband, Jack, turned out to be a man of Lucas's age, stockier, with rounded features and a jolly personality. He took his attention from the barbecue to greet Megan warmly and press a glass of something deliciously fruity into her hand.

'I hope you're hungry. Peg has laid on enough food to feed a small army,' he teased his wife, who poked her tongue out at him then excused herself to go and prepare the salads.

Having had her offer of help refused, Megan found her eyes drawn irresistibly to where Lucas was engaging in a rowdy game of football with the irrepressibly giggling twins. A smile curled the corners of her lips.

Following her gaze, Jack grinned. 'You like children, Megan?'

Painful fingers tightened about her heart, but her voice was soft. 'Oh, yes.' There had been a brief time when she couldn't stand the pain of being with her friends and their families, but that had passed. Now, although there were some things she still would not do, she took pleasure in watching the children grow, closing off her mind to her own emptiness.

'Good,' Jack pronounced, turning back to his sausages. 'Lucas is crazy about them.'

Megan caught her breath as once again she got the un-spoken message that the friendly couple thought she and Lucas were an item. What on earth had Lucas been saying to give them that impression? As soon as she could she would ask him, and get him to put the record straight. For now all she could do was shrug off the friendly teasing.

'Have you known Lucas long?' she asked, sipping at the refreshing drink.

'Since university, although I've only been working for

him for five years. We used to live in London, but neither
of us wanted to raise the children there. We didn't think
we could do anything about it, though, because I didn't
want to leave the company. It was Lucas who came up
with the ideal solution. He suggested I work from home,
and…here we are. It's all worked out perfectly,' Jack informed her as he removed the cooked food from the griddle
and refilled it.

Her eyebrows rose. Not many employers would be so
thoughtful, even for friends. 'He must be unique.'

Jack wiped his hands on the apron he was wearing and
came to join her. 'He is that. To look at him now, you'd
never guess he was the head of a multi-million-dollar company, would you?'

As if to illustrate the claim, Lucas collapsed onto the
lawn and the boys piled on top of him. Megan laughed as
they bounced and he groaned. Then the strangest thing happened. It was as if the earth shifted under her feet, as in
her mind she saw the same picture with different players.
Lucas was there, and the boys, but she was there too. They
were a family, and there was so much happiness in the
shared laughter, she could scarcely breathe.

Her heart lurched, and the scene vanished, leaving behind a sense of loss so sharp that she wanted to cry out.
Pain seemed to fill every part of her, and her fingers tightened around her glass so tightly that the slender shaft
snapped, cutting into her palm. With a gasp of shock she
stared at the welling blood as the pieces of glass dropped
to shatter on the patio with the noise of a thunderclap.

'Don't move,' Jack ordered as he grabbed up a napkin
from the table and pressed it to the wound.

'I'm so sorry,' Megan apologised thickly, feeling colour
come and go in her cheeks. Nothing like that had ever
happened to her before.

'It was just an accident,' Jack said easily, moving her

away from the slivers of glass at her feet as Lucas and the boys rushed up.

'What happened?' Lucas's sharp question made her glance up to find him frowning down at her in concern.

'Her glass broke,' his friend answered for her. Seeing his sons hovering anxiously in the background, he smiled at them reassuringly. 'Go and ask Mummy for the dustpan and brush, boys.'

Lucas took her hand from Jack's. 'I'll see to this. You'd better stay and make sure the food doesn't end up as a casualty too,' he said tersely, already steering Megan towards the house.

'Is she going to faint?' Michael wanted to know, walking beside them as his brother ran on ahead.

'I hope not,' Megan answered raggedly, feeling rather light-headed.

'Your face went all funny,' he went on seriously. 'Mummy faints when she cuts herself.'

'Poor Mummy.'

Michael shrugged. 'She's OK when Daddy kisses her better. Are you going to kiss her better, Uncle Lucas?'

Megan's heart leapt into her throat and she glanced up into Lucas's amused blue eyes. 'Do you think I should?' he asked the boy without looking away.

'Yeah,' Martin declared firmly. 'Mummy likes being kissed.'

'That settles it, then,' Lucas murmured, and opened the door to the downstairs cloakroom. Megan found herself hustled inside and made to sit on the toilet seat. Seconds later Peggy arrived.

'First-aid box,' she said, handing it over, and Lucas balanced it on the cistern. 'Go and help Daddy, Michael. Tell him I'll be there in a minute. Don't touch anything, and don't run off!' she called to his retreating back. 'How is it?'

'Fortunately it hasn't gone too deep. A plaster should do it,' Lucas assured her, holding Megan's hand under the cold-water tap.

'Thank goodness. I'll leave her in your capable hands, then,' Peggy decided, and gave Megan a sympathetic smile before vanishing.

Megan winced as he probed the cut for any fragments of glass. 'I feel like a sideshow at the circus!' she exclaimed fretfully.

'What do you expect if you will go in for these sort of dramatics?' Lucas challenged gruffly. 'How did you manage to do it?'

I had a vision of myself as part of a family, and the sky fell in, she said silently. 'I don't know.'

'Well, you were lucky you didn't do any serious damage. You'll live, though I don't think my heart can take too many shocks like that. You looked as if you'd been mortally wounded.'

It had felt as if she had. She had thought herself long past such emotional reactions, but that had been as sharp as in the early days. 'I didn't mean to shock you.'

Lucas studied the job he had done bandaging the wound. 'In future consider my constitution and check with me before you take up anything dangerous like knife-juggling, OK?' he ordered wryly, and she smiled faintly.

'You never used to be so worried about me. I was just a pest.'

'You're still a pest, Red. However, sometimes things change and take us by surprise. How's that?'

Now that the shock had worn off, Megan was very much aware of their closeness in the tiny room. 'Much better, thanks.'

'Now all I have to do is kiss you better,' Lucas pronounced softly, and when she automatically looked up he swiftly took her lips in a kiss that was as shattering as it was brief. It was so tender, it brought a lump to her throat, then he drew back, holding her gaze. 'Better?'

'Better' didn't come nearly close to describing her feelings. She cleared her throat, vaguely aware that she should break the spell which held them, but finding it strangely impossible. 'You're supposed to kiss the wound, not me.'

He half smiled, right down into her soul. 'Does that mean you didn't like it?'

Oh, she'd liked it all right. Far too much for safety. Her lips tingled, wanting more. This was getting out of hand. She had to put a stop to it before she closed the space between them, as every nerve she possessed was urging her to do.

Swallowing hard, she dragged her gaze free. 'I think we should go and join the others now.'

'You're right. This is neither the time nor the place,' Lucas agreed huskily, stepping back.

The small space this created between them allowed her brain to start working again. 'There will never be a right time or place.'

'There will be, and when we find it you won't be running away, Red,' he stated with such conviction that she shivered.

She said nothing, knowing words would not do. She would have to show him by her actions how wrong he was. Turning away, she walked back outside to where the others waited for them, Lucas a step behind her.

'We were about to send out a search party!' Jack called, and Megan was once more uncomfortably aware that both husband and wife were watching them with unfeigned speculation.

'What have you been saying to them?' she hissed at him as they crossed to the picnic table the boys already occupied. 'They think we're a couple!'

'We are,' Lucas observed calmly.

'Not in the way they mean! You must have said something.'

Lucas sighed. 'I told them who you were and what you did. I'm not responsible for any conclusion they might have jumped to. They wish the best for me and obviously like you. To them it's a natural progression.'

She could see that, but it hardly helped. 'You'll have to tell them they're wrong,' she insisted, and watched his eyebrows lift.

'I could, but they'll only be more convinced. You and I give off sparks, Red. They'll never believe we're indifferent to each other.'

'But there has to be a way,' she groaned.

Lucas's smile faded from his eyes. 'There is. We could tell them all we want to do is jump into bed with each other. However, I prefer not to shatter their romantic notions. If you insist, you'll have to do it yourself,' he said frostily, walking past her to go and throw an arm around Peggy and say something which made her laugh.

Megan was left to take her seat, knowing she had deserved his scorn. Knowing, too, that she could not do what he'd suggested. It might be true, but she'd rather nobody else knew just how basic their attraction was. Besides, for one afternoon it wouldn't hurt. She wasn't abandoning her position, just redefining the lines.

It was a wonderful meal, and Megan found herself relaxing although she hadn't thought she would. Lucas acted as if nothing had happened, but she was aware of the coolness in his eyes when he looked her way. Strangely enough, when she should have been welcoming it, she found herself regretting having put it there. She concentrated on the boys, listening to their tales of mischief and mayhem. By the time they began clearing up, the twins had wormed their way into her heart, and there was no getting them out.

Afterwards, the boys insisted on a game of cricket, and

for the next hour she found herself caught up in the wildest game she could ever remember playing. She called a halt then, collapsing onto a lounger. Not long afterwards, Peggy joined her, and they watched the game proceed without them.

'It's been nice having you here, Megan. It's good to see Lucas so relaxed,' Peggy remarked after a while. 'He worked so hard to get the company recognised worldwide, he forgot to take time off for himself.'

Megan watched Lucas allow himself to get run out by Martin. 'He's making up for it now with all the women he takes out,' she drawled with an unconscious edge to her voice which Peggy recognised.

'He plays hard, I know, but from the moment he finds the right woman you won't see him with any other. You can take my word for it!' Peggy declared forthrightly, and Megan had to smile.

The other woman was trying to reassure her that she had nothing to worry about, and Megan couldn't utter the words to refute it. Lucas was lucky to have such a loyal champion. 'I believe you, Peggy,' was all she said, and found her hand being squeezed before Peggy glanced at her watch and scrambled to her feet.

'I'll be back in a moment,' she excused herself, hurrying indoors.

Megan sighed and closed her eyes. It was warm, she had been well fed, and knew herself to be amongst friends. For the first time in ages she felt truly at ease. She sank a little lower on the chair, and must have drifted off, because some time later a sharp cry jerked her back to consciousness.

'Uh-oh,' Peggy groaned from beside her. 'Here, hold Annie for me, Megan. I'd better go and see who's hurt.'

Before Megan fully comprehended what was going on, a warm bundle had been placed in her arms and Peggy was trotting off across the grass. The bundle gurgled, and she found herself blinking down into the warm brown eyes of a tiny baby girl. Shock sent her rigid. Everything within her cried out, No! The one thing she had never been able to bring herself to do was hold a baby in her arms. It was a defence mechanism. As long as she'd kept her distance from those tiny scraps of life, she'd known she would be safe from the pain. And now here, suddenly, the very worst had happened.

She wanted to run, but there was no strength in her legs. She was totally disarmed by the tiny, trusting form. Horror made her heart race sickeningly. Then Annie smiled up at her, and deep inside her something cracked wide open. She gasped back a sob, and a tiny hand stretched out towards her face. With a strangled sound Megan found herself lifting her own trembling hand to take the smaller one, feeling her heart clench as those sausage-like fingers instantly clamped about one of hers.

Oh, dear God.

She closed her eyes and lowered her head until her cheek was gently touching the velvety one. Breathing was painful, but with it came the warm baby scents she had tried so hard to block out. It devastated her, and at the same time filled her with such aching tenderness that she felt she might explode with all the emotions going through her. Yet she didn't. Somewhere amongst it all came a deep sense of peace, and she opened her eyes, staring wonderingly at the little girl. Very slowly, she smiled.

She was so beautiful, so perfect. Eyes glittering like emeralds, Megan raised each tiny hand to her lips and kissed it gently, whilst Annie looked at her solemnly, as if she realised this was a momentous occasion for the woman who held her. All Megan's defences fell away like so many dried leaves in autumn as she stroked Annie's downy hair. She knew now that by locking her heart away she had hurt herself far more than anyone else could. She loved babies, and denying it because she wouldn't have any of her own only increased the pain.

A simple act had freed her from that torture, and she accepted the freedom gladly, drowning in a wealth of sensations, until she had to rise up and take a breath, and found herself speared on the end of an electric blue gaze. Lucas was no more than a yard or two away, standing so still, it was as if he had been afraid to move. A shock went through her at the strange expression on his face, and then he smiled and she found herself smiling back.

'Are the boys OK?' she asked, her voice sounding as rusty as if it hadn't been used in years rather than minutes.

'They'll have some bruises tomorrow, but that's par for the course for them,' he reported, coming to sit on the lounger Peggy had abandoned. 'Do you want me to take her?'

Megan glanced down at the little girl who was happily gumming her own fist. 'No, I…I think I'd like to hold her for a while, if that's OK?'

Lucas breathed in audibly, raising an eyebrow at Peggy and the family, who had come to join them. 'Sure. Take as long as you like,' he agreed, when the baby's mother nodded.

'When she starts becoming a nuisance you can give her back to me,' Peggy added for good measure, exchanging meaningful looks with her husband. As one they moved away towards the house.

'Mummy, why is Aunty Megan crying?' Michael's piercing treble piped up, and Peggy groaned.

'Oh, Michael! If I didn't love you so much, I would have drowned you at birth!' she exclaimed, dragging her son away to shut him up with ice cream.

For her part, Megan raised a hand to her cheek and felt the moisture there. She hadn't realised that silent tears had slipped from her eyes. No wonder everyone was looking at her so oddly. They must think her a complete idiot, she thought, and cast a glance Lucas's way. But he was lying back on the lounger, his eyes closed as he soaked up the sun. She relaxed again, with a sigh.

Time passed without Megan having a conscious thought. That would come, but right now she was content simply to sit and absorb the glimpse of paradise she had amazingly been allowed. Nobody disturbed her, but she was conscious of Lucas's reassuring presence beside her. She couldn't explain exactly how it made her feel, only that his being there felt so right.

Eventually Peggy came back, and Megan gave up the little girl with a pang of regret. 'She's beautiful, Peggy. I envy you,' she said huskily.

Placing her daughter in a baby chair, Peggy adjusted the shade to keep the sun off her. 'You'll have a baby of your own one day.'

The words cut with a surgeon's precision. With her defences down, Megan couldn't keep the pain from darkening her eyes. She felt emotion choke her, and abruptly jumped to her feet.

'It's awfully quiet. Where is everyone?' she asked jerkily, causing the other woman to frown at her as she straightened.

'Are you all right, Megan?' she asked in concern.

Megan was very much aware that she wasn't all right. Her insides were shaking badly, but she did her best to pull herself together. 'Of course I'm all right. Why shouldn't I be?' she challenged, with a laugh that fell away discordantly. Feeling eyes on her, she turned to find Lucas sitting up and watching her expressionlessly.

'Take it easy, Red,' he said softly.

It was an innocuous enough thing to say, yet it caused something to snap inside her. 'Don't tell me to take it easy!'

she shot back at him. 'What the hell do you know about how I feel?'

He stood up slowly, as if aware that any sudden move might make her bolt. 'You're right, I don't know. So why don't you tell me?'

She stared at him, standing there offering to listen, and the rage went out of her as quickly as it had come. He was offering her a shoulder to cry on, and his shoulders were certainly broad enough to bear anything, but she could not do it. She couldn't bear to see the pity fill his beautiful blue eyes. Pity was the one thing she could not accept from anyone. She'd carried her secret this long. She would carry it for ever.

She took a deep breath, feeling herself steadying by the second. 'There's nothing to tell. I think the accident shook me up more than I thought.'

She glanced at Peggy, who smiled and immediately stepped into the breach. 'I know what you need: a good cup of tea. Whenever I've felt a bit wobbly, a cuppa has done me the world of good.'

'I'll give you a hand,' Megan said firmly, walking away from the eyes she could feel burning into her back. When she glanced round a few seconds later, Lucas was talking to the baby. She bit her lip, sadly aware that she had made the mistake of overreacting and that Lucas was piqued enough to wonder why.

'You know if something is worrying you, Lucas really is the person to help,' Peggy remarked softly, drawing Megan's gaze.

Megan sighed tiredly. It had been an emotionally exhausting day, and a dull ache was starting up behind her eyes. 'He can't,' she denied firmly, then smiled at the other woman's troubled expression. 'No one can, Peggy. Believe me, there are just some things in this world that nobody can do anything about. Now, let's make that tea. I really can do with it, and I'd like to play with the twins a little before we go.'

'All right, Megan,' Peggy accepted reluctantly. 'But I want you to know that, even if we can't help, we can be here for you if you ever need us. You're welcome any time.'

The generous offer brought a lump to her throat. 'I might just take you up on it one day,' Megan responded, and that was the last either of them said on the subject.

They stayed for tea and scones, then Lucas declared that they really had to go. In the end, Megan was sorry to leave, for despite everything she had enjoyed the afternoon. The whole family saw them off, and she waved until they turned a bend in the road and the cottage was lost to view. She sank back into her seat then, aware that the nagging headache had increased its tempo. She hoped it wasn't going to develop into a full-blown migraine. She got them occasionally, usually brought on by stress, and the afternoon had been nothing if not stressful in parts.

Lucas concentrated on his driving, and it wasn't until they were almost home that he finally chose to break his self-imposed silence.

'You aren't going to tell me why Aunty Megan was crying, are you?' he asked idly, sending alarm shooting through her system.

She tensed, wondering where this was leading. 'No.' Out of the corner of her eye, she saw his lips twist wryly.

'I thought not. In fact, you aren't going to answer any questions, are you?'

Her own lips curved. 'That would rather depend on the question,' she replied evasively.

'Mmm, so if I was to ask you if you enjoyed yourself you would say…?'

'I enjoyed myself very much. They're a nice family,' Megan declared without hesitation.

Lucas shot her a considering look. 'But if I were to ask you why Annie made you look as if the world had come to an end...?'

The amusement left her as she realised just how much he had seen. 'I would say you were imagining things.'

'And can we please drop the subject, right?' Lucas added drily. 'OK, let me put it another way. For a woman who professes not to possess a maternal instinct, you held that baby as if she was the most precious thing you had ever seen.'

Megan swallowed to moisten a suddenly dry throat. Lord, just how much had she given away? 'Maternal instinct has nothing to do with it. I was afraid of dropping her.'

They reached the house and he pulled the car into the drive, switching off the engine, leaving them in sudden silence. 'You're lying, Red.'

Though she reached for the door-lock, she knew she had to say something. 'Why would I lie?'

Lucas turned in his seat to stare at her broodingly. 'That's just it—I don't know. But every instinct I have tells me you are. There's something you're not telling me.'

Megan welcomed the spurt of anger that that roused in her. 'You're forgetting something, Lucas. Lying or not, there's no reason for me to tell you anything. You don't own me. I'm not accountable to you.'

'Nevertheless, you will tell me.'

She caught her breath. 'Because you say so? I don't think so!' she shot back, thrusting open the door and climbing out.

Lucas moved just as swiftly, and faced her over the car roof. 'What are you afraid of?'

Megan sighed, dragging her hands through her hair as if that might ease the growing tension beneath her scalp. 'Let it go, Lucas. Sometimes the best thing you can do is walk away. So please, if you think anything of me at all, then just let it be.'

He looked grim suddenly. 'And if I won't?'

'Then damn you!' she said tautly, and turned her back on him, going inside and up to her room. The house was stuffy from being shut up all day and she threw her bedroom windows wide to catch what breeze there was.

She tried lying down, but she was too tense to rest, even though she knew it would be good for her. So much had happened in such a short space of time that she felt as battered as a punching-bag. She wished she had handled everything better, but she could never have anticipated Annie, and the emotional trauma she would produce. However tempted she might be to confide in someone, she knew she wouldn't, for no amount of sympathy could help her.

Restlessly she moved about the room, wondering what Lucas was doing. She wanted to avoid him until she had made the necessary repairs to her stricken defences. He was too astute, and that, she thought, with a wry smile, did frighten her. She didn't know why he couldn't leave her alone, but knew he saw her as a mystery he wanted to solve. It didn't occur to him that the mystery which intrigued him was anguish for her. He would keep on digging away until he had solved it to his satisfaction, leaving her to deal with the mess he left behind.

Only it wasn't going to be that way if she could help it, she decided as she changed into jeans and a shirt. She couldn't rest, so she might as well go down to the yard and do some work. Work had been the ultimate panacea in the early days, the only thing which took her mind off her troubles, and it was no less true now. Catching up her bag, she went downstairs again. She didn't know where Lucas had got to, but she saw no sign of him on her way out to her car and was grateful.

The yard was deserted when she unlocked the gate and

walked in. Ted had gone home ages ago. She usually didn't mind the quiet, finding it soothing, like her work. Only this time it proved to be different. She climbed onto her stool and picked up her pencil, following the lines she had drawn with a knowing eye. This was her baby, her brainchild, and it would be flawless. Totally without blemish.

She didn't know she was crying until a teardrop landed on the paper. Others followed, and her breath caught on a racking sob. Unable to stop, she dropped the pencil and buried her head in her hands, crying as if her heart would break, knowing that it already had. Virtually blinded, she stumbled to the nearby couch and collapsed onto it, knowing these tears had been eight long years in coming. She had never cried. She had made her decision, abandoning her dreams, and never once mourned the loss of what had been a vital part of her. This afternoon, holding Annie had torn open the shields she had locked her heart behind, and she cried out all the bottled-up anger and pain.

How long she cried she didn't know, and afterwards she fell into an exhausted sleep. What eventually stirred her was the piercing pain in her head. She recognised it at once for what it was: the migraine she had suspected. The emotional trauma, followed by a long-overdue bout of crying, had brought about the thing she had hoped to avoid. She needed her medication, but it was back at the house. Yet she had to try and get there, for if she didn't the pain would be all the worse.

Groaning, she pushed herself into a sitting position, breathing deeply to combat the rising nausea, closing her eyes as the room spun and shafts of pain lanced into her from the light hitting her eyes.

She knew then that she had left it too late. There was no way she could drive like this. That only left the telephone. She doubted if Daniel would be in, but Lucas had been at the house, and though she would rather not call him she wasn't stupid enough to suffer pain out of sheer pride. With a superhuman effort she somehow got to her feet, but the floor had become like jelly, bouncing under her. She managed two steps before her knees buckled and she crumpled to the floor.

She groaned again, longing for her bed and the dark, and as she lay there gathering her strength to try again she thought she heard her name being called. Freezing, she listened intently, and sure enough there it was again, followed by the sound of footsteps.

'Megan?'

It was Lucas. She didn't know what had brought him here, but right now all she cared about was that help was at hand. 'In here,' she called croakily, and seconds later he was there in the room.

'Megan?' His voice was sharp with concern. 'What happened? Are you hurt?' he demanded, dropping to his knees and bending to turn her gently over.

Megan went rigid, the breath hissing through her teeth as she pressed a hand to her temple. 'Migraine,' she bit out, sighing faintly when Lucas put his palm on her forehead as it felt blessedly cool.

'I thought you'd been attacked,' he growled fiercely, not missing the signs of the tears she had shed. Whether they were the result of the pain or the cause of it he couldn't tell. 'Do you have something you can take?'

'Tablets. Up at the house,' she informed him shortly, and in the next instant she felt herself being lifted then placed back on the couch.

'Right, I'll go and get them.'

'No. Wait!' Megan halted him. 'I'll come with you. I left my car round the back,' she said, getting to her feet by dint of holding onto the arm, and standing swaying even then.

Lucas's eyes narrowed. 'You're not driving like this. You'll wrap yourself round a tree!'

She glared at him through her agony. 'I'm not that stupid! You can drive—just stop wasting time,' she ordered.

'Gracious to the last!' he drawled mockingly.

She knew she had been rude, but the pain was increasing by leaps and bounds. When she looked at him, her eyes revealed the fact. 'Just get me up to the house, Lucas, please,' she gasped.

He didn't hesitate. 'Stay there; I'll bring the car round,' he ordered, and left her propped against the wall.

Licking her lips, Megan waited until he was gone then made her way unsteadily to her desk, picking up her bag and the office keys. By the time Lucas swung her car to a halt in front of the office, Megan had locked up and was leaning against the doorframe.

'I told you to stay where you were,' he reminded her as he climbed out, swung her up into his arms and carried her to the car. 'Don't you ever obey orders?'

'No,' she retorted, but sank into the seat with a sigh of relief.

'You're more trouble than you're worth. The next time you fall down I might not pick you up,' he warned, but she could hear the concern in his voice and was warmed by it. He joined her and set the car in motion again. 'Which could be any time. You aren't seeing yourself from my point of view!'

'Bad, hmm?' she asked, resting her head on the back of the seat and wincing at the tiniest bump.

'I've seen corpses with more colour!' he said drolly, keeping one eye on the road and the other on her. 'Does this happen often?'

'No.' Thank goodness, she added silently. 'Put it down to all the stress and strain I've been suffering lately.'

'Hmm,' Lucas mused. 'I saw you'd been crying. When you're feeling better, I really think we should talk, Red,' he added gently but firmly.

She didn't have the energy to fight him, and sighed with relief as they drew up before the house, making an answer unnecessary. She didn't protest when he carried her indoors. His arms about her were so strong and protective that strange things were happening inside her. She wished she felt well enough to appreciate it better. Then pain closed in again, and she closed her eyes on a groan as he began to mount the stairs. She wasn't exactly thistledown, yet he wasn't even breathing hard.

'You're very strong,' Megan murmured huskily. 'You make me feel very safe,' she added, not really aware of what she was saying, simply talking to distract herself.

Lucas let out a snort of laughter. 'You sure do pick your moments, Red.'

'I don't know what you mean,' she muttered, aware that he held her fractionally closer.

'I mean you're the most luscious bundle I've carried upstairs for a long time, and I'm taking you to your bedroom. It isn't the time for you to start flirting with me.'

She thought he sounded amused. 'Is that what I was doing?'

'Tell me again when you're feeling better and we'll take it from there,' Lucas advised, nudging open her bedroom door. Walking to the bed, he laid her down gently on the covers. 'Where are the pills, Megan?'

She winced as she lifted her head and pointed to the drawer of her bedside table. Seconds later Lucas held the bottle. Reading the label, he shook out the correct dosage and went to get a glass of water from the bathroom. With an arm steadying her shoulders, he helped her swallow the medication before easing her back onto the pillow.

Megan watched him cross to the windows and pull the curtains, sighing with relief as the light was dimmed and the pain in her eyes eased fractionally. It occurred to her then that he had turned up in the nick of time, yet he couldn't have known she was in trouble. 'Why did you come to the yard?'

'I was looking for you. I thought you might be upset, and I wanted to apologise. When I couldn't find you in the house, I tried the yard.'

She sighed heavily. 'You don't have to worry about me, Lucas. I can take care of myself.'

'I noticed,' he countered drily, coming back to the bed. 'I can't help worrying about you, Red. I think it's about time somebody did. Now, let's get these clothes off you. You'll feel better in bed.'

Megan knew she would, but the idea of Lucas removing her clothes sent the blood pounding through her head in alarm. She struggled to sit up. 'I can do it,' she argued, but Lucas pushed her back down.

'It will be quicker if I do it. Stop arguing for once, Red, and allow someone to help you,' he ordered shortly, and made quick work of removing her outer clothes. Then, when she was clad only in the skimpiest of underwear, he shifted her so that he could pull the duvet out from under her and replace it over her trembling body.

'Better?' he asked softly.

Megan was glad of the gloom, for it hid the heat in her cheeks. He had been totally impersonal, so there should have been no reason for her to be trembling, yet she was, and the pain in her head had nothing to do with it. 'Yes. Thank you.' The words were slightly slurred as the powerful painkillers began to take effect.

'Go to sleep, Megan. I'll look in on you later,' he promised, and as he headed for the door her eyes were already closing.

Lucas didn't leave, only made sure the door was shut before pulling her chair up beside the bed and sitting down. His eyes remained broodingly on her face, seeing the pain she was suffering, and beyond it a sadness that she probably wasn't even aware of.

He knew he had made the mistake of taking her at face value, seeing only the pest of a kid he had grown up with. Yet he realised now that she was a mass of contradictions. On the one hand she was cold, on the other incredibly passionate. Outwardly she gave the impression of being a woman in control of her life, and yet today she had looked so vulnerable that his heart had very nearly stopped. Nothing about Megan Terrell was as it should be, and he wanted to get to the bottom of it. No, *needed* to get to the bottom of it. He hadn't realised how desperately he wanted her to trust him, to confide in him, until she'd absolutely refused to.

Sighing, he stretched out his long legs, prepared to stay and watch over her. As he had told her, somebody had to, because beneath that iron veneer she was a vulnerable woman, and he wanted to protect her. He was surprised by just how much he wanted that, but he knew himself well enough to go with it. Something told him that the rewards would be worth the trouble.

CHAPTER SEVEN

MEGAN STIRRED, slowly drifting towards wakefulness, and as she did so two things registered in her fuzzy brain. Her pillow had grown hard and her head was still thumping. Usually the tablets knocked her out, so that when she woke the pain had gone, leaving her feeling hungover but recovering. This was different, and, frowning, she opened her eyes carefully, prepared to shut them quickly if the light hurt. Instead, what she saw had them widening. The reason her pillow was hard was because it had metamorphosed into Lucas's chest. The thumping she could hear was not her headache but the regular beat of his heart.

Shock rocketed through her. She couldn't imagine how Lucas—a virtually naked Lucas, her equally naked limbs were telling her—had come to be in her bed. Neither did she know how she had come to curl herself up against him so trustingly. Yet she had, and as her senses began to operate she peeped beneath the covers, and was relieved to find that they were both wearing underwear, even if it did nothing to disguise the shape and feel of the body underneath. Awareness set her nerve-ends tingling like crazy, sending messages to her brain which started a sensual glow inside her.

She knew she ought to move, for the position was extremely compromising, but the warmth and scent of him urged her to linger and savour a moment which would not come again. The temptation to run her hand over the smooth, taut flesh of his belly was strong, and she was fighting a losing battle when, from above her head, she heard Lucas sigh. Instantly she attempted to wriggle away to the safety of the edge of the bed, but a strong arm snaked up around her waist to prevent her.

Megan lost her breath, and barely had time to look up into glittering blue eyes before she was held against him, his lips brushing the warm flesh of her shoulder to devastating effect. She had to bite down hard on her lip to withhold a tiny moan.

'Mmm, you taste nice,' Lucas murmured drowsily, his free hand coming to rest on the curve of her hip. 'You're warm and soft, too. I think I like waking up like this,' he groaned, and her pulse rate shot off the scale.

It was stomach-twisting to realise that she liked it too. The outside world seemed a million miles away, this closeness the only reality. In the darkness before dawn, nothing else seemed to matter.

'How's the head?' he enquired softly, brushing his lips against her temple, and even as she shivered faintly in response his words brought her down to earth.

'It's fine,' Megan replied in a voice which was supposed to be cool, but sounded anything but. 'Lucas, I don't know how we came to be here like this, but you have to go,' she ordered shakily, pushing away enough to be able to see his face.

He was smiling faintly. 'We're here like this, Red, precisely because last night you refused to let me go,' he informed her shockingly.

Her lips parted in a gasp. 'I couldn't have!' she protested, even as the tiniest sliver of a memory fluttered in and out of her mind.

Lucas raised his hand and stroked her hair from her face. 'You don't remember asking me to stay? You told me you didn't want to be alone any more.'

Those last two words speared her heart, they were so

revealing. Dear Lord, what else had she said and done? 'I—' Her throat closed over.

He hushed her with a finger on her lips. 'It's OK. You wanted comfort, Red, and I was happy to give it. Where's the harm in that?'

Her lashes dropped. The harm was in knowing it was pointless to want things like this. To take comfort now would only make the loss sharper later on. And yet something inside her cried out for human warmth.

'It's wrong,' she muttered gruffly, trying to convince herself more than him.

Lucas only held her closer, his hand gliding gently down her spine. 'How can it be wrong?' he growled throatily. 'It sure as hell feels right to me. I want you here, and this is where you want to be too, don't you?'

She did, God help her, because it felt more than right. Yet it went against every rule she had made. Rules designed to save her sanity in a world gone suddenly mad. What price anything if she broke them now?

'You have to go!' she insisted breathlessly, feeling the heat coming from him turning her bones to water.

Lucas raised his head at that, and she found herself staring heart-stoppingly into fathomless blue eyes. 'And if I won't?' he countered, his voice a gravelly whisper which teased its way along her nerves.

Prickly heat broke out all over her flesh. 'Lucas, please!' she protested, only to watch as a beautifully lazy smile spread across his lips before he bent down to nuzzle the velvety skin of her neck. She forgot to breathe.

'I long to please you, darling. Just tell me what you want me to do,' he declared seductively, and she took a gasping breath as her senses came perilously close to rioting. She had to get away, or...

Instinctively her hands rose to push him away, but only came into contact with warm male flesh. Her breath caught in her throat as a dozen messages were transmitted to her brain, none of them sane, and she closed her eyes in desperation. But that only served to magnify the sensations which his exploring lips were producing. He was tracing a path up to her ear, sending shivers down her spine, turning up a heat that made her insides begin to melt. And she wanted to melt so badly that she knew that if she didn't stop him her already shaky defences would crumble into dust.

With an almost audible groan she made herself fight on. 'S-stop it, Lucas.'

He raised his head, but didn't release her. The sensual curve of his lips so tantalisingly close to hers was a refinement of torture. 'We have to finish this, Red, you know that.'

Her heart lurched and her eyes locked with his. 'It should never have begun,' she groaned, curling her hands into fists to prevent them from spreading across the strong planes of his shoulders.

Lucas shook his head, dipping it to kiss the corner of her lips before lifting it again to study the result of his foray with a brooding intensity. 'Maybe, but it's gone too far for us to go back. We want each other, Red. When I look at you my heart pounds and my stomach twists into knots. I ache for the warmth of you, and I know you feel the same.' He paused to trace one finger over the trembling fullness of her bottom lip. 'Why deny ourselves what we both need?'

Megan's heart pounded. Would it be so wrong? He was right, she wanted him, so why deny herself when she didn't have to? A brief affair with Lucas wouldn't hurt him because he did not want a commitment with her. It would not be like before. No way would it be the same because she wanted Lucas with a passion she hadn't known she possessed. There was nothing to hold her back except her scruples, and they had suddenly become redundant. For once in her life, she could let her defences drop without fear of the consequences. It was more than she'd ever expected, and she knew she would always regret it if she didn't reach out and grasp this moment with both hands.

Her head swam with the sense of freedom. Every breath she took dragged in the scent of him, heightening her senses. Her gaze dropped to his tanned torso, and she trembled like a leaf in the wind as need rippled through her. She wanted to press her lips to his heated flesh and taste him, know him, to assuage a burning craving to absorb him into her.

'Do it,' Lucas urged softly, and her nerves jolted violently.

'What?' she croaked back. Was he a mind-reader too?

'Touch me. Do anything you like,' he invited. When she hesitated, he raised her chin with his thumb. 'I want you to touch me, Red,' he insisted in a thickened tone. 'Don't you know I've been aching for you to?' he breathed, and lowered his head again.

It was like drowning, and Megan was going down for the third time. His kiss was a piercingly sweet persuasion against which she quickly discovered she had no defence. His lips enticed her to join him, to share in sensations so exquisite that she couldn't withhold the whimper of pleasure which escaped her tight throat.

With a soft sigh, her arms slipped about his neck, where they had always wanted to be, and she opened to him, welcoming the deep invasion of his tongue. She expected instant passion—the flash fire which overcame them every time they touched—but Lucas had other ideas. He was holding back, using every ounce of his considerable control as he tasted her, pleasured the deepest, most sensitive recesses, and invited her tongue to mate with his in sensually silken strokes.

Megan was lost in an instant. Her one brief affair had never offered her this enchantment of the senses. She had always suspected that Lucas was a magnificent lover, but nothing could have prepared her for the reality. She gave herself up to his undoubted mastery.

Lucas abandoned her lips to trace delicate kisses over her cheeks and eyes, then on down to the arched column of her neck. Behind her closed lids, Megan was dazed by a kaleidoscopic explosion of colours. His hand was so gentle as it discovered the fragile bones of her shoulder that she scarcely felt it, and yet not one part of her remained untouched by it. She held her breath as he lifted his head and watched his fingers tracing the tender skin of her arm until he reached her hand and raised it, bringing each finger separately to his lips before pressing a final one to her palm.

'So beautiful,' he murmured softly, and lowered his lips to the scented valley between her breasts.

A groan escaped her and she felt herself burning up. Sweet heaven, but he seemed intent on driving her out of her mind! She could not lie still. Her hands rose to his hair, gliding into the silky mass and rejoicing at the way it curled around her fingers. He found the catch of her bra, and she gasped, her body turning fluid as he stripped it from her.

Her breathing turned ragged, but Lucas's control was awesome as he traversed the planes of her belly and thighs with his hands and mouth. Her hips moved instinctively as he brushed away her final covering, and she began to tremble at the sheer beauty of what he was doing to her. He kissed the backs of her knees, her instep, and she hadn't known they could be so sensitive, as he glided down one silken leg and up the other. He moved with exquisite slowness, learning her, tasting her, making her heart pound and an ache begin to throb deep inside her.

'Every inch of you is perfect,' Lucas declared as he eased away from her to remove his shorts. His hands spanned her

waist, and very slowly rose towards her breasts, which were
swollen and aching for his touch. She bit her lip when he
paused short of his goal, lifting his eyes to hers.

'Last chance, Red. If this isn't what you want, say so
and I'll stop. But, God help me, beyond this point I don't
think I'll be able to.'

Any more than she could. 'If you stop now, I think I'll
kill you, Lucas Canfield!' she groaned, and it was all the
encouragement he needed.

The passion he had held back was released in all its
magnificent glory and, catching her tightly to him, he kissed
her with aching need. The pleasure she had felt only
minutes earlier was nothing to this. Before he had touched
her as if he had found a lost treasure; now she was all
woman, and he needed her.

A cry of pleasure escaped her as this time he set about
showing her exactly how much he wanted her. Released
from the spell she had been under, Megan was free to do
the same. They couldn't get enough of each other. Hands
and lips were everywhere as they gasped and moaned by
turns, and it was a visceral pleasure to hear Lucas groan
and feel him tremble when she touched him.

She gasped when he found her breast, feeling her aching
flesh swell into the cup of his hand, her nipple hardening
into a point which thrust into his palm. His thumb moved,
rubbing back and forth until she couldn't withhold a moan
of pleasure as coils of tension twisted deep inside her. Then
his mouth replaced his hand, his tongue laving the sensi-
tised nub until finally he drew it into the moist cavern of
his mouth and suckled strongly.

As her other breast suffered the same mind-blowing torture, her own hands were exploring, tracing down his spine
until she found his buttocks and pulled him against her, her
hips moving in an age-old invitation. Then her hands
slipped between them, finding the hardness of him, running

her fingers along the velvety length until Lucas groaned and his own hand dragged hers away. All then became a glorious storm of sighs and groans as damp flesh rubbed against damp flesh. Limbs entwined until it was hard to know where one ended and the other began.

When they could take no more, Lucas moved over her, parting her thighs, entering her with a shuddering sigh which measured the scantness of his control. Megan had lost hers long ago, and her legs rose, clasping about his hips, urging him deeper, meeting his thrusts with tiny cries which rose to a crescendo as the tempo increased in the final surge.

As, with a cry, Megan was forced out over the edge, the world exploded around her. She was dizzily aware of Lucas stiffening as he too climaxed and joined her with a guttural cry, his arms holding her crushed to him. Megan clung on, feeling weightless, boneless, aware of nothing but the pleasure to be found in this one pair of arms.

When they finally returned to the heated darkness of the bed, neither had the strength to move away. She didn't mind. She loved the feel of him, and his weight was nothing. Yet from somewhere Lucas found the strength to move onto his side, easing her with him so that they still touched from head to toe.

Her hand went to his cheek, her head into the curve of his shoulder. Replete, she slept.

THE NEXT TIME Megan woke, it was light. Lucas still slept, and she lay watching him, filled with a serenity she hadn't known before. He looked younger in sleep, more rested and carefree. She was tempted to reach out and brush away a stray wisp of hair which had tumbled onto his forehead, but didn't want to disturb him.

Her heart swelled with emotion. She wanted to preserve this moment for ever, because it felt so right, so perfect.

She had no regrets. Making love with Lucas had been the most magical experience of her life. She sighed contentedly. The steady beat of Lucas's heart was reassuring, his arm curving her waist protective. A sense of peace stole over her, so profound that she realised that what she had previously taken for that emotion had been a mere shadow of reality. She experienced it now because she was, quite simply, where she had always wanted to be.

Always? The concept rocked her with all the force of a powerful explosion. Disarmed by the contentment which filled her, she found the truth breaking through the remnants of her defences and shining like purest crystal. Yes, always—for she loved him. Boundlessly. Wholeheartedly.

It was perfectly clear now why she had continually ragged Lucas about his love life. The cause had been pure, instinctive jealousy. Instinctive because although she hadn't known it she had loved him even then. Now she had the explanation of why she had felt so alive these past few days. She had fallen in love with him on sight. The sense of peace she felt now came from realising she had finally come home.

There was no place she would rather be, nobody she would rather be with. Lucas was her destiny, and she wanted to stay with him for ever. But, even as a smile curved her lips, a drop of ice was forming in her heart, rending the fabric of that peace irreparably. Reality raised its ugly head, and would not be denied.

There was no home for her with anyone, and especially not with Lucas. To him this was just a romantic interlude. Last night, in her ignorance, she had thought it was the same for her. A once-in-a-lifetime opportunity to have some memories to cherish without any risk. Now she knew differently. Her emotions were involved, and that changed everything. Cruel fingers clutched at her heart, starting up an ache which no painkiller could deaden. How blind she had been. Lucas was everything she had ever wanted.

She felt the happiness trickle out of her, draining the rainbow hues from her radiant heart until all that remained was a despairing grey. He was everything she could never have. Not for ever, and not in the short term either.

There was no way she could have an affair with him now. To go on would only be to store up pain for herself, and she had already suffered enough pain for two lifetimes. Only by breaking off now could she limit the damage, for leaving it until the end would surely devastate her. Even now she hurt so much that she wanted to cry out, and it could only grow to an intensity which would shatter her. In a lifetime of painful decisions that had diminished her bit by bit, she now had to make the one which left the future bleak and empty.

Last night had to be the beginning and the end. She closed her eyes, wishing she could put the clock back, to save herself from the awful knowledge that, for her peace of mind, last night had been far, far too much. Whilst for her heart it would never, ever be enough.

Who would have thought it would come to this? An affair with Lucas had seemed to offer a moment out of time. Something to be looked back on with fondness and no regrets. It had blown up in her face all too soon, and now she had to extricate herself from this mess she had made. She knew she was going to have to put on the act of her life. Lucas must never know she loved him. They had shared a mutual desire which last night had satisfied. That was all. Hardly a novel situation for him. He'd probably shrug it off. It certainly wouldn't break his heart.

Hers, on the other hand, was in bad shape, and if she wanted to protect it then she must not be lying there when he woke up. Finding it one of the hardest things she had ever had to do, Megan carefully slipped from beneath his arm and slid from the bed. She turned her back on him mentally and physically, gathering up fresh clothes and shoes and hastening into the bathroom. She was determined not to cry, because that served no purpose. She knew what she had to do, so she must grit her teeth and get on with it.

She showered quickly, afraid that the noise might stir him, and once dressed she let herself back into the bedroom. Lucas hadn't moved, and with her heart in her eyes she allowed herself one last look.

She stepped closer to the sleeping form. Something inside her felt ready to burst. She had to say it, just once. Her voice was the merest breath of a whisper. 'I love you, Lucas. God help me, but I do. I...' Her throat closed over, and she pressed trembling lips together, turning away and slipping out into the corridor before she was tempted to do something really silly, like fling herself at him.

Wretchedly near to the forbidden tears, she hurried downstairs. The thought of breakfast turned her stomach over, so she avoided the kitchen and went in search of her car. She would go to the office, even though it was Saturday. Work had always helped in the past, and it was all she had to distract her on a quiet, sunny morning. The sun was an affront. After what she had just discovered, it should have been raining. Some days things never worked out right.

A little while later, she parked next to Lucas's car where he had abandoned it in order to help her the day before. Had it only been yesterday? It felt like for ever already. She rested her forehead tiredly on the wheel. She'd tried to avoid love, fearing finding herself wanting what she knew she could not have. But love had been cleverer, creeping up on her when she wasn't looking, so that she'd found herself in the middle of it, with no way to avoid the inevitable heartache. The funny thing was, Lucas had nothing to do with it. He'd never asked her to love him. She'd brought it all on herself.

Which, while true, was no comfort at all, she decided wanly as she let herself into the yard. She went to the boat shed first, to see how Ted had been getting on. He really was a wonderful craftsman, bringing her designs to life. Yet today she found no satisfaction in the sight of the half-built craft. Her heart wasn't in it. Her heart was back at the house with a dark-haired, blue-eyed man.

She turned away with a grimace. This was getting too maudlin. She hated self-pity. It was destructive and point-less. Sighing heavily, she left the shed, and was on her way to the office to make herself a cup of coffee when the sound of a car engine made her falter. Her heart thumped as she glanced towards the entrance. Could it be Lucas already? Half of her longed to see him, whilst the other half said it was too soon; she wasn't prepared. As it turned out, it wasn't Lucas who walked through the gate moments later but a total stranger.

He appeared to be in his mid-thirties, was built like a tank, and had a nose which had been broken more than once. Megan felt a shiver of apprehension run down her spine. This was not their usual kind of customer, and some-how she didn't think he wanted to buy a boat. She watched him approach, hiding her nervousness under a polite smile.

'Good morning. Can I help you?' she asked, wishing she weren't the only one there.

The man had a good look round before answering. 'I'm looking for Danny. Is he about?'

Megan caught her breath, alarmingly aware that only Daniel's new friends called him that, but that this man did not look very friendly right now. She didn't know what was going on, but instinctively she knew she had to play it cool. 'You mean my brother, Daniel? No, he's not here.

I've no idea where he is. I haven't seen him since the day before yesterday.'

He took another look round. 'There's another car outside,' he remarked suspiciously, and Megan's heart skipped. She resisted the urge to ask him what business it was of his—he might just tell her.

'That belongs to one of my employees. Daniel's taste runs to something red and flashy. If I see him today, can I give him a message?' she offered coolly, standing her ground. The man finally nodded.

'Yeah, darlin', you can. Tell him Vince wants to see him, sharpish,' he said with a mocking laugh, and, as she caught her breath, turned on his heel and left.

Megan stared after him, feeling distinctly uneasy. When she had sought distraction, this hadn't been what she'd had in mind. That man was bad news, and as she continued on her way to the office her heart thumped. She wondered what Daniel had done now.

The coffee didn't settle her and working was a joke, when her mind was seething like a bubbling pot. She needed to know what was going on and was on the point of going to find her brother when Daniel strolled in. She fully expected him to fling himself into a free chair in his usual manner, but today he crossed to the window and stood staring fixedly out of it, the tension in him so plain, it was almost tangible. What brought a worried frown to her forehead, however, was the fact that he still wore his evening suit from the night before.

'You're up early,' he remarked casually—far too casually for her peace of mind. He was hiding something.

'And you're up late,' she returned evenly. 'I hardly seem to see you these days, Daniel. Where have you been hiding yourself?' She had chosen the words carefully, and it did nothing for her unease to see his back tense even more.

'Don't be ridiculous—I'm not hiding. What have I got

to hide from?' he countered edgily, still with his back to her. 'Besides, I've stayed out all night before,' he added, stuffing his hands into his trouser pockets and attempting to look relaxed.

'I know,' she placated him gently. 'It's merely that I just had the strangest encounter.'

'Oh, yes? Of the third kind, was it?'

He might be joking, but he was bracing himself too, and her nerves jangled. What did he think she was going to say? What had he done? 'You had a visitor. He left when you weren't here,' she said levelly, and felt her tension increase with his patent relief.

He cleared his throat quickly, turning towards her, his face a colourless mask. 'Oh, well, I dare say he'll catch up with me later.'

Megan stared at him with a sinking heart. 'That was the impression I got too. He left a message.'

At the mention of that, Daniel looked sick. 'He did?'

'He said Vince wanted to see you. I got the feeling it had better be sooner rather than later. Daniel, what's going on?'

He jumped as if she had jabbed him with a pin. 'Nothing. What gave you that idea?' he denied instantly, and she sent him an old-fashioned look.

'You've been acting like a cat on a hot coal, hardly knowing whether it's better to jump off or stay put!'

He laughed, but it was not a happy sound. 'It's just that I've a lot on my mind,' he said, and came over to her, pulling up a chair and sitting down to lean forward eagerly. 'I've had this amazing idea,' he explained. 'I've been feeling in need of a holiday, and I can't remember the last time you went away, Meg. We could go together. What do you say?' His hand came out to cover hers as it lay on the desk, squeezing it encouragingly.

Megan didn't know what to say. All she could think was

that things must be pretty bad if he was having to resort to this. 'Why now, Daniel?'

His smile was cajoling. 'Because everything's so dead here. I need some fun. We could travel around. Just think of it!'

She was, and it left her cold. She shook her head. 'No.'

He hadn't expected a refusal. 'What do you mean, no?'

Megan gently pulled her hand away. 'I mean no, I won't go on holiday with you.'

Daniel shot to his feet, kicking the chair aside angrily. 'Damn it, I was banking on you. I have to get away!'

She had guessed that much, and it was making her feel very nervous. 'Why?'

For a moment it looked as if he wasn't going to answer, then he dragged a hand through his hair. 'I owe some people some money,' he admitted flatly, and the way he said it made a chill run up her spine.

'What people?'

'Not anyone you'd know. I...borrowed some money to place a bet. All I needed was one win and I'd have been able to pay back all my debts!' he exclaimed, as if the fault hadn't been his in gambling in the first place.

Megan tried not to look as alarmed as she felt. 'I take it you lost?'

Daniel laughed raggedly. 'I asked for more time to pay, and they gave me forty-eight hours.'

It was like something out of the worst kind of B movie. 'How much do you owe?'

The amount he quoted made her feel sick. 'The bank won't help, nor any of the other sources I've tried. I've been going out of my mind trying to find a way out, and all my friends have turned their backs on me!'

It was not the time to say, I told you so, although she was tempted. 'Can't you go back to these people and explain the situation?'

'Damn it, Meg, if I go back to them without the money, they'll break my legs, or worse! I have to find some cash, and quick!'

His urgency transmitted itself to her, and she knew instinctively not to doubt it because Daniel was really scared. 'What can you do?'

'Leave the country.'

'If these people are as nasty as you say they are, they'll have long memories. If you went you could never come back,' she said, trying to think clearly but finding it hard as she'd never been in this sort of situation. 'Can't you go to the police? Say you've been threatened?'

Daniel snorted. 'Get real. There was no threat as such; besides, imagine how well that would go down with them. I'd end up as part of the next motorway!'

That wasn't even remotely funny. 'Oh, Daniel, how could you get mixed up with these people?'

'Because I needed the money! Haven't you been listening?'

His anger came from fear, and she pressed her trembling hands together in an effort to hide her own alarm. 'I am listening. I know you need help, but I can't see how I can give it to you.'

He looked up at her then, eyes hopeful. 'That's just it—you can. OK, maybe the holiday wasn't a good idea, but couldn't you use some of your inheritance to help me? I promise to pay it back.'

She bit her lip, knowing she was going to dash his hopes, but she couldn't offer what didn't exist. 'I don't have that sort of money, Daniel,' she said softly, and he frowned irritably.

'Of course you do. You inherited thousands when Dad died.'

'I know,' she agreed grimly. 'But I don't have it any more. How on earth do you imagine this place has kept running? I've been paying the bills with my own money for months now. I'm almost broke, Daniel.'

To give him his due, he looked stricken, and for once it wasn't because of his own problems. 'Good God, why didn't you tell me?' he croaked.

She sighed tiredly. 'Because you haven't been listening.'

Daniel let out a very shaky breath and combed trembling fingers through his dishevelled hair. 'Lord, I'm sorry, Meg,' he apologised, and held her eyes, his own anxious. 'All of it?'

She raised a shoulder resignedly. 'Almost.'

'God!' Daniel groaned, rubbing his hands over his sickly face. When he looked at her again, his eyes were dull. 'It started out as a joke, you know. A bit of a lark. A bet here and there. Then I went to the casino and…the next thing I knew I was hooked. Only instead of winning, I lost. I kept on losing. That's why I went to Vince. He doesn't take kindly to welshers, but I can't pay him back. It's all gone. What am I going to do?'

Megan left her chair and went to him, putting an arm about his shoulders. She could only see one solution. 'I think you should go and talk to Lucas,' she proposed, knowing that Lucas would not refuse to help his friend, but Daniel looked appalled.

'You're joking! How could I tell him what a fool I've been?'

Now he'd admitted what she had known all along! 'You'll have to decide what's more important to you, Daniel. Your pride or your life,' she declared bluntly, and saw his colour come and go.

'You don't pull your punches, do you?'

'Kindness isn't going to help you, but Lucas can. He's your friend. Talk to him, and be honest for once,' Megan urged him.

Daniel sighed, but at least when he looked at her he had

more colour. 'You're right. God, I've been an idiot, but I'll make it up to you, I promise. You know, if Lucas lends me the money, this place will have to go.'

She stared at him in dismay. 'But you can't sell Terrell's!' It was her life. What would she do without it? She would have nothing left.

Unaware of her thoughts, Daniel stood up, squaring his shoulders. 'I don't want to, but it may be the only way to pay him back, and you. I know Terrell's means a lot to you, Meg, but you're good enough to work anywhere.'

Megan swallowed hard. She wanted to protest further, but for once Daniel looked more like his old self, and she could not destroy that. 'You must do what you have to, Daniel,' she said huskily, and he gave her a half-smile.

'I'd better go and clean myself up before I see him,' Daniel decided, taking a quick inspection of his crumpled appearance.

'You do look the worse for wear,' she agreed. 'Good luck,' she added softly, and, with a wry look, Daniel took himself off.

Megan crossed to the window, flinging it wide and breathing in a lungful of the warm fresh air. She couldn't lose this place. The one part of her world she had always relied on not to let her down, no matter what else she had had to give up, had been Terrell's. It was her rock. She had given it all the passionate devotion she would have given to her own family, had things turned out differently. It had become a kind of surrogate family, and if she was asked to give that up her life would become barren once more.

Yet it was out of her hands. The whole fabric of her world was slowly crumbling around her, and all she could do was put on a brave face and pretend she didn't care. It ought to have been easy, with all the practice she had had, but it wasn't. Something told her it would never be easy again.

CHAPTER EIGHT

'I THOUGHT I'd find you here.'

Megan jumped at the sound of Lucas's voice. She was sitting on the grass in the tiny bay, lost in her own thoughts. She had locked up the yard hours ago, but hadn't wanted to go home, so she had come here for peace and quiet, and now Lucas had found her.

At once the air became electric, and all her senses sharpened, so that she could almost feel him. Intimate memories flashed into her mind, and she knew she would never be unaware of him again. She wondered how she would live with that, and yet keep it hidden. He was part of her; to deny it made her only half-alive. Yet deny it she must. She had to be strong—for her own good.

'Nice work, Sherlock,' she quipped, glancing round with a mocking smile, only to have her stomach plunge and her heart lurch wildly. Lucas was dressed in the most disreputable thigh-hugging jeans she had ever seen, whilst his shirt was unbuttoned, as if he had just slipped it on, leaving his tanned, muscular torso temptingly bare. Suddenly drymouthed, and with her hands prickling with the urge to touch his warm male flesh, she hurriedly turned her gaze back to the river, very much aware that he was crossing the ground towards her.

Sure enough, seconds later he dropped down beside her, stretching out his long legs, taking his weight on his arms. She could feel his eyes on her, but refused to look round, making a pretence of finding the river fascinating, when in fact she saw nothing at all.

'I missed you when I woke up,' he said huskily, trailing a finger down the velvety flesh of her arm. 'Why didn't you stay?'

His touch made her want to close her eyes, but she fought it. 'Sorry, but I never could lie in bed when the sun was up,' she replied coolly, hoping he couldn't hear the way her heart was hammering.

'I could have made it worth your while,' Lucas countered seductively, his fingers lingering on the pulse at her wrist, and she very nearly groaned aloud.

This was worse than she had expected. He was too good at this, and she was far, far too susceptible. She had to make him stop, and said the first thing which came into her head. 'Have you seen Daniel?' she asked, and felt the stillness in him an instant before his hand dropped away. Ridiculously she felt bereft, chilled by the withdrawal she had sought.

'No, I haven't. Should I have?' he replied in a voice which told her he had registered her mood. By now his mind would be doing rapid calculations.

She managed an offhand shrug, licking her dry lips nervously. His eyes were boring into her skull, making her heart race, and she shifted uncomfortably. 'I sent him to you.'

'For any particular purpose?' He sounded lazy, but the vibrations coming off him were anything but. She knew she couldn't avoid looking at him for ever, and steeled herself to glance round.

Her eyes were met and held by stormy blue ones. 'To ask for your help,' she enlarged faintly. He was so close, it would take only the smallest effort to reach out and touch him, to feel his warmth. Yet she couldn't give herself even that comfort.

'What's going on, Red?' he demanded softly.

'Daniel must tell you himself,' she insisted, just as Lucas reached out to brush a wisp of hair from her cheek. She froze instantly, her breath locked in her throat.

'I'm not talking about Daniel's gambling problem,' he corrected her, and she gasped.

'You know?'

He sent her an old-fashioned look. 'Of course I know. I'm neither blind nor stupid. I've always been able to tell when Dan is in trouble. A telephone call told me what other facilities the club offered, and some careful questioning did the rest. I was hoping he would come to me of his own accord. Which it appears he will, thanks to you. But that isn't what's important right now. You know what is. I want to know what's going on with us, Red.'

The confrontation she had anticipated was upon her with a vengeance, and her lashes dropped, shielding her emotions from his all too perceptive gaze. 'Nothing is going on,' she denied brittlely.

His expression grew sceptical. 'Then why did you run away?'

Because I couldn't stay, her heart answered achingly. Aloud, she set her chin determinedly. 'I didn't run away,' she said, with only the faintest quaver in her voice. 'I told you. I simply got up.'

'Even though we had made love together last night?' His voice had dropped to a lower key which worked on her senses, stirring them up, reminding her of the achingly beautiful loving they had shared.

And, because she was not proof against it, she knew her answer to that had to be totally convincing. To back it up she forced her eyes to meet his in mild consternation. 'What has that to do with anything? We made love. We enjoyed it. End of story.' If only that were true, but she knew this story would run and run. She would not be free of it until the day she died.

Unseen by her, something dangerous flashed in Lucas's eyes for a moment, then was gone, as his face lost all expression. 'I see. So that's it, is it?'

Relieved not to be in the middle of an ugly scene, Megan enlarged on the tack she had chosen to take. 'You were expecting more?'

His blue eyes narrowed but never left hers. 'Frankly, Red, I was expecting a whole lot more. I enjoyed last night, but it was nowhere near enough.'

Her lashes fluttered. She knew the feeling, but they were experiencing it for different reasons. Hers was love, whilst his was merely desire. Whilst it was flattering to know that Lucas's interest hadn't been satisfied so quickly, it only confirmed how he saw their relationship. She was doing the right thing.

'I'm sorry—' she began, a faint huskiness tingeing her voice, but Lucas interrupted her.

'Sorry doesn't cut it, Red. I'm not some callow youth. I know when a woman wants me, and, sweetheart, you *do* still want me,' he pronounced confidently, making her nerves leap anxiously.

Colour rose in her cheeks and she swallowed hard. Suddenly this was not going the way she had expected. She had decided he would give in gracefully when he realised she wanted to end their brief affair, but for reasons she couldn't fathom he was determined to change her mind. She wouldn't, and even though he was right about her still wanting him she had to convince him he was wrong.

'I think I know better than you what I want, Lucas!' she countered with all the firmness she could muster.

'Why are you denying it? We both know I could make love to you right here and you wouldn't fight me.'

Her senses rioted at the idea and she knew it was true.

When he touched her, she melted. She knew she always would. Yet she had to deny it. 'Don't flatter yourself!'

'Do you want me to prove it?' Lucas challenged softly, and her eyes registered her despairing anger.

'It would be against my will!' she choked out, and immediately saw his expression soften.

'I know, Red, and the person you would be fighting is yourself. The question is, why? The air buzzes when we're together. We send sparks off each other even now. We both know it isn't over, so why are you doing this?'

Megan's throat closed over. His understanding of her was uncanny and frightening. It made her feel as if there was nothing he didn't know about her. Yet there was no way he could know that she loved him, and that was the way it had to stay. The affair was over. He *had* to accept it.

'A woman has the right to say no,' she reminded him thickly, and he nodded his acceptance of the fact.

'And the man who cares about her has the right to know why,' he returned, sending alarm signals skittering along her nerves.

Megan caught her breath. What was he saying? She began to feel panic claw at her stomach. No. It wasn't true. They were just words! He couldn't care. He *mustn't* care! Alarm slowly trickled icily into her veins. She had to put an end to this right now. 'You don't care about me, Lucas,' she denied sickly, her heart starting up a faster tempo.

This time there was the faintest hint of a smile in his eyes. 'Don't I, Red? I think I know how I feel better than you do, darling,' he drawled, using her own words against her.

Her colour faded at his insinuation, her alarm increasing in leaps and bounds. 'Don't call me that!'

One eyebrow quirked. 'Why not? It's how I think of you,' he countered at once, and her heart stopped. This couldn't be happening! It was her worst nightmare come to life!

She jumped to her feet, hands bunched into fists at her sides. 'Stop playing games with me!' *Tell me that's all it is,* she begged silently. *Tell me it's just a wicked game!*

Lucas was on his feet too, and he wasn't laughing. 'This is no game to me. This is for real. What are you running from, Red? Why can't you trust me enough to tell me?'

She lost her breath. She was going crazy. She had to be, for why else would he have almost sounded as if her lack of trust hurt him? It couldn't be true. She wouldn't let it be true. Lucas didn't care. He was just frustrated at having lost a potential sleeping partner!

She made herself look at him coldly. 'What do you want me to say? That I'm running from a broken heart? That I don't want to be hurt again?' she charged derisively, and saw his head go back as the words struck home. She told herself she couldn't have hurt him. He had to care to be hurt, and he didn't care. He didn't!

A muscle flexed in his jaw. 'Either, if they're true,' he returned grittily, and Megan shook her head.

'They're not. The truth is no man has hurt me. They can't. I'm more likely to hurt them. I'm trying not to hurt you, Lucas.'

'Why?'

The soft challenge shook her to the core. 'Wh-what?'

Lucas smiled grimly. 'It's a simple question, darling. Why don't you want to hurt me? You've never worried about the others, have you?'

Her mouth went dry as she saw where his clever brain was taking him. She wouldn't go down that road. She dredged up a likely explanation. 'No, but I've always considered you a friend, Lucas. That's why I don't want to hurt you.' She waited for his reply. It wasn't long in coming.

'I don't believe you.'

She hadn't counted on such a blunt denial, and it left her floundering. He wasn't responding the way he should. He read things into what she said that shouldn't have been there. The man defied all logic! Alarm skittering along every nerve, she saw red. 'Damn you! Why can't you just be angry like a normal human being?' she cried, and he had the gall to laugh.

'Is that what you want?' he asked silkily, and her nerves screamed.

'It's what I expected,' Megan shot back, crossing her arms defensively when she saw the speculative gleam grow in his eyes.

'Well, sweetheart, you got what you expected, because I am angry, though not in the way you think. I'm not angry for the things you've done, but for the things you won't do. You say you don't want to hurt me, and yet you won't trust me. *That* hurts me, Red.'

Megan felt a ball of emotion swell inside her. There was no doubting his sincerity, but she didn't want it. Couldn't take it and what it implied. Yet, loving him, she was discovering how much it hurt her to hurt him, and she felt compelled to compromise. Her throat worked like crazy in order to allow her to speak. 'I do trust you, Lucas. You know I do.'

Lucas took the few steps necessary to bring them face to face, and took hold of her shoulders. He shook his head. 'Not in the ways that count. For God's sake, I can feel your pain. Share it with me, Megan.'

The plea very nearly broke her. How could he know the agony she suffered? She had hidden it all these years, and nobody had ever suspected before. Lucas seemed to know so much. He offered comfort she hadn't realised she needed until now. Yet old habits died hard. She didn't want his pity. The secret must stay locked inside her.

She wasn't aware just how much of her anguish showed on her face, but Lucas saw, and with a muffled oath he brought his mouth down on hers. For Megan the world shut down. She was rendered defenceless by the tingling pleasure of his lips teasing hers, and when she opened them the silken stroke of his tongue plundered with devastating need. She could not deny him what she needed so badly herself, and for vital seconds she responded, rising on tiptoe to press herself against him as the kiss deepened to fever pitch.

Then Lucas's hands tightened, pushing her away, and she stumbled backwards, fingers pressed to her throbbing lips. 'Why did you do that?' she croaked, licking her lips and tasting him there, instantly wanting more.

'Because your eyes begged me to,' he answered equally huskily, and she looked away in dismay, aware that one kiss had undone a thousand words. 'Don't worry, I'm not about to leap on you. I'll leave you alone for now. Just don't think this is over. One way or another, there will be truth between us.'

With those words of warning, he ran a gentle hand down her cheek and across her lips, before abruptly turning and walking away.

Megan watched him go with an anxiously beating heart. Nothing had turned out the way she had expected. Lucas had implied that his feelings for her were more than simply sexual, but it couldn't be true. Whatever it was, it wasn't love. He couldn't love her. He just wanted her and hated being thwarted. Yet if he loved her... No! She couldn't think that way! Lucas did not love her! He never had and never would. She didn't want him to. It wouldn't bring her joy. It would be the worst possible thing to happen. She could cope with anything but that.

Dropping down to the grass again, she hugged her knees up to her chest and wrapped her arms around them. 'Please,

God, don't let him love me,' she prayed over and over in
a litany of despair. She didn't cry, but, physically and emotionally exhausted, she stretched herself out on the soft turf
and closed her eyes against the sun. She welcomed its
warmth easing over her like a blanket. Without realising it,
she slept.

HOURS LATER she woke. The sun had moved round, leaving
her in dappled shade, and she sat up, feeling slightly
chilled. A glance at her watch told her it was the middle
of the afternoon, and she scrambled to her feet, heading
back along the path to her car. Lucas's Jaguar had gone,
and she wondered where he was. Almost immediately she
told herself it didn't matter. She had no business thinking
about him. They would soon be going their separate ways,
and she would have to pick up the pieces of her life.

She drove home, bracing herself to face Lucas again, but
his car was missing, although her brother's was parked outside. Daniel didn't answer to his name, though, when she
went indoors, and she presumed they must have gone somewhere together. She hoped it boded well. She didn't doubt
that Lucas would know what to do.

She forced herself to eat a sandwich she didn't want,
then took herself into the garden to spend the rest of the
afternoon weeding. The sun had already gone down by the
time she stopped, and the only interruption had been Ted
ringing to tell her he was going out to dinner. Wearily she
made her way upstairs to shower, then changed into a large
baggy T-shirt and grey leggings over a frivolous pair of
silk panties. She was just fastening gold studs in her ears
when she heard the sound of a car and knew the two men
had returned.

She found Daniel in the lounge. He was sitting on the
couch, his legs propped up on the coffee-table. Glancing
round tensely, she realised he was alone. 'I thought I heard

Lucas,' she remarked casually, feeling anything but casual. Sitting beside him, she curled her legs up under her.

Daniel stretched luxuriously. 'You did. He's gone through to the study. He said he had a call to make,' he explained genially, causing her brows to lift questioningly. When he said no more, however, she was forced to prompt him.

'Well? What happened?'

Daniel tried to keep his face straight, but it was impossible. Giving in, he gave her the wry smile he used always to have. 'Lucas came up trumps, Meg. Just like you said he would.'

Megan felt her heart swell at the knowledge that she hadn't been mistaken. 'He said he would help?'

Daniel let out a relieved breath. 'He already has!' he exclaimed wonderingly. 'I nearly bolted, I was so ashamed of myself, but I knew I had almost ruined you as well as myself, so I had to speak out. Lucas was marvellous. He didn't criticise, just listened to what I had to say, then asked me how much I needed.'

Megan felt light-headed with relief. 'Just like that?'

Daniel looked sheepish. 'Well, not exactly. He said he thought a thrashing might do me good, but that as you wouldn't like it he'd agree to help with my debts providing I seek proper counselling. I know I've been a fool, Meg, but I'm not such a fool that I don't know when I need help. I jumped at the chance. I need to get my head together if I'm going to square things with you. First, though, I've got to get Terrell's back on its feet.'

Megan frowned. 'I thought you were going to sell Terrell's?'

'Lucas doesn't think it's a good idea. Rather than selling, he says we need an injection of cash. He suggested he becomes a partner; that way he can supply the money, and I can pay both of you back out of my share of the profits.'

Megan didn't know what to say. Lucas's generosity was breathtaking. She had expected him to help, but not to go that far. He was taking an awful risk. She couldn't imagine why he had done it. 'And you agreed?' she asked unnecessarily.

'Did I! This is just what we need. Terrell's can be great, Meg, but it will take hard work. That's my fault. I should never have let things slip so far. But I'll make it up to you, I promise.'

Megan bit down hard on her lip. Daniel was no saint. She knew he would keep his word about the gambling, but he was too restless to stay here and slog away at rebuilding the business. He had to be up and doing, and she couldn't see them competing with the best for some time to come.

Before she could venture any of what she was thinking, Daniel spoke again. 'By the way, you've got another commission. Lucas wants you to design a boat for me to race. That way I can promote Terrell's the way it deserves. We're going to be up and running in no time, Meg, and I can't wait!'

Though it did her good to see the enthusiasm returning to her brother, her head was reeling from all the plans he was telling her about. All of them inspired by Lucas.

As if by magic he appeared in the doorway, looking far too handsome in a blue silk shirt and white chinos. A cut-crystal glass holding some golden liquid nestled in his palm, whilst his other hand was slipped casually into a trouser pocket.

'Well, children? Is God in his heaven and all right with your world?' he drawled ironically, running an eye over Megan, which set her heart thumping. Without waiting for an answer he drained his glass and set it down on the nearest table. 'I won't be in for dinner, so you two will have to celebrate on your own. Don't drink too much, Dan. The holiday is over, remember.'

A second later he was gone. They heard his car start up, the noise fading as he drove away.

He left behind an uneasy silence as brother and sister looked at each other.

'I don't know what's the matter with him,' Daniel declared, frowning. 'He's been acting out of character all afternoon. Usually he has great concentration, but today his mind has been elsewhere. Has he said anything to you, Meg?'

'No,' she lied, well aware of where his thoughts had been. On her.

'Well, I'd say it was a woman. What's the betting old Lucas has fallen in love, and the woman of his choice is playing hard to get?' Daniel laughed, though not unkindly.

Unfortunately it was too close to her secret fears, and Megan got to her feet jerkily, nerves all on edge. 'Don't be silly. You know Lucas plays the field.'

Daniel shook his head, his expression serious. 'Not since he got here, he hasn't. In fact, the only woman I've seen him with is you.'

Her heart leapt into her throat and she turned on him angrily. 'If you make the stupid suggestion that Lucas is in love with me, I swear I'll hit you, Daniel!' she warned fiercely, taking him aback.

He held up his hands. 'Hey! I haven't said anything. Besides, what would be so wrong with that?'

Watching the possibility cross his mind and find approval, Megan felt angry, helpless tears stinging the backs of her eyes. 'Everything would be wrong with it! Can't you see that? It would be… It would be…' She couldn't finish the sentence, and, pressing her lips tightly together, she crossed to the window and stared blindly out.

Daniel gaped at her back in shock and growing understanding. He'd never seen Megan so uptight. 'You're in love with him, aren't you?' he asked gruffly, though he knew he didn't really need her answer.

Megan gritted her teeth. Emotions seethed inside her, so that it hurt to breathe. 'Lucas does not love me,' she said firmly, but naturally Daniel did not understand that she was trying to convince herself more than him.

'I think you're wrong, Meg. It wouldn't surprise me if Lucas did love you. Come to think of it, he's always had a soft spot for you, right from when we were kids!' He sought to reassure her, to give her the hope he thought she needed, unaware that it was the very last thing she wanted to hear.

A bubble of hysteria broke out of her, and she laughed achingly as she turned round. 'Don't you understand? I don't want him to love me! I don't want anyone to love me! I couldn't bear it!'

Daniel stared at her. 'But…if you love him…?'

'I want him to love anyone but me.'

'That doesn't make sense, Meg!' Daniel protested, floundering.

She smiled tiredly. 'Yes, it does. Oh, yes, it does,' she countered thickly, and took a deep breath. 'Now, if you don't mind, I'd rather not discuss it. Just tell me what you want for dinner.'

Daniel looked as if he wanted to argue at the abrupt change of subject, but in the face of her determination he was forced to bite the words back. 'I've lost my appetite. I think I'll go and do some work in the study.'

Megan bit her lip as she watched him go to the door. 'I'll make you a sandwich. You might get hungry later,' she said softly, and he glanced at her over his shoulder.

'I don't understand you, Meg.'

She blinked back tears. 'I know. You'll just have to trust that I know what I'm doing.'

Daniel shook his head in defeat and disappeared, leaving

Megan to bury her face in her hands. What on earth was she doing, ranting at Daniel like that? She was falling apart. The whole fabric of her life, so painfully built up, was dissolving before her eyes. All because she loved Lucas.

Yet love had never been an option for her, so why did it hurt so to cut him out of her life, when she had always intended to do so? Her heart had the answer her mind could never have seen. She loved Lucas. A living, breathing man, not an abstract idea. To deny herself something in the abstract was easy; to deny the reality was like ripping out her heart. She had never thought it would be so hard, but it was, and the longer it took, the harder it was. This morning had been difficult enough. She had the distinct feeling that if she didn't get Lucas to accept that whatever had been between them was over, and soon, she would shatter into a million irretrievable pieces.

Which meant she had to try again. Tonight, when he came home, she would be waiting for him. This time she would succeed. She *had* to succeed. To envisage anything else was unthinkable.

The hours passed slowly, with nothing holding her interest on the TV. Eventually she went up to her room, curling up on the window-seat to wait until Lucas returned. She hadn't intended to sleep, but she must have, for something woke her with a start, and, glancing at her watch, she discovered it was almost midnight. Sitting up, she listened, just faintly hearing the sound of a door closing. It had to be Lucas, for Daniel had gone to bed before her for a change. Clambering stiffly from the seat, she ran her fingers through her hair and let herself out into the corridor.

Lucas's room was at the other end of the hall, and when she reached it there was no light showing under the door. She debated going away again, but was reluctant to leave the matter hanging. If Lucas was asleep already, he would just have to wake up.

For the first few seconds after she entered the darkened room Megan thought it was empty, but when they probed the gloom her eyes finally picked out Lucas's figure stretched out on top of the bed, his shoulders propped against the headboard. What faint light there was caught the glitter in his eyes and told her he was looking right at her. Closing the door, she leant back against it.

'I have to talk to you,' she said firmly.

'Naturally it couldn't wait until morning,' he responded, and she heard the mocking amusement behind the words.

'No,' she confirmed, aware, now that her eyes were getting used to the dimness, that Lucas wore a towelling robe and probably nothing else. It was a distraction she could well have done without. All she could do was ignore it—no easy thing when everything about him drew her like a magnet.

'So tell me, what is so important that it brings you hotfoot to my room in the witching hour, at great risk to your reputation?' Lucas went on drily, and Megan gritted her teeth, knowing he was taking devilish delight in drawing the moment out. She raised her chin, determined to keep her cool.

'First I wanted to thank you for helping Daniel. You were more than generous.'

Lucas drew one leg up and rested his arm on his knee. 'He's my oldest friend. You knew I wouldn't let him down,' he said simply, and even in the gloom Megan felt her eyes lock with his.

Her heart kicked, and she had to moisten her lips with her tongue in order to carry on. 'Yes, I did know, but even your loyalty has limits. I never expected you to offer to become a partner, or commission the boat for Daniel to race. I appreciate it, but I don't understand why you went to those lengths.'

'Don't you?' he challenged her softly.

Megan's skin prickled at the waves of energy coming from him, and she realised it had been a mistake to come. She should have waited until morning. But it was too late to back out now, so she forged on. 'I know you have a good heart, Lucas, but—'

'But nothing,' Lucas interrupted immediately. 'I didn't do it out of the goodness of my heart, Red. I did it for you.'

The simple statement stunned her defenceless heart. 'For me?'

'I know just how important Terrell's is to you,' he replied, and Megan caught her breath.

For a moment she thought he really did know, but she got a grip on her anxiety when logic told her he was simply speaking generally. However, he had made her too edgy to stand still, and she pushed away from the door, taking several steps into the room. 'Naturally. It's been in the family a long time.'

Lucas shook his head. 'It goes beyond that. For some reason I have yet to discover, Terrell's is your life. And I find that a strange thing to say of a woman who has so much more to offer,' he declared thoughtfully.

The words found targets he had no conception of, and she winced, glad of the shielding darkness. The laugh she forced past her lips was ragged. 'You know that's not true,' she said edgily.

Lucas did not laugh. 'No, I don't know. You've got me turned inside out, so that all I really know right now, this minute, is that I need you.'

Her heart constricted at the words. It was unbelievable how much pain could be caused by something which was supposed to bring only joy. Next to 'I love you', they were the words a woman most wanted to hear, but to Megan they spelled only horror. Her composure was shot to pieces. Needing someone implied an emotion beyond caring, and that plunged her into her worst nightmare She didn't want to hear this. She had to stop him before he said anything more. Before he said words which would explode in their faces.

'Now listen, Lucas, you have to stop this!' she protested shakily. 'It's not funny any more. We both know you don't need me!'

'Oh, but you're wrong; I need you very much,' he declared huskily.

Oh, God! She curled her nails painfully into her palms. 'What you're talking about isn't need, it's plain old-fashioned lust!' she decried, willing him to retreat and not drive her to say things she would always regret.

In the next instant shock waves chased along every nerve as Lucas swung his feet to the floor and closed the gap between them. She took a half-step backwards then forced herself to retreat no further, biting back a moan when she felt his hands close on either side of her head, tipping her face up to his.

'It's never been that, for either of us. You know it; that's why you keep trying to deny it. I know it frightens you, but, honey, you aren't the only one. I've never felt this way before either. You feel it the same as I do. Feel it!' he ordered throatily, and she didn't have to try because already that electric charge was passing from his flesh to hers.

When his head lowered, a whimper of despair forced its way from her throat. His mouth found hers, lips scorching with the faintest caress, barely touching and yet possessing her very soul. She wanted to sink into his embrace and never surface. Heaven was here for the taking, but it had the sweetness of hell.

'I don't want this.' She forced the necessary lie from an achingly tight throat.

Lucas uttered a sighing laugh. 'You do,' he murmured, trailing a line of kisses along her jaw and up to her eyes, which closed as if they were weighted. 'Just give in to it, Red. I'll keep you safe. I swear it.'

His closeness made it incredibly difficult to think just when she most needed to be clear-headed. 'You have to stop doing this!' she protested once more.

'It would be easier to stop breathing than to stop wanting to make love to you,' Lucas declared with a groan.

Megan shivered, staring up into midnight-dark eyes which invited her to drown in them. She felt as if knives were being driven into her heart. 'Don't make me hurt you, Lucas,' she pleaded thickly.

'You're going to have to do your worst, Red, because, like it or not, you're the woman I want,' he said softly, and she caught her breath.

Megan felt the burn of tears behind her eyes. 'This wasn't supposed to happen!' She was supposed to be fighting, rejecting him, not clinging as if she would die if she let him go!

Lucas paused, pulling away enough to be able to look at her, and her heart ached when she saw the tenderness in his deep blue eyes. 'Wasn't it? Remember, I told you in the beginning you couldn't dictate to love,' he breathed, and lowered his head.

This time his kiss was a sensual ravishment. He allowed her no space to retreat, plundering and claiming her mouth with blatant hunger. Megan felt an answering need well up inside her. For sanity's sake she tried to quell it, yet it was inevitable that she should fail.

It hurt too much to refuse herself what her tortured heart cried out for. She knew she would live to regret it, that she would pay a high price for stealing these moments, but she was willing to pay it for a few more hours of the joy that only Lucas could give her. With a muffled sob she capitulated, sinking against his strong body, sliding her arms helplessly up around his neck and burying her hands in his hair.

At the same time his arms enfolded her, holding her close, letting her feel for herself the power she had to arouse him. It was heady and exciting, and her mind and body claimed him. Right or wrong, he was hers! And, as if he had been able to hear that silent assertion, Lucas dragged his mouth free of hers and gazed down into her molten eyes.

'You're mine, Red,' he declared huskily.

Megan closed her ears to words of caution. She didn't want to think. 'Yes,' she sighed back. For tonight she would be his. Tomorrow... Tomorrow would look after itself.

He ran the ball of his thumb over her bruised lips, making her eyes close. 'What, no fight?'

Her lids rose up; her eyes were a seething caldron of emotions. 'Don't let me think, Lucas. Make the night last for ever!' she beseeched, and his lips curved.

Lucas bent to swing her up in his arms. 'Anything for you, Red. You have only to ask,' he declared thickly, carrying her to the bed and lowering her gently on to it.

CHAPTER NINE

THERE WAS A MOMENT when Megan awoke when she felt quite blissfully happy. She sighed and shifted her head on the pillow, a slow smile beginning to form.

'When you look like that, is it any wonder that I love you?'

The smile vanished and her eyes shot open. Lucas was lying on his side, his head propped on his hand. His hair was mussed, he was gloriously naked, and he was waiting for a response.

For the moment Megan was blessedly numb. 'What did you say?' A pained whisper was all she could form in a throat as tight as a drum. Lucas had been as good as his word—he had allowed her no time to think last night—but she was thinking now, and she knew the time of reckoning had come.

Lucas smiled at her, misinterpreting her shock. 'I said, I love you,' he repeated simply, lowering his head to brush his lips over hers.

Megan twisted her head sharply, so that his kiss fell on her cheek instead. She felt him tense, then ease away to look down at her. She couldn't look at him, not yet. The numbness began to evaporate. 'You don't know how much I wish you hadn't said that,' she murmured in distress, and his hand came out to capture her chin, using gentle force to turn her to face him.

The tension in him was tangible, but the only sign on

his face was the nerve ticking in his jaw. 'I was hoping for a different reaction.'

Emotion deepened the green of her eyes, for she knew she must put an end to this, and there was no way to do it without causing pain. Yet she had to do it, and she hardened her heart. 'You didn't seriously expect me to say I loved you, did you?' she challenged mockingly, wishing he would let her go, because his gentleness was surely killing her.

Lucas's nostrils flared as he took an angry breath. His eyes flashed and his smile was grim. 'Why not? It wouldn't be the first time,' he responded shockingly, calling her bluff, and her eyes widened in dawning horror.

Dear God, no! 'You couldn't possibly. . .!' she cried, appalled.

'Oh, yes, I was awake,' he told her tersely, keeping a tight rein on his anger and watching the colour drain out of her.

'No!' Megan denied desperately, thrown on the defensive though all her weapons had been effectively stripped from her in one telling blow. She sat up, moving as far away from him as the bed would allow, searching for something to cover her nakedness. There was only the pillow, and she clutched it to her like a shield.

Lucas sat up too, a wry smile twisting his lips. 'You can't hide from me any more, Megan. I won't let you, no matter what you say to try and make me angry or change the subject. I was awake when you came out of the bathroom. I heard you tell me you loved me, but I also heard your fear. I didn't understand it, but I knew you needed time. So instead of revealing that I wasn't asleep I gave you that time. Only to discover when I did talk to you that you'd gone into full retreat.

'I didn't know why then, and I still don't. Even after a night spent making love to each other, you were prepared to deny it, if you could. But I'm not going to let you. I love you, Red, and I know you love me. I want to hear you admit it.'

Breathing raggedly, Megan stared at his, trying to think although her brain had turned to mush. 'Why? It won't change things,' she countered tightly, feeling a wild trembling start deep within her. She had to get out, and her eyes gauged the distance to the door.

Lucas shook his head. 'You'll never make it, but you can try if you like,' he said levelly, and when she didn't move he took a deep breath. 'OK, now tell me what sort of things won't change.'

He had her trapped, and though he looked relaxed he knew he wasn't. He was prepared for anything, and that included getting some answers. Well, since he had asked, she would have to tell him. 'I don't want you to love me,' she ground out painfully, and immediately Lucas shook his head.

'It's too late for that, Red. It was too late the moment I saw you again.'

She looked away, biting her lip against the pain of words which tore her heart apart. She could feel him willing her to open up and let him in, but she couldn't do it. 'Then I want you to stop loving me,' she ordered jerkily.

'Sorry, no can do,' Lucas replied bluntly, bringing her head round again.

'But you have to!' she cried, eyes shimmering with lashed tears. 'I can't bear for you to love me! I'd rather you hated me!' Because hate would cauterise the hurt, and she *would* hurt him.

The softening of his blue eyes stole her breath away. 'I'm sorry, Red, but I can't do that. I intend to keep on loving you until the day I die,' he informed her with such gentleness that it brought a sob of despair to her lips.

'Don't say that!'

'It's the truth, and the truth can't hurt you, Red,' he countered.

It could! It was driving a stake through her heart. Megan felt the trembling intensify until she could barely control it. She knew she had to get away before she broke down completely. 'I can't take any more of this!' she exclaimed in anguish, and leapt from the bed. Lucas was right behind her, catching her before she reached the door and hauling her into the prison of his arms. She fought him wildly, but he was much too strong, and finally she collapsed against him, panting for breath.

'What are you so afraid of? What is so awful about having me love you?' he demanded, his breath brushing her ear as he spoke.

Megan looked up, seeing beyond his anger to the pain in his eyes, and it was a like a dagger in her soul. The fight went out of her. She wanted to cry, and closed her eyes against the sting of tears. 'Because I'll hurt you, the way I'm hurting you now,' she confessed in a cracked whisper. 'Please, Lucas, just let me go,' she begged.

He took a deep breath, not denying her claim, but he didn't let her go. 'No. I want to know. Don't you see, I *have* to know? I've been waiting for you all my life. Do you honestly think I would give you up without a fight?'

Megan pressed a hand to her trembling lips. No one had ever spoken to her with such a depth of emotion, and it was as beautiful as it was deadly. He was baring his soul in an attempt to get her to trust him, unwittingly giving her weapons to hurt him with. And she would have to hurt him, because he wasn't going to back down, not this time. A whimper escaped her. 'You expect too much of me, Lucas!' she croaked, praying for numbness to take away her own pain, but knowing it would not come.

The passionate blue eyes locked on her distressed green ones. 'Because I want you to love me?'

'But that's not all, is it?' she groaned. He had told her what he wanted when he met the right woman. It was everything she wanted him to have, and everything she could never give him. 'Don't you want to marry me? Have a f—' Her voice broke, and she willed herself to go on. 'Have a family?' she finished faintly, desperately wishing he would let her go, because it was a refinement of torture to be held so close.

Lucas tensed as he sensed her agitation. 'Naturally,' he confirmed cautiously.

Megan would have given a fortune not to go on, but there was no turning back. Knowing it, suddenly she felt a strange calm steal over her, distancing her. There was nothing she could do to avoid the outcome he insisted on, so he could have his truth, even if it destroyed them both.

'Natural to you, maybe, but not to me. I don't want those things.' Her tone was flat, unnatural, and he frowned down at her.

'But you love children. I saw that for myself,' he countered, and she winced.

'I've told you more than once that I don't want children,' she reminded him coldly, and he eased away from her a little, trying to catch her eye but she refused to look at him.

'A lot of women say that, but they change their minds,' he pointed out, quite truthfully. It happened, but not to her.

'I won't change my mind,' she declared, and Lucas uttered a grim laugh.

'You might have to,' he said shortly, and she stared at him blankly.

'What do you mean?'

'Hasn't it occurred to you? We've made love several times, without any thought of protection. You could already be pregnant,' he informed her, and she could tell that part of him hoped she was.

Megan laughed, but it was harsh and painful, totally

without humour. Of course it hadn't occurred to her because she knew it couldn't happen. 'No, I could not be pregnant. I've been on the Pill for years, and have no intention of coming off it.'

That, finally, made him release her, and she felt instantly chilled. Rubbing her arms, she spied her T-shirt in a heap on the floor and retrieved it, slipping it over her head with relief. Clothed she felt less vulnerable. Taking a deep breath, she turned to face Lucas and found him frowning at her.

'Even for me?' he demanded tersely. Careless of his nakedness, he looked handsome and proud, and Megan hoped his pride would get him through, because he had given her an opening she could not refuse.

'There are definite limits to what I will do for love,' she declared bluntly. She produced a faint smile. 'So there's no risk of the dreaded patter of tiny feet. For which I am heartily grateful,' she lied. It had never been easy, and never would be.

Lucas didn't seem to know what to say. Shaking his head, he dragged both hands through his hair then automatically picked up his robe and pulled it on, tying the belt with restrained anger. Megan watched him sadly, wanting to offer comfort but knowing she couldn't. When he glanced her way, she quickly summoned a smile and a shrug.

'And, as you know, I've never been a candidate for marriage. It would stifle me.'

He stared at her as if she had suddenly grown another head. 'Yet you say you love me,' he said tautly, and she sighed.

'I told you I didn't want to hurt you, Lucas. Yes, I love you, but I don't want the same things you want. I'm sorry,' she said huskily, and took a step towards him.

He held up a hand, palm out, to ward her off. 'Thanks,

but I don't want your pity!' he snapped disgustedly. 'I don't particularly care for your brand of love either.'

Megan turned away on the pretext of picking up the rest of her clothes. Her hands were shaking so much, it was a wonder she managed it. She felt dead inside. Finally, he believed her, but she had had to hurt him to achieve that and she would never forgive herself for that. Straightening, she licked dry lips and prepared to drive the final nail into the coffin.

'You'll get over it. You might think you love me now, but you won't tomorrow. When you give yourself some time to think, you'll come to the conclusion you never loved me in the first place.' She couldn't say any more. The words would choke her. Squaring her shoulders, she headed for the door.

'What about you?' His question halted her with her hand on the knob. She didn't turn around, so failed to see the arrested look on his face. 'Will you still love me tomorrow?' he asked in the strangest voice.

I'll love you for ever, her heart replied. 'Oh, I've a very fickle heart, but maybe I'll love you till the next man comes along!' she quipped, and made her escape.

Outside she collapsed against the wall. The old saying was right: you could take what you wanted, but you had to be prepared to pay for it. She was paying for last night. She should not have stayed, but she had wanted to steal a little more time. Now she had for ever to remember that she had destroyed something fine: Lucas's love.

Uncomfortable with her guilt, she straightened and continued on to her room. Sinking onto her dressing-table stool, she dropped her head in her hands. What an awful mess her life had become. In the space of a few short days she had broken all her rules. She had thought she knew what heartache was, but nothing compared to this.

A tear trickled down her cheek, but she brushed it away

and pushed herself to her feet. She didn't have time to break down now. In a few hours she would have to face Lucas again, and nothing of the misery she felt must show on her face. She just had to keep telling herself she had done the right thing. She had left him free to find someone who could give him all the things he wanted—things he deserved, because he was a kind, loving, honourable man, who had had the misfortune to fall in love with a woman who, through no fault of her own, must deny him that most precious of gifts—a family of his own.

IT WAS ALMOST nine-thirty when Megan went down to breakfast. She had gone through the motions of showering and dressing in fawn trousers and a green silk blouse. She had felt the need for make-up too, to give her face some much needed colour. A glance in her mirror had shown her a virtual ghost. She felt as ephemeral as one, too. Her spirit had been beaten down until now she was running on empty. It felt as if it wouldn't take much to crush her altogether.

She had hoped to find the kitchen empty, but when she pushed open the door she found Lucas seated at the table, lingering over a cup of coffee. Her instinct was to retreat, as her heart twisted painfully, but then she stiffened her spine. She wasn't a coward and she had made her choice. She wasn't about to back out, so the sooner she got used to meeting Lucas, the sooner her defences would strengthen. One day she might even be able to face him without that deep sense of loss.

He hadn't noticed her yet, and she found herself studying the top of his head. It was funny how vulnerable it made him seem, and she had the urge to go and run her fingers through the silken strands soothingly. She couldn't, though. Such automatic signs of affection were strictly forbidden if she was to hide her feelings from him. He must be given no reason for supposing she had lied.

Still as she was, she must have made some noise, for he suddenly looked round, spearing her on the end of a hooded glance. Then, to her utter surprise, for it was the last thing she ever expected, he smiled. To her beleaguered spirit, it was as if the sun had come out inside her. It was simple and beautiful, and yet it hurt more than anything ever had. She could not have spoken if her very life had depended on it.

'Good morning. I still don't suppose I can interest you in a marriage? No? Then how about a cup of coffee? You look as if you could do with one.'

Megan made it to the nearest chair and sat down abruptly, knocked sideways by his disconcerting behaviour. 'Wh-what...?' she managed to mumble incoherently, and Lucas smiled wryly, poured her a cup of coffee from the pot in front of him, and set it before her. She stared at it as if it might explode. Thrown off balance, she had no idea what was going on.

Lucas appeared to have no such problem ordering his thoughts. He spoke as if they were discussing the weather. 'I suppose you realise you are the only woman I will ever marry?' he said softly, and Megan stared at him incredulously. How could he have said that? They had been through this.

She turned her gaze blindly to the coffee in her cup. 'You'll find someone else,' she declared thickly.

'It's you or no one, Red,' Lucas returned doggedly, and her stomach lurched.

She stared at him, eyes glittering with anger and a boundless hurt. 'Why are you doing this? I thought...' The words tailed off painfully.

Lucas relaxed back in his chair, his intent gaze never leaving her. 'You thought it was over? Unfortunately for you, I have a good memory.'

Megan couldn't seem to draw her eyes away from his.

Like a rabbit caught in the headlights of a car, she could only wait for the moment of impact. 'And what is it you think you've remembered?' she charged, feeling rushed and trapped and totally unaware that it showed in her eyes.

Lucas saw, and his jaw clenched briefly before he sighed and climbed to his feet. Walking round the table, he came to a halt behind her, setting his hands on the back of her chair, making her tense. Ambivalently she found herself torn between not wanting him to touch her and dreading that he wouldn't! Her skin began to burn with the reflected heat of his, and she shivered as his nearness sent tingles chasing along her nerves. She wanted to lean back against him. To close her eyes and breathe him in. God help her, she was such a mess!

His voice broke into her despairing thoughts. 'I remembered what you said after your date the first night I was here. You'd just broken off with him, and you said he didn't love you, but that even if he did he wouldn't tomorrow. Does that sound familiar?' he enquired softly.

Megan closed her eyes, recalling those words all too clearly and realising the enormity of her mistake. She hadn't expected him to put two and two together like that. She had forgotten how dangerous he was. 'That doesn't mean anything,' she denied shakily.

'Then why are you trembling?' he asked, hands shifting from the chair to her shoulders, thumbs rubbing back and forth in a rhythmic movement which started flash fires on her skin.

'I—I'm cold!' she lied, then wished she'd remained silent for she was burning up and he knew it. He knew exactly what his touch did to her.

'Uh-uh. I think you're afraid, Red. Afraid of what I might find out. And you should be, because I'm not giving up. I'm never going to give up on you,' he told her huskily, bending to press a kiss to the top of her head.

Megan shuddered with a mixture of pleasure and horror. She jerked away. 'You have to!' she insisted raggedly, rising on unsteady legs and turning to face him. He was expressionless, tensed to do battle for as long as it took.

'Why?'

'Because I say so!' she shouted back, then, alarmed by the wildness inside her, she caught her breath and walked over to the sink, gripping the edge like grim death. 'You have to let me go, Lucas. Oh, why can't you be like other men, who would walk away without a thought?'

'Because I'm not like other men. I'm the man who loves you,' he told her simply.

Her knuckles grew white with strain. 'It wouldn't be enough.'

'Enough for what?' he asked her quietly, and Megan took a shuddering breath.

'To stop me hating myself,' she replied, and, straightening her spine, turned around. 'That's why you have to stop this. We both know you could wear me down, make me give in, but I'd still end up hating myself. I'm begging you not to go on.'

Lucas stood watching her without saying a word until she felt like screaming. Finally he sighed. 'I'll tell you what I'll do. I'll make a deal with you. All you have to do is tell me the truth. The complete, unvarnished truth. Then, and only then, will I walk away,' he proposed evenly.

Tears stung her eyes. He was asking the impossible. 'I can't,' she denied thickly, and Lucas breathed in deeply

'You're a stubborn woman, Red. If I didn't love you so much, I'd probably throttle you. I'm going out before I give in to temptation. But don't worry, I'll be back. You can count on it!'

He went out, leaving Megan feeling as if she had gone fifteen rounds with a heavyweight boxing champion. Lucas would not give up. How painfully ironic it was that the measure of his love for her was the very thing which was hurting her. Yet she couldn't tell him. She had her pride, and she did not want his pity. Somehow, there had to be a way to make him stop before it was too late.

But what?

The telephone rang out in the hall, and Megan took a steadying breath before going to answer it.

'Hi, Megan, it's Peggy. I thought you might like to come over for coffee. Jack's taken the boys fishing, so there's just me and the baby. We can have the whole morning to ourselves.'

Megan found the idea instantly tempting. To get away from the house for a while would be wonderful. There would be no chance of running into Lucas, either, because he would be working with Daniel. 'OK, I'll come.'

'That's marvellous!' Peggy declared in relief. 'You remember the way? Good. I'll see you in about an hour, then. Bye.'

Megan put the receiver down slowly. Thank goodness for Peggy. She was a life-saver. More than that, she could be an ally. If anyone had influence over Lucas, Peggy did. If she could only get her onto her side, perhaps Peggy could persuade Lucas to give up this dangerous game he was playing.

Encouraged by the thought, Megan quickly cleared up the kitchen, collected her bag and car keys, and headed out the door. She had no difficulty finding the Lakers' cottage, and her spirits had improved noticeably by the time she pulled up outside the gate. Peggy was there to greet her, a gurgling Annie in her arms.

'I'm so glad you could make it. The children are marvellous, but it's nice to have a conversation with an adult now and then!' she joked, slipping her arm casually through Megan's as they made their way round the house to the patio.

Megan made herself comfortable on one of the loungers set out there whilst Peggy put the baby in her shaded baby seat before coming to join her.

'How are you, Megan? I have to admit to being worried about you after you left,' Peggy confessed.

'I'm fine,' Megan instinctively replied, then sighed tiredly. 'No, that's not exactly true. I'm ashamed of myself for creating such a scene. It was very rude of me.'

'Nonsense. Where can you have a scene, if not with friends?' Peggy dismissed easily.

Megan studied her hands. 'Yes, but you're Lucas's friend, not mine.'

Peggy frowned at the younger woman's lowered head in concern. 'I hope I can be a friend to both of you,' she said gently.

Licking her lips, Megan gave Peggy a shaky smile. 'I was rather hoping you would say that, because I have a favour to ask of you,' she said gruffly, clearing her throat nervously.

Peggy tipped her head curiously. 'Yes?' she invited, and Megan sighed again.

'I want you to persuade Lucas to get out of my life,' she declared scratchily, holding onto her composure with some difficulty.

'But, Megan…' the other woman began to protest gently, and Megan reached out swiftly to clutch at her wrist and halt the refusal she knew was coming.

'You must! If you're his true friend, then you must do this for me. You have to tell him it's in his own best interest!' she insisted hardily, unaware of just how deeply her fingers were biting into the other woman.

Peggy ignored the pain doggedly. 'But is it?' she asked, her lips parting on a tiny gasp as Megan tensed.

'Oh, yes!'

'I can't pretend to know what's going on, but I can't

help feeling this is wrong. You love each other,' she protested worriedly.

The claim brought a frown to Megan's brow, and she
released Peggy's abused arm abruptly. 'How do you know
that? Have you seen Lucas?'

Peggy rubbed at her arm automatically, and shifted uneasily in her seat. 'He…telephoned. He sounded very upset.'

Megan set her jaw. 'That's all the more reason for you
to do this for me. He refuses to let me go, no matter what
I say. You'll have to persuade him that he must.'

Peggy's troubled gaze never left the younger woman. 'I
can see it means a lot to you, Megan, but I can't be expected to persuade Lucas to do something without knowing
why. I have to understand why you want this. Can't you
tell me that?'

Megan stared at her, caught between the need for help
and the reluctance she had always had to reveal the truth
to anyone. Yet Peggy was her last and best hope. Her heart
thudded sickeningly.

'If I agree to tell you, you have to promise never to
repeat what I say to another living soul,' she demanded
huskily.

Peggy caught her breath and, out of sight, crossed her
fingers tightly. 'Of course I promise. I won't tell anyone.'

Still Megan hesitated, swallowing to moisten a tight
throat, feeling emotion roiling inside her. 'I've never told
anyone,' she began awkwardly. 'I swore to myself I never
would. But it's the only way, isn't it?' She sought confirmation with cloudy emerald eyes.

It was impossible for Peggy to remain unmoved by that
look, and her face softened into a smile. 'You don't have
to say anything if you don't want to,' she advised gently,
and Megan shook her head.

'No. I've got to tell you because I need your help. Everything has gone so wrong. I never meant to fall in love with Lucas, and when I did I tried to end it without hurting him. He won't listen. He just keeps telling me he loves me, and it's me or no one. Even though I've told him I don't want children, he refuses to accept it. He's leaving me no choice but to tell him I can't have them!' she exclaimed despairingly, not hearing Peggy's gasp of shock. 'Lucas loves children.'

'I always say he wants a football team of his own!' Peggy responded, her voice wavering disastrously on the verge of tears.

Megan's bottom lip trembled betrayingly, and she pressed it tightly to the other. 'Well, I can't give them to him. The thing is, I know he'll say he can accept that, but I can't! Oh, it would be so easy to give in, to take what he offers, but I'd never forgive myself. With another woman he could have that football team! I *want* him to have them! I've never seen a man more suited to have children, and he deserves them, Peggy,' she added huskily, looking at the other woman through glittering eyes.

Peggy reached out and captured Megan's hand. 'Are you sure you can't have children? There are so many tests these days, so many ways of achieving the impossible,' she said unevenly, and Megan dropped her eyes.

'You don't understand. I told you I can't have children, but the truth is, I can, but I won't.'

Peggy froze. 'I…you…'

Megan removed her hand, clutching it with the other in an attempt to stop it shaking. 'I have what they call a genetic disease. My mother had it, but I didn't know that until after she died. It's passed on through the female line, but it's only harmful to boys. When I heard…'

She paused, swallowing hard to conquer the emotion rising in her. 'You can't imagine what it's like to know you will condemn your own children to the same horror you feel. To know that your daughters will suffer the agonies you do. To live with the knowledge that they, like you, will have to watch their sons die before the end of infancy.

'I couldn't do it. No matter how much I long to have children of my own—and that's all I ever really wanted, you know—I couldn't do it. I couldn't do to them what has been done to me. I decided I had to be the one to end the chain of misery. Call it playing God if you want, but I don't regret my decision. I won't have children. I won't inflict heartbreak where there should have been love.'

'Oh, dear Lord!' Peggy's exclamation was the merest thread of sound.

Megan wiped at the tears which were slowly and silently trailing down her cheeks. 'It was easy to decide never to marry either. I wanted to avoid the pain of yearning for things I couldn't have. It was working, too, but, like a fool, I didn't allow for falling in love.

'Then this morning Lucas told me he loved me, and… It hurts, Peggy, knowing I can't give him what he needs. So it's got to end, only I can't tell him why because I don't want his pity! I couldn't live with that! And I'm so afraid he'll persuade me to marry him, but if I stay with him I'll just hurt him more. He'd have this great big emptiness inside him, all because of me, and I couldn't take it. So you see, you have to persuade him to let me go! You just have to!' she ended desperately, and finally dropped her head in her hands and cried as if her heart would break.

Beside her, Peggy stifled her own tears behind her hand. Looking towards the house, she stared into Lucas's pale, strained face, helpless to know what to say or do. He came over to her and she clasped his hand. 'You heard? Oh, Lucas, what an awful, awful thing…!' She shook her head in distress.

Lucas stroked her cheek. 'Take Annie inside,' he said

softly, and as she did so he walked round to sit on the edge of Megan's lounger, reaching out to pull her into his arms.

She stiffened at once, recognising the scent and feel of him. She looked up, her face an agony of pain and betrayal. 'No!' she cried hoarsely, struggling to be free, but he caught her face between his hands and held her eyes with his.

'Don't fight me, Megan,' he ordered in a voice choked with tears. 'As you love me, don't fight me any more,' he added in a whisper, and drew her into the loving shelter of his arms.

She could not move then, for even to breathe hurt beyond measure. He had heard. He knew everything, and now there was nowhere for her to hide. She tensed at the feel of his hand smoothing her hair, feeling her last fragile defences crumble into dust.

Lucas breathed in deeply, trying to absorb some of her pain. 'Oh, Red, Red, how on earth could you think I would pity you, when I think you're the bravest woman on this earth?' he groaned.

Megan caught her breath, her fingers clutching the material of his shirt. 'You can't think that!' she challenged, and a laugh escaped him even as he closed his eyes.

'You'll have to get rid of this habit of arguing with me, darling. I do think it, and it's true. You're brave and proud, and quite helplessly fat-headed!'

That jerked her out of her cloud of despair. Her head came up at once. 'What?'

Lucas's smile was still shaky, but it was a smile. 'Only a fat-head would think I would chose marriage with a woman I didn't love in order to have children, because the woman I did love had made the heartbreaking decision not to have any of her own.' His hand slipped into her hair and cupped the back of her head. 'Don't you see, sweetheart?

If I can't have you, I don't want anyone else. Speaking
selfishly, I'd rather be childless with you than without you.'

Her eyes swam. 'How can you say that?'

'Because I love you,' he groaned, and brought his mouth
down on hers in a kiss which stole her soul from her, but
gave her his in return. When he drew away, her tears were
gone, replaced by a look so defenceless that he felt like
crying himself. 'I kept trying to tell you that you hurt me
more by not trusting me. That is the only way you can ever
hurt me.'

Megan reached out to press trembling fingers to his lips
in mute apology. 'It wasn't a case of not trusting you, Lucas. I love you so much, I just want you to be happy. No
matter what you say, you want children. You know you
do!' she insisted.

Lucas sighed, brushing his lips across her forehead. 'Not
being able to have children with you will be a sorrow, but
it isn't the end of the world. We'll have each other—if ever
I can get you to agree to marry me!'

Megan bit her lip. He made it sound so easy, so simple.
'But will it be enough for you?'

'Will it be enough for *you?*' he countered softly, and she
blinked at him.

Strangely she had never thought of that. She hadn't
wanted to hurt him. Had wanted to see him happy. She had
never asked herself if she could be happy with him. It was
a sobering thought, when she had always sworn that, if she
couldn't have it all, then she'd rather have nothing. Years
ago that had been true, but she knew it wasn't now. If only
she could be sure that Lucas was happy, truly happy, then
sharing her life with him would be all she would ever want.

'Oh,' she said at last.

Lucas started to laugh as some of the enormous tension
left him. 'Why is it I never get the response I expect from

you?' he asked wryly, and Megan felt an answering smile start to curve the corners of her mouth.

'Because I'm a contrary creature. You'll just have to get used to it,' she said softly, releasing his shirt to run her hand caressingly over the silky material, feeling the strength of him beneath it.

He stilled her hand by catching it in his and bringing the palm up to his mouth. 'How much time do I have?' he asked throatily, kissing the tender flesh and curling her fingers around the spot protectively.

Megan felt her heart expand as she finally allowed hope to enter. Maybe they had a future together after all. 'How does for ever sound?' she breathed, and the gleam in his eye was all the answer she needed.

'Sounds good to me,' he responded, drawing her close and closing his eyes on a wave of relief. 'Does this mean you're going to marry me?'

Megan lifted her hand to run the backs of her fingers over his jaw. 'Oh, yes, though I shouldn't. I'm just beginning to realise you set me up!'

He caught her hand and pressed it to his heart. 'What else could I do when you'd left me no choice? You wouldn't explain what was going on. I was desperate. All I could think of was getting you worked up enough to talk to someone, and Peggy agreed to help. Neither of us expected to hear what we did! It tears me up to think of you bearing all that on your own all these years. I wish you'd told me.'

Megan sighed wistfully. 'I didn't know I loved you then. I was afraid of anyone pitying me. I didn't want that. I would have taken my secret to my grave if you hadn't forced it out of me.'

'Forgive me,' he said gruffly. 'I never meant to hurt you. I just remembered seeing your face when you held Annie, and other times too, when you looked so sad. I knew you were hurting, and I wanted to ease your pain. All I ever wanted was for you to trust me enough to let me help you.'

She had been blind, in more ways than one. 'I had no idea. I thought you were playing some devilish game of your own. I got used to fighting my own battles.'

'Not any more. You have me now, Red. Whatever happens, you know I'll always be there for you. I love you so damned much, your happiness means everything to me. Don't shut yourself off from me ever again,' Lucas ordered, and she had to smile.

'I won't, I promise,' she confirmed huskily, reaching up to seal the promise with a kiss.

He drank from her lips until they were both breathless, then pulled away to smile down at her. 'You drive me out of my mind. Lord knows what I'm letting myself in for!'

Megan let out a gurgling laugh and made herself more comfortable against him. 'Does that frighten you?'

With a laughing groan, Lucas caught her and pushed her backwards so that she was pinned underneath him. 'Hell, no! Whatever it is, it's going to be good.'

Megan smiled as he kissed her. She liked the sound of that. Liked the sound of it very much indeed.

EPILOGUE

MEGAN GLANCED UP from the paper boat she was making as she heard the car drive up to the house. Her heart lifted instantly and a smile curved her lips. She looked over to where her son and daughter were splashing about in their paddling pool.

'Daddy's home!' she called out, and immediately the splashing stopped as, with squeals of delight, they abandoned the water for the greater pleasure of greeting their father.

Megan laughed as she watched them go, knowing Lucas would end up soaking wet but also knowing he wouldn't mind. He loved getting into a mess as much as they did! A scratching at her leg made her glance down, and she pulled a rueful face, handing the boat to the infant who waited for it so patiently.

'Was I ignoring you, James? I'm sorry. Here you are, darling. Isn't it a lovely boat? Shall we show it to Daddy?'

'Da-da-da-da,' baby James gurgled in response, and she took it as a yes and picked him up, settling him securely on her hip as she went to find Lucas and the children.

As she suspected, he hadn't made it much further than the front lawn of the lovely old cottage they had moved into shortly after their marriage. His briefcase, jacket and tie were strewn haphazardly in his wake and he was on the grass, tickling the life out of five-year-old Amy, whilst four-year-old Jonathan was clinging to his back like a rodeo rider.

Her heart swelled as she heard him laugh just before he collapsed and the two whirling dervishes piled on top of him. She had never dreamt that she could be so happy, and it was all due to Lucas. He had been the one to suggest adoption. Maybe they couldn't have babies of their own, he had said, but there were children out there just crying out to be loved. She hadn't needed much persuasion. Freed of her own nightmares, she had seen that they didn't have to be childless. There were other ways—good ways—for them to have the family they both wanted.

That was how they had come to get Amy and Jonathan. They had been an orphaned brother and sister who had stolen Megan's heart the minute she'd seen them. The love that she and Lucas had given them these past two years had made them blossom into the boisterous pair who had easily accepted the arrival of baby James, whom they had adopted six months ago. They were a lively, happy family, something Megan had never expected to be part of.

Seeing Lucas's hair caught in insistent fingers, she winced and went to rescue him. Dancing blue eyes met hers as she knelt down beside the giggling group.

'Do you know how much I love you, Lucas Canfield?' she asked with a grin.

'Enough to rescue me?' Lucas suggested breathlessly, reaching up with his free hand to tousle James's vivid red hair.

'You don't need rescuing, you love it!' she declared blithely, and gasped as he caught hold of her T-shirt and began pulling her towards him.

'Not nearly as much as I love you, Megan Canfield,' he breathed against her lips.

'You'd better not look. Daddy's going to kiss Mummy,' Amy pronounced, quickly putting a hand in front of her brother's eyes.

'Yuck!' Jonathan exclaimed with a toothy smile, and the

pair of them fell about laughing whilst Lucas proceeded to do just that, very satisfactorily.

'Happy?' Lucas asked seconds later, sitting up to take James from her.

'Very happy,' Megan confirmed, welcoming Amy into the curve of her arm, whilst Jonathan tried to make a whistle out of some grass. Her heart was full. Everything she had ever wanted was right here, and the man responsible for it all sat with his children about him, making grass whistles. Later, when the children were in bed, and they were finally alone, she would make sure he knew just how very much she did love him and always would.

Modern Romance™
...seduction and
passion guaranteed

Tender Romance™
...love affairs that
last a lifetime

Sensual Romance™
...sassy, sexy and
seductive

Blaze
...sultry days and
steamy nights

Medical Romance™
...medical drama on
the pulse

Historical Romance™
...rich, vivid and
passionate

27 new titles every month.

*With all kinds of Romance for
every kind of mood...*

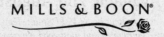

MILLS & BOON®
STEEP/RTL/16
The STEEPWOOD Scandal
REGENCY DRAMA, INTRIGUE,
MISCHIEF...AND MARRIAGE
A new collection of 16 linked
Regency Romances, set in the villages
surrounding Steepwood Abbey.
Book 16
The Missing Marchioness
by Paula Marshall
Available 2nd August
Available at most branches of WH Smith, Tesco,
Martins, Borders, Eason, Sainsbury's, Woolworths
and most good paperback bookshops.

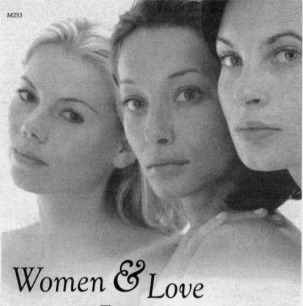